D0189451

The Sciences
Good Study Guide

Andrew Northedge,
Jeff Thomas, Andrew Lane
and Alice Peasgood

The Open University

Acknowledgements

Grateful acknowledgement is made to the following sources for permission to reproduce material in this book:

Text

Collee, G. (1989) 'Food poisoning', *New Scientist*, 21st October 1989, IPC Magazines Ltd. Diagrams by Peter Gardiner;

Figures

Figure 3.1 (top): Biophoto Associates; *Figure 3.1 (bottom):* Meidner, H. and Sherriff, D. W. (1976) *Water and Plants,* Blackie and Sons Ltd.

The Open University, Walton Hall, Milton Keynes MK7 6AA

First published 1997. Reprinted 1997, 1998, 2000, 2002

Edited, designed and typeset by The Open University.

Printed in Great Britain by The Cromwell Press.

ISBN 0 7492 3411 3

This publication is a set book for the Open University courses S103 *Discovering Science* and S280 *Science Matters* and has been designed for use with other OU courses. If you would like a copy of *Studying with The Open University,* please write to the Course Enquiries Data Services, PO Box 625, Dane Road, Milton Keynes MK1 1TY.

The Sciences Good Study Guide was designed to be studied alongside specially written introductory modules in maths, science and technology, the first of which will be available in late 1997. To find out more about these modules and other Open University materials, please write to Open University Educational Enterprises Ltd, 12 Cofferidge Close, Stony Stratford, Milton Keynes MK11 1BY.

Contents

See page 302 for Maths Help contents

Preface

This book is for students of mathematics, the sciences and technology (including engineering). It is designed to help you to improve your study skills, whether you are just starting out or have been studying for some time.

If you are a 'beginner' you may be unsure about how well you will cope with serious study. You may have difficulty concentrating, or wonder how and when to make notes. Perhaps you feel anxious about your writing skills. This book will help you to work out ways of facing such challenges. If, on the other hand, you are a more experienced student, you may want to refresh or advance your skills in a particular area, such as writing essays or preparing for exams. The book is designed to make it easy to look up any study topic on which you want fresh ideas and should be something to keep by you over many years of study.

This is not a pious book, one which preaches to you to be good, work hard and be super-efficient in your studies. We take a realistic view of studying, building on the experiences of many Open University students and their tutors over the years. The book works by presenting you with real examples of study challenges and inviting you to think about your own responses. It discusses the underlying nature of study problems and talks you through practical solutions. It does not offer quick, 'off-the-shelf' remedies, but is written in the belief that becoming a good student is a long-term process of changing habits of working and ways of thinking.

The book was written, in the first instance, for Open University students. But we always had it in mind that many other students could benefit from the book. You will find that the examples used sometimes assume that you are an adult, part-time student, studying independently from home and working with structured open-learning materials. But most of the advice is equally relevant to other contexts. (In any case, many other universities and colleges now have large numbers of part-time, adult students and use open-learning materials.) All you need to do is to translate the examples and advice to your own situation.

We were keen to produce a book that would be relevant right across the fields of mathematics, science and technology. Naturally, some sections will be more relevant to some disciplines than to others. For example, Chapter 5, on working with numbers and symbols, may appeal more to science and technology students, who need to work with units, handle data and get their calculations correct, rather than come to grips with all the underlying mathematical principles. Chapter 4, on working with mathematical relationships, may have more appeal to beginning mathematics students. Incidentally, we found it cumbersome to keep writing 'mathematics, science and technology', so to save space and avoid tedium we refer in general to the 'MST' subjects.

One part of the book works differently from the rest: the Maths Help section. People vary a great deal in the mathematical knowledge and skills they bring to higher-level study of MST subjects. Some need only a little rust knocking off here and there, or an explanation of a few very straightforward points. Some may get along fine at first but then run into something they haven't seen before and then waste a lot of time trying to work out what to do. To cater for these students, Maths Help is a 'trouble-shooting' section, covering the most common mistakes and misunderstandings of students who have not worked with numbers or mathematics for a while. Of course, the way you use it will depend very much on your particular course of study – and you shouldn't assume that you have to understand all the material in Maths Help before you start studying. It may, however, be enough to get you moving again if you're stuck, or it may help you see the nature of your difficulty. If it isn't enough, look for further help – from the course material you're studying, or from your tutor, or from a more detailed introductory teaching text.

To keep the book a manageable length, we have had to be selective. Not everything you need will be covered, but we hope the book will give you enough skills and confidence to find what you need from other sources. You can either read the book from cover to cover, or study each chapter independently. You may find it works best as a reference source, somewhere to search out topics that are relevant to your current study or solutions to problems. Make full use of the index at the back of the book and the contents list at the front. In addition, the text has a variety of features – section headings, boxes, lists of key points and hints and tips – that will help you to locate advice relevant to your needs.

Authors' acknowledgements
In the best OU traditions, this book reflects the efforts of many minds from a wide range of disciplines. The course team that planned and wrote it included staff from the Faculties of Mathematics and Computing, Science, Technology and the School of Health and Social Welfare. It would be impossible to identify all who contributed, but some deserve a special mention. We owe a special debt of gratitude to Sonia Morgan of the School of Health and Social Welfare at the Open University, who as Course Manager has tirelessly and diplomatically helped steer *The Sciences Good Study Guide* from the first moments of conception to successful delivery. We are also particularly indebted to Judith Daniels of the Mathematics and Computing Faculty and to Hilary Holmes and Frank van der Molen who acted as consultant authors. From the OU, Heather Cooke, Nigel Cutress, Jane Williams and Ruth Williams made valued contributions to the production of the text. We would also like to acknowledge the help of Judy Ekins, Judy Emms, Linda Hodgkinson, Judith Metcalfe, Isabella Pottinger and Graham Weaver. We also benefited greatly from the comments and support of members of the OU course team involved in the production of S103, *Discovering Science* – in particular, Evelyn Brown (who kindly contributed material to Chapter 9), Stuart Freake, Isla McTaggart and Annie Payne. In addition, we received helpful comments from anonymous student testers in different parts of the UK.

Special thanks also to Val O'Connor and Tanya Hames for secretarial support and to all those involved in the OU production process, especially Janis Gilbert (graphic artist) and Sarah Hofton (designer). Our editor, Mark Goodwin, displayed all the expertise necessary to produce a coherent and readable book from a range of differently authored manuscripts. We benefited a great deal from the help and guidance of our external assessor Dick Evans, Principal of Stockport College of Further and Higher Education. This project was made possible by money from the OU's *Plans for Change* initiative and from the Higher Education Funding Council of England.

Of course, any small errors and shortcomings that proved resistant to collective scrutiny remain the responsibility of the authors. We would be pleased to receive feedback on the book, favourable or otherwise, from students and tutors alike (please write to JT at the address below).

Andrew Northedge, *Access Unit, School of Health and Social Welfare*
Jeff Thomas, *Centre for Science Education, Science Faculty*
Andrew Lane, *Systems Department, Faculty of Technology*
Alice Peasgood, *Access Unit, School of Health and Social Welfare*

The Open University, Walton Hall, Milton Keynes MK7 6AA

CHAPTER 1

Getting started

The hardest part of a journey is taking the first step.

An old saying

1 The first step of the journey

Starting a course of study is rather like starting a long journey.

A*ctivity Break* Think of some long journeys you have taken. Why should the first step be any harder than the other steps? Get a piece of paper and write down a few thoughts before reading any further.

Here are some answers to compare with yours.

◆ Before you can start you have to *plan* your journey, making difficult strategic decisions about how to travel and what route to take.

◆ You also have to make lots of *routine preparations*: looking up train times, making bookings, working out money arrangements, stopping the papers, packing, switching everything off and locking up the house.

◆ But perhaps the greatest difficulties are *mental*. You have to *commit* yourself. *This* is the day – there will be no more putting it off. And *this* is the journey, as opposed to other journeys you might have made instead. You have to let go of all other plans – of all those other things for which you could have used the time.

Even then you may take the first step with an uneasy feeling that you have forgotten something. Later, as you settle into a travel routine, you may come to see that many of your worries were unnecessary, but at that first moment you feel raw and vulnerable.

1.1 Preparing for study

What can starting a journey tell us about starting to study? One thing we see is that it is not the step itself – putting one foot forward – that is difficult. It is all the things you have to do to make the first step possible. Similarly, the first study tasks in a course are usually designed to be easy. The difficulties lie in the planning, the preparations and the state of mind you have to adopt to get yourself started – and in feeling edgy because you haven't yet settled into a 'study routine'.

Planning

There are more ways than one to make most journeys, and there are different routes through your studies. Consequently, you need to plan your way ahead. And if, for any reason, some paths are not open to you (say, you cannot participate in some elements of your course because of limitations on your time, your resources, or some other impediment) you can still work out a route to your destination. Arriving is what counts. How you get there is up to you. The key is to find out what your options are, draw up a plan that will work for you and then follow it. I shall look at planning in Section 3 of this chapter.

Preparation

Preparation for study, as for most journeys, does not have to be enormously complicated – but there are a few essentials you need to sort out if you are to be successful. What these are will depend on your circumstances, so you need to take the time to think ahead. Section 3 will also help with your preparation.

Mental readiness

Are you mentally ready to set out on your study journey? Sections 2 and 4 of this chapter offer assistance with your mental preparations. As you will see, I suggest (on page 19) that you keep a kind of 'travelogue' of your thoughts and plans in the form of a *Study Diary*. In fact, it's worth starting this now, before you read any further. It will bring your own thoughts on studying to the front of your mind, and so help you to engage effectively with the rest of the chapter. And it will be interesting, later, to look back and see how the experience of studying has changed your thinking.

A ctivity Break

1 Why have you committed yourself to this particular course of studies?

2 What kinds of highs and lows do you expect to encounter?

3 How well do you think you will cope?

4 Where do you think you will have arrived at the end?

Jot down some answers to each of these questions on a sheet of paper and put it in a folder marked 'Study Diary'.

I cannot say what your answers should be. These are questions only you can answer. I hope that, by the end of this chapter, you will have plenty more thoughts to add to your notes.

1.2 Working out your own answers

In this book you will keep meeting 'Activity Breaks', in which we ask you to write down your own ideas. We believe that *you already know a lot about how you learn.* We imagine, too, that *you have already had advice about studying* – people telling you to be organized, to keep to time, to plan before you write, to present your work neatly, and so on. Advice is easy. The difficulty lies in connecting it up to studying as *you* experience it.

To develop techniques you can use in your studies, you will often have to work things out for yourself. This book aims to present you with thought-provoking activities that will connect with your own experience. These activities will include questions to stimulate you to reflect on your situation and your personal capabilities. The intention is to bring to the fore what you already know about yourself and the way you learn, so that you can work out your own study solutions.

We assume that you will acquire study skills through:

◆ an active engagement with genuine problems
◆ making connections with your own experience
◆ thoughtful reflection on your study strategies.

There is more on this topic in Section 4.1.

1.3 Capturing your thoughts

Finally, in doing the two activities in this section you have already encountered a key 'study skill'. By asking you to *think* and then *jot ideas down on paper*, I was introducing a basic study technique. You do not learn simply by 'soaking it up' like a sponge. You need to work with pen and paper beside you at all times, so that you can write as thoughts come to you. If you make a habit of noting thoughts down, you will find that, while some are soon thrown away, others turn out to be very useful. Once you have ideas on paper, you can *work* on them – refine them, extend them and connect them to each other. In becoming a student, you have entered 'thinking' territory. You need to get as much out of your thoughts as you can.

> ## Key Points
>
> ◆ Studying involves:
>
> – *planning* your route (don't just set off in hope)
>
> – making a few essential *preparations* (after working out what these preparations should be)
>
> – getting yourself into the right *frame of mind* (be clear about why you are studying and what you want to achieve).
>
> ◆ We learn study skills in an active manner, by thinking about our experiences and working out our own solutions.
>
> ◆ As you study you should make a habit of writing your thoughts down, so you can look at them and work on them.

2 Why read about studying?

If you can work out your own solutions, why should you need a study skills book? Isn't studying a fairly straightforward activity anyway? You read the books, attend tutorials, do the practical work and complete your assignments. What could be simpler than that? But is it so simple?

Mark looked up again and saw that it was 7:20 – nearly an hour since he'd started and he was still on page 3. In another hour he'd have to walk over to collect Amy from her class. Would he ever start again after that?

'Early morning tomorrow – can't afford to be late tonight. And there's the police thriller from 9:00 till 10:00 – only two more episodes – can't miss this one. I wonder if the step-daughter is involved? … No! Must get back to the reading – or perhaps a cup of coffee would help me concentrate – although I had one only 20 minutes ago.'

Mark looked at the page again. His eyes glazed over. He'd been staring at it for so long now and nothing was going in. There was a diagram marked with arrows and letters, with two equations next to it. 'What am I supposed to do with this lot?' He got up to straighten a photo on the mantelpiece and sat down again. He flicked ahead to some complicated-looking pages and wondered how he would ever cope. 'At this pace I'll never reach them.'

The first page hadn't seemed too bad: a bit dry, too many long words, not many jokes – and he didn't see what they were going on about with the experiment so he'd skipped that. Then there was some stuff he'd done back at school, which he also skipped. But when he ran into the table and the equations at the bottom of page 2, he was lost. He just couldn't make them out, so he'd left them and carried on. And now he had ground to a halt at these equations on page 3.

'Who am I kidding, trying to get into this stuff?' He went back to the previous paragraph, but found his attention slipping away again halfway through it. 'Am I supposed to remember all this? If Amy asks, I won't be able to tell her a thing about it.'

'Why am I so bored? I thought it would be interesting when I saw the cover.' Mark looked at his note-pad. The topic was written at the top. The rest was blank. They said to make notes as you study – but notes of what? 'No point copying out the whole book. "Sum up the key points." How? Perhaps I'll just sort out my desk.'

The phone rang. It was Ryan …

Mark brought back some coffee and sat down again. 'Only half an hour left. Must concentrate. Let's go back to page 2. On second thoughts, why not go right back to the start and try to get some notes down? Or what about that table? I could try the calculation. No, I don't know what that symbol means. Oh, forget it! It's too late to get anywhere now. Let's slip down the pub for a jar before getting Amy. I can always give it another go after the serial.'

Meanwhile, in another room a few streets away …

Sushma dropped another crumpled ball into the waste-paper basket and stared blankly at the pad. What now? She had made a half a dozen starts and she still couldn't see where to begin.

'How can I be stuck when I've hardly started? How long is this whole thing going to take? Will it ever be done? Not at this rate! … "What are the physical limitations on the transfer of bacteria by insect vectors?" Where do you start with a question like that? I can't give them the whole chapter. Should I start with a definition, or a diagram, or a summary of the different bacteria and insects involved? What are insect vectors anyway? I thought I knew about infections before I started reading this. Biology always was my weak spot. I just can't make anything of those diagrams … What if I set it all out as a table? Or perhaps I could just take a few sentences from here and there in the textbook and change the words around a bit – at least they couldn't say I'd got it wrong. But the tutor said to write in your own words and to include diagrams.'

As her mind slipped back to the classroom she winced. Why hadn't she kept quiet, as she'd meant to do? She knew she didn't really understand what those articulate types were spouting about, with all that technical jargon – but the tutor seemed so keen for everyone to speak. When she'd finally wound herself up to say something the tutor had looked straight at her, so she'd blurted out her question too fast for anyone to understand. The tutor thought she was asking something really simple and had explained it to her so carefully – she'd felt about ten years old. She hadn't had the nerve to interrupt. She'd made a right idiot of herself. How could she face going back again?

'Anyway – I didn't come away with that much. Nothing I can't get from the book. Why not give it a miss this week? Would the tutor be offended? … Oh, well – I'll think about that later. Must get back to this stupid assignment. I wish I could remember where I put the assignment notes. I suppose I'd better search the house again. No – waste of time – I've looked ten times already. Where else could they be? Forget it! How about looking up "vectors" in the dictionary and starting from there? … Why am I doing this to myself?'

Is it really as bad as that? Surely not … at least not all the time. Yet there are some times when studying feels pretty bleak. Mark and Sushma are fictitious, but their problems are real enough – and they are not problems only for *new* students or *'weak'* students. They are *general* problems of a sort we all face when we study – problems of *struggling to understand*, of *managing time*, of *completing a task*, and of keeping up one's *morale*.

---

*A*ctivity Break   Have you experienced any of Mark and Sushma's problems? What do you think they are doing wrong? Write down what you see as Mark's main problems and some ideas as to what he could do about them. Then do the same for Sushma.

One of Mark's problems is *finding time* for study given his social commitments, his work commitments and his leisure interests. And both Mark and Sushma have problems *using* their time *effectively*. Both are concerned about *what* they should be doing and *how long* it should be taking them. Both are 'stuck' and cannot see a way forward. Mark is repeatedly distracted – by a phone call, by his own thoughts, by making coffee, by tidying his desk and the mantelpiece, and most of all by the boredom he experiences when he reads the text. Sushma is distracted by her feelings of inadequacy: she sees herself as a very weak student and feels overawed by the tutor and the other students. As a result, she approaches the assignment in a very tentative way, which makes it difficult to get to grips with the subject. She is also feeling stupid and annoyed with herself for having lost her assignment notes. She is sitting there, almost hypnotized by the question, casting around desperately for some way of getting the assignment done. Both Mark and Sushma feel fed-up; they have lost the enthusiasm with which they started their studies and are in danger of giving up. They need some help.

On the other hand, Mark and Sushma may be doing better than they think. Studying *often* feels like a struggle. It is in the process of struggling that important learning starts to happen. We dropped in on Mark and Sushma at particularly low moments, but let's join them a few weeks later when things are looking up …

Sushma squeezed between the plastic chairs and put her cup and plate on the canteen table. 'I'm starving. I came straight here from work and I missed lunch today. I thought my stomach rumbles would drown out the tutorial.'

'*I wouldn't stuff in that sandwich so fast if I were you,*' said Mark. '*Don't forget our old friend* Clostridium perfringens.'

'*Yes,*' chipped in Kathy, '*the curse of the canteen. That sarnie's been sitting under a warm light-bulb for hours, I'll bet. Exponential growth of bacteria, you know.*'

'*Disgusting orgy of reproduction in your gut right now, I shouldn't wonder,*' added Mehmet. '*Toxins pouring out all over. Still, you won't be on the run till tomorrow morning.*'

'*Oh, don't! I can't eat it now.*'

'*Don't worry,*' Mark encouraged her. '*You'll be right again by Friday. Unless you're pregnant of course.*'

'*Oh, shut up! Anyway, you're all breathing in millions of bacteria just laughing.*'

'*Did anyone see that programme about microwaving food that's been in the fridge?*' asked Mehmet. '*Now that was enough to spoil your appetite.*'

'*Yeah,*' replied Kathy, '*and it felt dead good, being able to understand how the microwaves heat the food by exciting the water molecules. My family was dead impressed.*'

'*My molecules haven't had much excitement lately,*' Sushma said. '*After I'd finished that last assignment I was far too exhausted to even think about enjoying myself.*'

'*It's amazing how much you can pick up from those science programmes, you know – when you've got a bit of background. But you can see how they only give you one side of the story,*' said Kathy. '*I'm saying, "Hey – what about the ecological impact?" And my family's saying, "Get her – two months of education and she's telling the boffins where to get off."*'

Naomi joined in: '*My John still tries to show he knows it all – but I reckon he's getting a bit worried. I caught him sneaking a look at one of my books.*'

'*I found I was stopping myself using long words at work, so they wouldn't think I was a wally,*' said Mark. '*Only a few weeks ago I thought I'd never crack that scientific jargon. I was completely lost.*'

'*Well, I'm still struggling,*' said Sushma. '*I had a terrible problem with that maths on the growth rates of bacteria.*'

'*Oh, yeah. So did I,*' said Kathy. '*It was a pain. I gave up and 'phoned Naomi. We sorted it out between us. But you're so good at it, Sushma. You got a great mark for that last assignment.*'

'*You should have seen me sweating over it. Nearly drove everyone in the house to a nervous breakdown. I find the assignments the worst. Though I don't much like the look of the next topic in the book either.*'

'Oh, I don't know – it looks quite interesting,' said Mark. 'You just run yourself down, Sushma. I could cope with your grades. Hey – break-time's over – we'd better get back.'

And off they go to have a stimulating, friendly tutorial, while violins play in the background, and we see that studying can be wonderful after all … Well, I just wanted to show that, though studying is often frustrating and tough, it can also be rewarding. It's a bit like climbing mountains. You have to do a lot of hard slog on the way, and sometimes when conditions are hard you wonder why you bother, but when you reach the peaks it can be very satisfying. Many students say that studying not only teaches them about the subjects they study, but also gives them *more confidence, broader interests*, and *more purpose in life*. They begin to achieve more at home and at work. This is another reason for reading about studying. If you develop your study techniques, not only will you improve as a student, but you will also strengthen your abilities in other walks of life.

A *ctivity Break*   Are there any parallels between the stories about Mark and Sushma and your own experiences? Look back at the Activity Break on page 2 and at the answers in your Study Diary folder. In the light of Mark and Sushma's experiences, would you change any of your answers now? If you would, write down the new answers and put them in your folder.

3 How to get yourself organized

When you begin, studying is difficult simply because it has no 'shape' for you. Until you have developed some kind of *'system'* for organizing your studying – for deciding *what* needs to be done and *when* – you can spend a lot of time dithering about, starting one thing and then another, all the time wondering whether you are really getting anywhere. Mark clearly suffered from a lack of purpose or plan, and this left him with a major problem: how to *manage* his study time.

3.1 Managing time

In fact, Mark had *two* kinds of problems with time: *finding* enough time, and *using* it effectively.

Finding time

Mark had *social* commitments (picking up Amy, talking to Ryan on the telephone), *work* commitments (an early start the next day) and *leisure* interests (watching the police thriller). All of these things are important, but is there enough space in between for studying? Students always have to make very difficult decisions about priorities. When studying comes into your life, it generally means that something else has to go. And yet we know what 'all work and no play' does. Even students have to have some fun. So one of the first skills you have to develop is 'a juggling act', keeping an extra ball in the air. Studying often requires a lot of time in good-sized *chunks*. You have to become an expert at *creating* time. One way to set about this is to draw a chart of a 'typical' week and try to spot gaps for your studying. Figure 1.1 shows one student's chart.

	Monday	Tuesday	Wednesday	Thursday	Friday	Saturday	Sunday
Morning	Housework	Study 1 hr	Study 1 hr	Visit Mum	Housework/ Shopping	Study 2 hrs	Study 2 hrs
Afternoon	Work	Work	Work	Work	Work	Free	Free
Evening	Evening Class	Study 1 hr	Study 2 hrs	Aerobics	Study $1\frac{1}{2}$ hrs	Free	Free

Figure 1.1

When she had looked at her chart, the student wrote:

'This was my first shot. When I saw that it gave me a total of ten and a half hours of study, I decided to make more time by doing two hours on Tuesday evening and an extra half hour on Saturday, to make a total of 12 hours. If I needed to, I could make some extra time at weekends (for writing an essay, say). And if I'm going out on one of the days, I can study for longer on another. Actually, now that I come to think about it, I'd rather have one weekend day completely free to relax. So, I think I'll study for five to six hours on Saturday (in two sessions of two to three hours). This gives me a revised table containing about 13 hours of study.'

Figure 1.2 shows the student's revised chart.

	Monday	Tuesday	Wednesday	Thursday	Friday	Saturday	Sunday
Morning	Housework	Study 1 hr	Study 1 hr	Visit Mum	Housework/ Shopping	Study 5/6 hrs	Free day
Afternoon	Work	Work	Work	Work	Work		
Evening	Evening Class	Study 2 hrs	Study 2 hrs	Aerobics	Study $1\frac{1}{2}$ hrs	Free	

Figure 1.2

A ctivity Break Draw a chart for yourself like the one in Figure 1.2. Work out the total study time you can reasonably expect to set aside and where in the week it falls. Try to identify where clashes may occur and where you might have to cut back on some things.

You don't need to go into great detail; you are just trying to give more 'shape' to your week. Don't be alarmed if you find this activity difficult. It is. Moreover, having made a plan, it is even harder to stick to it. Yet sticking to it is not necessarily the point. Even if you find that you keep having to change your plans, it is still worth making them, because even changing your plans forces you to think about *what* you are doing and *why.* Planning makes you think *strategically,* instead of just drifting.

Using time

Mark was having difficulty not only in finding *enough* time, but also in *making effective use* of time. He had not worked out what to do in the two hours he had allocated to his studying. By flitting about, he ended up finishing the session early, without having achieved much. To avoid this problem you need to develop ideas about *how much time* you require for *particular types of task* and about how long to stick at those tasks if you are running into difficulties. You will find you can do some tasks – such as studying a difficult passage or writing a report – only when you are *fresh* and have a *good-sized chunk of time* ahead of you. Other tasks – such as organizing your notes or reading through a draft of a report – you can squeeze into odd moments, or do when you are tired. You need to think about how long you can concentrate and whether you find it easier to work late at night or early in the morning. *People vary a lot in their patterns of working, so you must experiment and find out what works for you.* You need to *reflect* from time to time on whether you could parcel out your study time in different ways and get better results. Don't just plod on ahead, vaguely hoping for the best. You need to *manage* yourself more actively than that.

3.2 Completing a task

So far I have talked as though studying comes neatly bundled into clear-cut tasks. But, as Mark found, a lot of your work as a student is very *weakly defined.* In order to have a task to complete, *you* need to *define* the task for yourself.

Defining tasks

First, you need to have an *overall idea* of what you want to accomplish in a given week. Then, you need to define a number of *smaller tasks,* such as 'reading the next five pages of the chapter', so that you can decide how much *time* to give to each task. This enables you to *manage* yourself – that is, to:

◆ get yourself started
◆ keep yourself going
◆ decide when to stop and move on to another task.

With a big task, such as writing an assignment, it is particularly important to be able to break it down into a series of smaller tasks, so that you can see the way ahead. *When you have a task that is clearly defined, it is easier to focus your attention and keep yourself working*, resisting the kind of distractions to which Mark succumbed.

Why is it so easy to be distracted when you are studying?

Studying sometimes produces a sense of drifting in a sea of meaninglessness. This leads you to clutch at any straws of distraction you can find. When you don't really understand the text, or don't know what you are trying to achieve, you feel restless and uneasy.

Distractions offer you a chance to focus your attention on familiar and meaningful parts of your life and so escape from the uncertainties of studying. Our urge to avoid uncertainty is very strong. That is why it is so important to define tasks for yourself to create a pattern and a meaning to your work.

If you find that you keep stopping as you work, try setting yourself a smaller and more tightly defined task – particularly one with an active component. For example, if you keep 'drifting off' as you read, get a highlighting pen and search for key words or phrases. This will give you a specific task on which to focus.

There are many study tasks you can define for yourself. For example, you could:

◆ read the next section of the text you are studying

◆ make notes on an article you have recently read

◆ sort out and file all the notes you've made over the past couple of weeks

◆ watch a video-cassette

◆ do some practical work

◆ gather together notes and ideas for your next assignment

◆ plan your next assignment

◆ write the first draft of a report

◆ make contact with other students

◆ attend a tutorial

◆ go over your study plans for the coming week.

You will get a fuller picture of the range of tasks you can define for yourself as you work through the rest of this book.

When you have identified some tasks to be done, you can divide out the time available between them. It is unlikely that you will be able to stick exactly to your plans. Studying is too unpredictable. But you can *set broad targets* to help you to decide when it is time to stop doing one thing and start on the next. And you can keep reviewing and adapting your plans to take account of reality as you go along.

Time versus task

Time management and *task management* are closely bound up with each other. You need to balance one against the other. If you become too obsessed with *time* (as Mark was) then you tend to think in terms of the 'hours put in' rather than in terms of what you have achieved. You may start 'filling up' the time with relatively unimportant tasks, whiling it away until you can finish your session feeling virtuous. To avoid this 'time serving', you must start with the aim of completing certain tasks (even if you don't always succeed). On the other hand, if you focus *too* much on the task, you may let it drag on for too long. You need to keep switching your attention between *task* management and *time* management to strike a reasonable balance.

3.3 Practical arrangements

A ctivity Break

1   Where are you reading this book?

2   Will you be able to concentrate without disturbance?

3   Have you enough space in which to work?

4   Have you pen and paper handy in case you need to write?

If you are not properly set up, sort yourself out now.

Setting up a place to study

Does it matter where you work? Yes, it matters a lot. You may be able to find study time in your work breaks, or on the train, and you may choose to do some work on the sofa, or in bed. But there are some tasks, like writing an assignment, for which you need to be able to work undisturbed, with space to spread your books and papers out, and easy access to your files. You may also need room for a computer and a printer, and space for doing experiments. Ideally, you need good lighting and heating too. But for many people, the most important thing is simply to have a *regular* study place, so you can settle into the right mood quickly and find things easily. You may not be able to arrange everything just as you would like, but try to get as close as you can.

If you live with other people, you need to negotiate specific times when you can use a particular table or a particular room and be left undisturbed.

Those around you often don't realize just how hard you need to concentrate when you are studying. They want attention, or simply can't resist the delights of your conversation. Make sure they understand your study plans and know when you will be unavailable. Unless you can be left alone for substantial spells you are in for a very frustrating time.

The equipment you need will depend on the course you are studying, but here are some general suggestions: a supply of pens and pencils, a ruler, A4 plain and lined paper, graph paper, a calculator, a box of index cards, cardboard pocket files, filing boxes, labels, shelf space and a good dictionary. For some courses, you will also require a television, a video-recorder, a radio or an audio-cassette player, and possibly a computer (see Chapter 7).

If you study for any length of time you will soon accumulate large amounts of printed material: handouts, your own notes, old assignments and so on. In the early weeks, Sushma simply let the papers pile up. She had not worked out where to put things; that was how she came to slip her assignment notes into the back of one of her study texts and forget about them. Later, she wasted nearly an hour fruitlessly searching through piles of papers and magazines all over the house, before giving up defeated and demoralized. It is important to be systematic about storing your study materials. You need to develop a filing system, using folders, boxes and plenty of sticky labels. In the end, you will find that, as a student, it is not so much what you can remember that counts, *as what you can lay your hands on when you need it.*

Figure 1.3 *A typical study 'kit'*

A further preparation for study is to investigate the bookshops and libraries in your area to find out how much they have on your subject. When you start to study 'for real', you'll be concentrating on the main teaching texts, but consulting other sources of information can be very useful – *if time allows*. It can be intimidating when you first visit a large library or bookshop, and it may be hard to locate the particular section you need, especially if you are not sure what it is called. Assistants can usually help if you take the plunge and ask. You may be surprised at how much relevant material there is. Alternatively, you may be disappointed and realize that you need to learn how to order books through the library, or take part in book exchange schemes with other students (although, increasingly, CD-ROMs and on-line databases offer alternative routes to the information you need – see Chapter 7).

Key Points

As you start out on your studies, think carefully about the following issues.

- How to *manage* your *time*; in particular, how to:
  - *find* time, by planning your week
  - *use* time effectively, by doing work of different kinds in the most suitable time slots.
- How to *define tasks* for yourself, and then, how to:
  - *allocate time*
  - *monitor your progress.*
- Setting up a *place* to study.
- Negotiating your study times with *family* and *friends*.
- How to *equip* yourself for studying.
- How to *organize* things so that you can find them.
- Exploring *bookshops* and *libraries*.

Activity Break

1 Think back to Mark and Sushma's experiences and to what I've said so far about getting yourself organized. Then make two lists detailing things about you and your circumstances which:

   (a) may interfere with your studies

   (b) may help with your studies.

2 In the light of these two lists, what are the few essential preparations you need to make as you start your studies?

3 Sketch out a quick plan for tackling your next week of study (assuming that you are currently studying).

4 What is studying all about?

4.1 What do we mean by study skills?

The word 'skill' is rather beguiling. It conjures up images of learning a few tricks. You take a little training, put in some practice and then, 'hey presto', you are skilled. But study skills are not like that. They involve picking up *practical 'know-how'*, stopping to *think* about what you are doing, *managing yourself* shrewdly, and *keeping up your spirits*. You improve your study skills, not so much through hours of repetitive practice (as with skill in a sport, or playing a musical instrument), but by trying out new ways of doing things, reflecting on how well they work, being aware of your strengths and weaknesses, and thinking strategically.

Practical know-how

By 'practical know-how' I mean the insights you pick up from day-to-day experience. For example, Sushma had not been studying long enough to realize the vital importance of a filing system. A more experienced student would have known that you need a special folder for important documents like assignment notes. Getting hold of folders and boxes and designing your own filing system is not a high-level, technical skill. It does not require hours of practice. It just takes experience, thought and a willingness to experiment. Other kinds of practical know-how include knowing:

◆ where to get information
◆ who to go to for help and support
◆ what to do when you are stuck.

You can also pick up know-how about what courses tend to expect from you, and where to go to find out (for example, book lists, past exam papers and former students). And know-how enables you, when facing a task, to judge:

◆ what kind of a task it is
◆ how well-equipped you are to tackle it
◆ how long to allow for it.

You accumulate all this knowledge through doing and reflecting.

Getting to grips

Successful study also involves a determination to 'get to grips'. It is easy to let a course just 'happen to you' – simply 'coping' from day to day, instead of taking control and making sure you get good value for your time and money. As we have seen, you have to be ruthlessly *practical* when it comes to arranging a place where you can work undisturbed with your study materials around you. You can't afford to be half-hearted about such things. You also have to be *realistic*, and alert to the danger of kidding yourself.

Beware of:

◆ 'filling in time', rather than really studying
◆ telling yourself you understand when you don't
◆ avoiding facing up to approaching deadlines.

To succeed you need to *take charge of your studies*, recognize things as they are, and keep working towards your targets.

Keeping your spirits up

There is nothing more damaging to your studies than sagging morale. We saw how little progress Mark and Sushma made when they were filled with doubt and despair – starting one thing and then another, frittering away time without achieving much. To stay on top of your studies, you have to *believe in your own abilities* and be clear about *why you are taking the course*. This self-belief is not easy. We all experience disappointments, confusion and self-doubt. The skill lies in knowing how to come to terms with these lows.

You can boost your morale by 'positive thinking'.

◆ Think about your strengths.
◆ Recognize the progress you have made.
◆ Remind yourself of what you are getting out of the course.

This is why a Study Diary is a good idea, and why I suggested starting one with your answers to the questions on page 2.

Also, try to organize your studies so that you take advantage of your strong points. And tackle weaknesses head on, by working out ways to develop your skills. Finally, be ready to recognize your own human needs.

◆ Seek out the fun in studying.
◆ Mix tasks you don't enjoy with ones you like.
◆ Don't drive yourself too hard – take a break from time to time.
◆ Make contact with other people when you feel down.

Being a 'reflective self-manager'

It is most important that you take a systematic, *analytical, strategic* and *reflective* approach to managing yourself and your studies.

Being systematic

Think back to the study chart on page 9. Drawing a chart like this is being *systematic*. You are saying, 'OK – I need to find 12 hours. Let's set the week out, so that I can see all seven days together. I'll divide each day into three parts and mark in the time that's already committed. Then I can sketch a plan that spreads the work over the remaining time.' Instead of muddling along, you take a rational, structured approach. (Being systematic means organizing what you do according to a 'system'. In this case, the system is to draw a chart and fill it in carefully.)

Being analytical

When I talked about the importance of 'defining tasks' (on page 10) I was taking an *analytical* approach. You weigh up what kind of tasks you face, and break them down into their component parts, working out what each task requires of you. (Analysis means taking things apart to see what the components are and how they fit together.)

Being strategic

When I talked about 'using time' – weighing up which tasks to do when you are fresh, and which to squeeze into odd moments – I was suggesting taking a *strategic* approach. You pay attention not only to the goal itself, but also to your motivation, your energy level and your powers of concentration – key resources if you are to reach your goals.

What is a strategic approach?

The terms 'strategy' and 'strategic' are important in this book, so you should be clear about what we mean by them.

A strategy is a broad plan for tacking a particular challenge.

Taking a strategic approach involves:

◆ working out exactly what you are trying to achieve and why (your goals)

◆ deciding which of your goals have the highest priority

◆ reviewing the resources available to you

◆ working out a plan that makes the best use of your resources to achieve your goals.

Being reflective

Having looked systematically and analytically at the tasks ahead of you, and having worked out a strategy, the final stage is to *reflect* on how successful you have been. Did your plans work out? Did you misjudge the task, or the time required? Did you learn anything that may help you to get it right next time? Taking a *reflective* approach means that you reflect on your past plans and achievements to develop principles that will shape your future plans.

A reflective approach gives you the flexibility to tackle a wide range of tasks (important in an age when the technology and organization of education are changing rapidly). You can learn and adapt continually, and *your abilities as a student improve throughout your life.*

This approach – systematic, analytical, strategic and reflective – is summarized in Figure 1.4. Acquiring study skills is shown as a spiral: you start in the middle and circle around in a continuous process of development. The central process is developing insights and skills from your own experience, though you may also pick up ideas from talking to others (and from reading books like this one). (You should begin at the middle of Figure 1.4 and read the diagram as a sequence of connected phrases.)

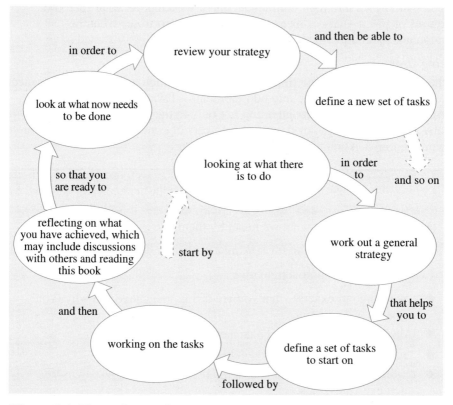

Figure 1.4 *The study spiral of a reflective self-manager*

Showing the sequence of analysis, strategic planning and reflection in a diagram highlights the general principles. But don't think of it as a formal process – as a set of steps to be performed on a daily basis. Managing your studies strategically and reflectively should become an unconscious habit. You may have to do it consciously at first, step by step, but eventually it should become second nature.

Becoming an independent learner

The older you get and the higher you go in the education system, the more responsibility you take for your own studies. In school, teachers take most of the responsibility for *what* you learn and *how*, and put pressure on you to work hard. As an adult, you make your own choices. You decide your own priorities, set your own targets and work out strategies for achieving them.

You also take responsibility for your own ideas and points of view. You are expected to think for yourself and to question. For example, I started this chapter with a saying about the first step of a journey being the hardest. You might very reasonably have reacted by asking whether the saying is true. Is it supported by any evidence? What about all the other steps, some of which can be very hard – for example, when you miss your connection, or lose your luggage? A proposition being old and often repeated is no reason to treat it as 'true'. Indeed, at higher levels of knowledge the 'truth' is assumed to be *uncertain*. Your studies are understood to be an inquiry which *you* are undertaking into the nature of the world. You are expected to *weigh up* ideas, not just '*learn*' facts. You read critically, make your own observations, conduct investigations and draw your own conclusions. You learn to present evidence, supporting one idea against another using the facts available. The whole emphasis changes from being a passive *receiver* of 'knowledge' to being an active *seeker* of 'understanding' and a *maker* of 'sense'.

This does not happen all at once, especially if you are returning to study after a long break. Nevertheless, your target is to become an 'independent' student, to be able to find your way around a subject for yourself. You study to find out what you want to know.

Keeping a Study Diary

As I've already mentioned, one way of encouraging yourself to take a reflective approach is to keep a diary of your studies. Writing a page each week about what you have achieved, and how you feel about it, will set you thinking about why you have approached things in particular ways. It will also stimulate the production of new ideas. Looking back over a few weeks or months will enable you to identify patterns in your work and help you to think strategically about whether you are achieving as much as you could. Write your Study Diary under headings such as 'Feelings about my studies', 'Main achievements this week', 'What went badly', 'Lessons learned', 'Major tasks ahead', 'Strategies for tackling them', and so on.

You will have already started your Study Diary if you did the activity on page 2. (It can be a loose-leaf diary – just sheets clipped together in sequence and kept in a folder.) Even if you only keep a Study Diary for short spells, every now and again, it can produce a reflective and strategic pattern of thinking which continues long after you have abandoned it. On some courses you will be advised to keep a Study Diary … but don't wait to be asked.

A life-long process

Developing study skills is not only for beginners. Whatever stage you reach, you can always gain from attempting to refine your technique. And, strangely enough, it is not always a matter of learning something 'new'. There are many basic truths you can come back to and understand again at a new level. Some sections of this book will be just as revealing if you return to them in a year or two with more experience of studying.

Key Points

Study skills are not a set of routine 'tricks' you learn once and apply for ever. Becoming a skilled student involves:

◆ accumulating practical know-how, on the kinds of things you have to do as a student, and on how to set about doing them

◆ being determined to get to grips with study challenges in a practical and realistic way

◆ knowing how to keep your spirits up, by positive thinking, playing to your strengths, tackling your weaknesses and being kind to yourself

◆ becoming a reflective self-manager, by taking a systematic, analytical, strategic and reflective approach to study tasks

◆ becoming an independent learner, by taking responsibility for your own studies and for making your own judgements about ideas and knowledge.

Moreover, your study skills should continue to develop throughout your life.

4.2 What is learning?

The purpose of studying is to learn. But what does it mean to 'learn' something? At degree level, learning is not just memorizing information. It is more about *ideas* than information, about *understanding* rather than pure memory.

Understanding ideas versus memorizing facts

TV shows like *Mastermind* and *University Challenge* give the impression that being 'clever' involves knowing lots of facts. Clever people usually *do* know lots of facts – but they can answer the questions quickly because of how the facts are *organized* in their minds. What really distinguishes people who know a lot about a subject from those who don't is the '*understanding*' they bring to bear – the ideas they can use to analyse and discuss the topic. You will have to do a certain amount of memorizing, especially just before an exam, so that you can produce the information required quickly. But your exam result will depend more on the work you put into understanding key ideas.

I am using the word 'ideas' here to include 'concepts', 'principles', 'laws', 'models' and 'theories'. Learning ideas involves three things.

◆ *Taking in new ideas* (and by 'taking in', I mean 'making sense of', not simply seeing, hearing or memorizing).

◆ *Thinking them through*, and fitting them alongside your existing ideas to build up a better 'general understanding'.

◆ *Using newly formed ideas* (both in the sense of using them to do things and using them to communicate with others).

Taking in new ideas

When you look at an unread textbook on your shelf, you know that there is a lot of information in it – information that you want, somehow, to get into your head. This is what I mean by 'taking in' – taking ideas that are part of the outside world and making them your own. This means much more than simply passing your eyes over lots of words, numbers and pictures. It means 'making sense' as you read, so that you 'understand' the meaning. You can look at and memorize the symbols without too much difficulty. But that does not mean you have 'made sense' of the equation, or that you 'understand' what it is saying to you. To 'take in' such an equation you have to read it within a flow of other words and symbols, as part of a whole framework of ideas. So, when you are trying to 'take in' a text, a lecture or a TV programme, you need study techniques which emphasize 'making sense'. That is why this book talks a lot about taking notes as you read, listen or view. Deciding what to note makes you pay attention to meaning. Chapters 2 to 7 of this book are about ways of 'taking in' various types of ideas from different kinds of source.

Thinking them through

It takes time before you can really get new ideas properly into focus. You have to connect them with other ideas already in your head. And when new ideas conflict with old ones, you have to work out where that leaves you. Various study activities help with this 'thinking through' process. For example, when you are jotting down assignment ideas, drawing a diagram, working through a mathematical problem, or 'boiling down' your course notes for exam revision, you are working your ideas into shape. These activities appear to be incidental chores around the edges of mainstream activities such as reading and writing. But they are *not* marginal to studying. The odd moments when you are jotting down bits and pieces to yourself are the times when you are doing important 'thinking through'.

Using ideas

You don't *really* understand an idea until you put it to use. It is when *you* are the one pushing the thinking along that you really grasp the full force of an idea. So some activities, like working on problems, doing experiments and writing assignments, play a key part in establishing new ideas as part of your mental 'repertoire' – that is, in making them your own. Chapters 8 to 10 are about this 'doing' side of learning, about using ideas.

'Taking in', 'thinking through' and 'using' are all active processes. None of them just 'happens', while your mind quietly dozes. Each requires purposeful, thoughtful action on your part. In fact, making a distinction between these three aspects of learning is artificial; in practice, they overlap. Yet the distinction is useful, because it emphasizes that learning happens at many different points during your studies, not just when you are reading a book, or listening to a lecture. It reminds you to give just as much effort to the 'thinking through' and the 'using' as you do to the 'taking in'.

The learning spiral

These three aspects of learning are part of a continuing cycle of advancing understanding. We have enquiring minds and are never satisfied for long with what we learn. As you answer one set of questions you become aware of new questions. If you start from the middle of Figure 1.5 (overleaf) you will see what I mean.

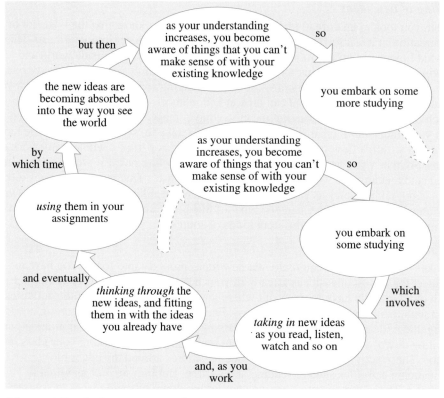

Figure 1.5 *The learning spiral*

Learning does not really happen as neatly as this, of course. You are usually starting on new ideas at the same time as writing assignments using established concepts. And this week's new ideas often connect with last week's, so that you begin to understand them in a new way. In fact, there is no identifiable moment when you learn a particular idea. You just find it 'turning up' in your thoughts as you work on other things. As you move around the learning spiral, you look back and realize that ideas you once struggled with now somehow seem obvious. You realize you must have 'learned' them, but you can't pinpoint when. In other words, learning is not a neat, sequential process. It proceeds by lurches as you circle around new ideas. Yet it is not completely haphazard either, nor out of your control. The learning spiral in Figure 1.5 should give you an idea of the nature of the process, so that when you 'reflect' on your own learning (as part of your 'reflective self-management'), you can make some sense of what is happening in your head and plan your way forward.

> ### *Ideas and skills*
>
> Throughout this chapter I have emphasized the learning of ideas, but have not mentioned the learning of MST skills as such – for example, being able to draw graphs, carry out experiments, use a computer data analysis package or apply mathematical techniques. This is a distortion, since in the MST subjects learning skills goes hand in hand with learning ideas. Acquiring a practical competence often provides the basis for understanding an idea, just as understanding broad principles helps in developing a skill. I just thought it would over-complicate the discussion, and Figure 1.5, to include skills as well. In practice, you must give equal attention to learning MST skills.

Key Points

- Learning at higher levels is a lot more than just memorizing information. The core task is understanding ideas.
- To learn new ideas you have to take them in, think them through and put them to use.
- Learning does not proceed along straight, neatly marked-off lines. It is better thought of as a process of spiralling through different stages of understanding and competence.

Activity Break Now you have read about the nature of study skills and the learning process, take one more look at the questions in the Activity Break on page 2. Would you answer the questions differently now? Write down any new thoughts in your Study Diary.

In this chapter, I have described how to plan and prepare for the start of a course of studies and how to get yourself in the right frame of mind. I have also discussed the nature of studying and learning in general. In the next chapter, we shall get down to some real studying.

CHAPTER 2

Reading and making notes

1 Getting into some reading

When you are studying MST subjects, the texts you work with can take a variety of forms. In some subjects, the pages are covered with numbers and mathematical symbols. In others, you might find lots of chemical symbols, diagrams of experiments, systems flow diagrams, electrical circuit diagrams, and many other things. In this book, we have divided these different kinds of study material across four chapters. The next three chapters look at how to study texts which contain:

◆ diagrams (Chapter 3)

◆ mathematics (Chapter 4)

◆ numbers and symbols (Chapter 5).

In this chapter, I shall concentrate on how to study words – that is, I shall be concerned with 'reading'.

Reading is one of the key challenges of studying. Why? Since you already know how to read, what is the problem? Think back to Mark in Chapter 1. Why was *he* experiencing difficulties? His problems were having *too much* to read, finding some of it *hard to understand*, and worrying that he would *not be able to remember* things. In other words, when you are studying, the challenges of reading lie in:

◆ coping with *large amounts*

◆ trying to *understand* the difficult parts

◆ finding ways to *remember* what you have read.

To begin to explore these challenges, you really need to have a go at some reading. You will find an article at the end of this book by Professor Gerald Collee of the University of Edinburgh. It first appeared in the popular UK science magazine *New Scientist* in 1989, shortly after a public panic over salmonella contamination in eggs. For much of this book, we're going to concentrate on this article. Of course, the particular texts that you'll come across in your studies may be quite different in terms of subject matter and approach, but I want to outline some general study approaches that should prove helpful whatever you're reading.

> ### *Photocopy the article first*
>
> It is a good idea to make at least one photocopy of the Collee article (on pages 396 to 402) before you start to work on it. Then you can scribble notes on a photocopy without worrying about what you write. You may be able to get access to a photocopier in your local library.

*A*ctivity *Break* Now read the article by Gerald Collee on pages 396 to
402. (This chapter and later ones will assume that you have read the
article.) Then write down your thoughts on the questions below.

1 Did you enjoy reading the article?

2 Did you experience any difficulties as you read?

3 How long did it take you?

4 In a sentence, what was the article about? (Don't look back – work from
   memory.)

5 What two or three points stuck in your mind as especially worth
   remembering?

6 Will you be able to remember what the article was about in two or three
   weeks' time?

7 Did you make any marks on the article as you read, or make any notes?

Obviously, I can't discuss your answers here, but to give you something to
compare them with, here are my reactions on reading the article for the first
time.

> I had no great urge to read about food poisoning, but the article opened in
> a fairly chatty, informal style, and I found I got along reasonably well.
> However, I became bogged down in the detail at times. Paragraphs 5 to 8
> seemed a bit rambling, as though searching for answers to a question that
> hadn't been spelt out. After paragraph 10 there was a shift in style, and the
> article became a list of different types of food poisoning bacteria. I
> couldn't quite see where it was all going, or what the point was – and I
> wasn't sure what would be worth trying to remember. Yet I found the whole
> thing quite interesting – especially the drawings of the different micro-
> organisms and the diagram showing how fast bacterial populations can
> grow.

So, my answers to the questions were as follows.

1 Yes – looking back – I did enjoy it quite well, although I was a little
   reluctant in the early stages.

2 I found some of the technical terms and Latin names off-putting, and I
   wasn't sure whether I should try to remember them.

3 It took me about 20 minutes. I wasn't concentrating particularly hard, so I
   moved along fairly quickly.

4 The article seemed to be about the causes of food poisoning.

5 The thing that particularly stuck in my mind was the poison that can kill
   millions of people with just one gram. (I wondered about who might be able
   to get hold of it!) I also remembered the bit about bacteria multiplying very
   fast on food that's warm and damp.

6 Afterwards, the article was rather jumbled in my mind, lots of detailed information and unfamiliar names – so I wasn't sure I'd remember much of it a few weeks on. For example, I knew the last part was about salmonella, but apart from unpleasant images of infected chicken carcasses and eggs, I couldn't remember much at all. I just got the idea that, although only a small proportion of eggs are contaminated, we eat so many that quite a lot of people get sick.

7 I underlined some words as I went along, but I didn't make any notes on this first read-through.

Were your reactions similar? Perhaps not. We all react differently to reading matter. It depends on:

◆ what you are interested in

◆ what you already know

◆ how much experience you have of reading in the particular subject area

◆ how hard you are trying.

Nevertheless, I hope that seeing my reactions helps you to think about yours. As a student, you are going to be very much involved with 'managing' your approach to reading, and this involves a good understanding of your reactions to various kinds of texts.

2 Reactions to reading

2.1 Feelings about reading

Did you enjoy reading the Collee article? (What did you write down for Question 1?) Does it *matter* whether you enjoy reading something? It certainly matters if you hate it, since it's very difficult to concentrate on making sense of a text you really dislike. It is also difficult to keep yourself studying for long spells if you are not enjoying the work. Worse still, the things you read tend to slip from your mind if there's nothing about them that you find interesting or thought-provoking. It is generally much easier to study and to learn things you enjoy.

> ### Key Point
>
> You cannot learn effectively unless you become *interested* in your subject to some degree and get some *enjoyment* out of studying it.

Normally, when you are reading in your own time, this is not an issue. You simply choose to read what you enjoy. But one feature of studying a *course* is that although the course overall is interesting – after all, you've chosen to study it – you sometimes find yourself reading texts you don't get on with, or subjects which don't appeal to you at first sight. So, how can you make yourself learn as a reluctant reader?

The basic answer is to look for ways of overcoming your reluctance – ways of taking an interest in the subject. Any subject can be interesting if you look at it in the right way. Whether you are interested depends on what is on your mind. I began to take an interest in the Collee article when I found myself remembering a residential conference I had attended: people rushed out of the sessions, heading towards the nearest lavatory. I remembered the emptiness of the dining hall at the next meal, as rumours circulated about conditions in the kitchen. I also recalled the visit from a health inspector, and notices going up telling us not to be alarmed.

As I read on, I started to wonder which of the bugs described in the article might have caused the problem. I compared the symptoms I have experienced at various times with those outlined by Collee. I also began to wonder about the conditions in which we keep food at home. In other words, I began to make connections between what I was reading and my own life and experience.

But it is easy to relate to sickness. Not all subjects have such a direct link to everyday life – for example, quantum physics or multidimensional geometry. With subjects like these the interest lies in exploring intellectual puzzles, in learning how to place complicated problems into conceptual frameworks that enable you to work on them. The key to getting involved is to grasp the problems the text is trying to solve – to see why the subject was interesting to those who developed it. Following how scientists tracked down the cause of an unexpected finding can have all the excitement of a detective story. And once you are into a subject, the sheer elegance of an explanation can be tremendously stimulating. It is no good simply forcing yourself to 'learn' what is on the page; you have to try to engage with the underlying quest of the text.

As you start reading a text, you hope that the writer is going to pose some interesting questions, that he or she will give you something to think about and help you to search for meaning as you read. Sometimes, you will be unlucky. The writer may fail to put across the questions he or she is trying to explore. Professor Collee, for example, rather takes it for granted that we want to know about lots of different ways in which bacteria can cause sickness. Looking back now, I can see that he is pursuing questions such as: 'What are the most common causes of food poisoning?', 'Is food contamination unusual?', 'In what circumstances are the body's defence mechanisms overwhelmed by food contamination?', 'What are the main mechanisms of intoxication?' and so on. Other biologists would probably assume, from their own experience, that this is what an article on food poisoning is likely to be about. This is one of the things you pick up as you become used to an area of study. You begin to know what sorts of questions are usually thought to be important. As a beginner, however, you often have to work out these questions for yourself.

I had not imagined that there would be much to say about food poisoning – perhaps a few descriptions of major outbreaks of sickness and a few hygiene tips – so my hopes were not high. However, as I read, I began to build up a picture of food poisoning as just one aspect of a broader pattern of organisms living alongside (and inside) each other: feeding, reproducing, competing and protecting themselves against each other. I began, unconsciously, to recognize the questions Collee was addressing, and I found the article much more interesting. This came about partly because *I* was now asking questions of the article: 'Is food poisoning important?', 'Do I want to know about it?', 'Is it likely to affect me?', 'Is this something I already know enough about?', 'What is Collee telling me?', 'What conclusion is he leading up to?', 'Why is *he* interested in the subject?' ...

Setting yourself questions

Questions make reading interesting. Unless you are reading with a question or two in the back of your mind ('Can food poisoning be eradicated?', 'Should I still be eating soft-boiled eggs?') it can be very hard to 'engage' with the words on the page in front of you.

When you can't get 'involved' with the text you are reading, it is probably because you cannot see *what* questions are being addressed, or because you cannot see *the point* of the questions being addressed. At such times, you may need to stop reading and look back to an earlier chapter, or skim ahead over some later ones, or read the preface to the book, or the conclusion – anything that helps you to 'get inside' the questions the text is addressing.

Here, I asked you to read about food poisoning out of the blue – you had no particular motivation to grapple with this subject. (Although food poisoning is quite an easy subject to find interesting – especially if, as was the case when the Collee article was written, it has just been in the news.) But normally, in a course of study, you read a text within a *context*. It is linked to other work you are doing, to other texts, tutorial discussions or an assignment. This context usually gives you clues to the text's meaning and its underlying questions. However, if a text simply does not stimulate your interest, then you have to shift your strategy and work out a way to *create* an interest.

Hints and Tips

To develop an interest in a subject, you can try to:

◆ link what you are reading to questions that already interest you – the questions that made you interested in the subject in the first place

◆ figure out why other people have found the topic interesting – the questions that interested *them*

◆ connect the subject to your own experience.

If none of this works, just work out a strategy for 'getting through' the reading – for example, you could search for information on a specific aspect of the topic, or pick out techniques you need to solve a problem in your next assignment. In other words, if you cannot find an 'intrinsic' purpose for yourself in the text, then *create* a purpose by actively seeking out something. If all else fails, just cut your way through the task quickly and move on to something else. You are not doing yourself or anyone else any favours if, like Mark, you sit and wallow in a topic that is not engaging your thought processes. As was noted in Chapter 1, a key aspect of skilled studying is 'getting to grips': 'taking charge' and drawing from a course what *you* need and what interests *you*. Don't just let it all 'happen to you'.

> ### Key Point
>
> *You* are the person who has to *do* the learning and *you* are the person the learning is *for*. So *you* have to take charge and find a way to construct a positive approach to what you are studying.

2.2 Coping with the words

It's easy to find yourself reacting against the very words used in study texts, regardless of the subject matter. It often seems as though you are struggling with a foreign language. For example, as I was reading the Collee article, I found myself wondering:

> *... what exactly is a microbe? Is it the same as a micro-organism? Does it matter whether I know? Do I need to be able to distinguish viruses, bacteria, fungi and protozoa from each other? Does an intoxication have anything to do with being drunk? Do I need to stretch my mind around* Clostridium botulinum *and all those other Latin names, or can I let my eyes just skim over them? How do you pronounce them anyway, and why are they written in italics in the article? And although I'm as familiar as I would wish to be with diarrhoea, will I ever remember how to spell it?*

Difficult words

Should you stop and look up difficult words in a dictionary?

It depends. Of course, it will slow you up if you do it a lot. You have to decide whether a word seems important. Does it come up regularly? Do you seem to be missing something?

For example, even if you haven't come across the word 'misnomer' before, you can probably guess what it means well enough for the purposes of the Collee article. (And you'll find it isn't very common in science texts anyway.) With a word like 'genus' – you can get by for now without knowing what it means – but it will keep on turning up if you study life sciences. Eventually, if it hasn't been explained in one of your texts, you ought to check its meaning in a dictionary. You'll have to make your own judgement as to whether not knowing the exact meaning of a word is interfering with your understanding of the text.

Unfamiliar words not only make it a struggle to squeeze meaning out of the text, they can also make you feel excluded from the 'in-crowd' of people who casually bandy these terms around. Are these terms really necessary? Or are they just a way of keeping ordinary folk off the territory?

Technical language

Everyone finds unfamiliar specialist language off-putting and frustrating.

Yet specialists *have* to develop their own 'language'; it gives them extra power in analysing their subject in a detailed and systematic way. In fact, as you study a subject and become more of a 'specialist' yourself, *you* will gradually find yourself using the same language without noticing it.

It is not done deliberately to annoy students. Developing new concepts and fitting new words to them are part of the process of producing new knowledge. At times, the technical language may be overdone. On the other hand, you cannot hope to enter a new subject area without learning some 'specialist' language.

So, don't let irritation and confusion over words hinder your progress. Instead, work out ways of tackling the problem.

Scientific vocabulary

When I looked for 'protozoa' in my dictionary, I couldn't find it. Instead, I found 'protozoan', which turns out to be the singular of protozoa. That's one of the problems with Latin names – apart from their unfamiliar look and sound – you don't just add an 's' to make the plural. 'Data', for example, is the plural of 'datum', just as 'bacteria' is the plural of 'bacterium'. Yet you hardly ever hear of a 'datum', and people often use 'data' as if it were the singular, saying 'that's what the data tells us' instead of 'that's what the data tell us'. It can get quite confusing. However, as you become used to studying in a particular field, you gradually get used to the odd-sounding words. If there are lots of Latin names in your subject, you could decide to look up a couple each study session and gradually build up your own list of definitions.

You'll come across difficult Latin names as the proper names of biological organisms (for example, the bacteria mentioned in the Collee article). Don't feel that you have struggle to pronounce or remember these mouthfuls; as a beginning student, you'll probably be expected to do no more than use the organism's common name, if it has one, or refer to it in some other way (for example, as 'the bacterium that causes botulism'). But remember, if you do use the Latin name of an organism, it must be in italics (or underlined, if handwritten): for example, *Clostridium botulinum.*

One way to tackle the problem is to buy a specialist dictionary for the subject you are studying (although these are sometimes quite difficult and technical in themselves). It may also be a good idea to keep a good-sized general dictionary close at hand as you study (for example, *The Concise Oxford Dictionary*). I looked up 'micro-organism' in my dictionary, and it said 'any organism of microscopic size' (which is pretty much what it sounds like). The definition of 'microbe' was very similar, so that answered one of my questions.

The definition my dictionary gave for protozoan was 'any minute invertebrate of the phylum Protozoa'. This wasn't a lot of help. If I don't know what a phylum is, I now have to look that up as well. And basically, the definition was telling me that a protozoan is very small, has no backbone and is one of those things we call 'protozoa'. I didn't feel that my understanding had moved on. It's often that way with dictionaries: you keep looking things up, but you don't always find what you want.

With a specialist science dictionary, much more information is given under 'micro-organism'. First, I'm told it's an organism that can be seen only with the aid of a microscope. Then, I'm given a list of examples: bacteria, some fungi, viruses, and single-celled plants and animals, including protozoa. Then, there is some general information on beneficial micro-organisms – the part they play in decay and decomposition, and their importance in food chains in the sea. If I look up bacteria, some information is given on their appearance, how they are classified, how they reproduce, and so on. There are a lot of unfamiliar words, and more information than I need to make sense of the Collee article. It's important that I'm not side-tracked by words and ideas that I don't need to grasp at the moment. I can always come back to these entries in the dictionary when I need to.

Dictionaries

A dictionary is an important resource to have handy, but don't expect it to be infallible. Some specialist words will not appear in a general dictionary – and, as you'll see in later chapters, words that do appear may not be defined the same way in your subject area. A dictionary is a useful guide when you are lost, but often you can get a better insight into the meaning of key terms from your study texts.

You might want to develop a system for writing down words that seem important as you come across them, so that you can add new clues to the meaning when you see them used in other ways. You could use a card index, starting a new 'concept card' for each word you think is worth the trouble (see Figure 2.1 overleaf). If you keep the cards filed alphabetically, you can find them quickly and add new bits of information each time you come across the word in a new context. Try starting your own collection and see whether this system suits your style of studying.

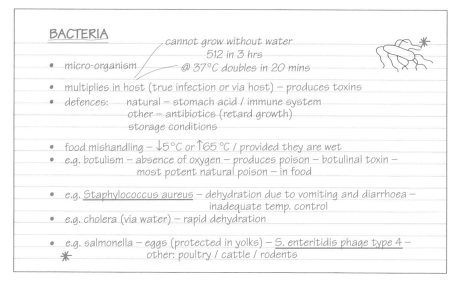

Figure 2.1 *A 'concept card'*

2.3 Scientific writing style

The *style of scientific writing* can sometimes be off-putting. Although Collee's article is chatty and friendly (for a science text), it packs *a lot of information* into a small space. Collee also *draws fine distinctions*, the importance of which are not necessarily obvious to a beginner. For example:

> Salmonella typhi *is the cause of typhoid fever, transmitted by contaminated drinking water. It is quite separate, however, from the large group of salmonellae that also belong to this genus and are linked with food-borne infections.*

> *While the typhoid bacillus causes disease only in humans, the salmonellae associated with food poisoning occur in many animal species as well as humans.*

Reading this passage requires you to hold several abstract categories in your mind at once, so that you can pop various items into the correct category boxes. Gradually, as you become familiar with the subject, these categories become part of your mental apparatus and can be brought into play quite easily. When you reach this stage, it becomes an advantage to have a lot said quickly. But while you are still getting used to it, this type of writing can seem dense and dry.

Science writing strives to be *precise*. In other words, scientists are supposed to say *exactly* what they mean – no more, no less. For example, Collee is uncomfortable with the term 'food poisoning', because the poison isn't always in the food itself. Sometimes, the poison is produced in the body *after* the food has been eaten. In addition, Collee uses the more specific term 'toxin' instead of the general term 'poison'. He also suggests that instead of 'food poisoning' we ought to say 'food-borne infections and intoxications'. (I can't see it catching on, can you?) In fact, Collee spends a whole paragraph making this, perhaps rather pedantic, distinction. But in the context of a scientific analysis it is important to be absolutely clear what we are talking about. Later in the article, when he is explaining to us the mechanisms by which sickness occurs, Collee is able to assume that we understand this crucial distinction.

And talking of writing style – what about a sentence like this one?

The cause of such an attack may be difficult to determine.

Why doesn't Collee put it like this?

I am often unsure of the cause of an attack.

Wouldn't it be simpler and more direct to write this way? It might be – but Collee isn't saying that he *personally* isn't very good at identifying causes. He is speaking on behalf of the community of scientists, and is saying, in effect: 'Using accepted scientific standards of rigorous proof, causes tend to be difficult to determine.' As it happens, my next-door neighbour never has any difficulty pointing to causes of things, but then he isn't weighed down by the rules of scientific enquiry. His certainty arises from self-belief. He assumes other people have as much respect for his views as he does. But I wouldn't sit down to read an article by him on food poisoning – whereas I am prepared to take notice of Collee, not because I respect him personally, but because he speaks on behalf of a well-established community with a high reputation for saying only that which can be proved (within known limits) to be true.

Collee's language signals this state of affairs. He deliberately leaves out 'who' is doing the determining – leaving us to assume that it is scientists (or perhaps bacteriologists) in general. When things are said in a way that does not specify *who* is 'doing' whatever it is, this is called 'using the *passive* voice'. If instead of saying 'I broke the window' you said the 'The window was broken', you would be using the passive voice. Scientific writing often uses the passive voice. It tells you *what* was done, but not *who* did it. The idea is that, in science, it shouldn't matter who is doing the enquiring, or what state of mind they are in. The result ought to be the same if an appropriate method is properly applied.

Note the use of 'may be'. Collee does not say 'is', because sometimes it isn't. All academic writers tend to be cautious and leave themselves a 'get-out'. (Did you notice I said 'tend to be', rather than 'are'? I don't want to get caught out, do I?) Some things *can* be said with certainty (this statement being one of them). For example, water pressure increases the deeper you dive. But many things hold only under certain conditions. And many other things are merely thought to be the case, according to current 'theory', but may turn out not to be so when investigated further. Academic writers say things in ways that signal the degree of confidence they wish to claim. To the newcomer, this sometimes seems like a wishy-washy and time-wasting approach – but it reflects a careful, academic approach to knowledge and enquiry.

Finally, most writing in science textbooks is deficient in what the mass media would call 'the human-interest angle'. Only information which is directly relevant to the scientific point is included. The frustrations and triumphs of the medical researcher hunting for a food-invading microbe are assumed to be irrelevant, so they are left out. Science textbooks are not written as swirling dramas detailing the excitement of discovery. They consist of descriptions, analysis and argument presented in a calm, detached and impersonal style. It can take a bit of getting used to, but the disciplined scientific style is actually quite exciting in its own way once you get used it, since it enables you to focus a clear, steady intellectual 'gaze' on intriguingly complicated problems.

Key Points

◆ Scientific writing is densely packed, and deliberately leaves out whatever is considered not directly relevant.

◆ In order to be precise, it has its own language and is very strict about using this language in a consistent, rule-based way.

◆ It also strives to be cool, impersonal and detached – often using the *passive* voice.

◆ It is careful not to make rash claims to truth – often finding ways of saying things that leave the author a 'get-out clause'.

◆ As a result, until you are used to it, scientific writing can be off-putting and slow going.

2.4 Keeping up your motivation

The reason I am discussing your reactions to studying is because it is not a simple or painless process. It is easy to lose heart, especially if you are studying independently as a distance student. By its very nature, studying often makes you feel edgy and uncomfortable. Constructing new ideas in your head can be a confusing, frustrating struggle. It takes effort and determination. It is immensely satisfying when you feel you have grasped something, but you never know when that moment will arrive. And in any case, you soon seem to be off again, forging ahead into the unfamiliar – sometimes, the painfully difficult – looking back with nostalgia at last month's work (which now seems a little more comfortable and familiar than it did when you first struggled with it). Perhaps you didn't find the Collee article too bad, but at some point you are bound to meet material you do find difficult.

How you feel when you are studying a text makes a big difference to how well you get to grips with it. So, to study effectively, you need to be able to 'manage' your feelings. This involves:

◆ recognizing how various types of studying make you feel

◆ reflecting on the effect these feelings are having on you, and then

◆ working out what to do about it.

You have made a beginning with the first two of these tasks by reading this section of the chapter. The third task you will have to explore as you go along, by trying out different patterns of study, switching activities when you begin to feel weighed down, and talking to other students or your tutor. If you start to feel dispirited, look back at the things you *have* learned, the things that you didn't know or understand before. Remind yourself of the progress you are making. It is vital to work out how to make your studying enjoyable, interesting and satisfying if you are to learn well and keep on studying over a long period.

Key Points

It is very important to be able to manage your feelings towards your studying. You need to be able to find ways of:

♦ building upon your enthusiasms

♦ avoiding sinking into despair when the going gets hard.

Specifically, you need to:

♦ be able to make the subject interesting

♦ accept technical language and take it in your stride

♦ accustom yourself to the scientific style of writing.

3 Reading strategically

Were you aware of having a 'strategy' when you started to read the Collee article? For most people, I guess the answer would be 'No'. This doesn't mean that you didn't have a strategy, just that you took your strategy for granted, and didn't think about it. After many years of reading, it would be surprising if you didn't have quite well-established ways of setting about a piece like this. For example, you might have skipped to the end first, to see how long it was and how much time it would take to read it. You might have looked at who the author was, to decide whether it was worth the effort. Or perhaps you studied the pictures first, to get a feel for the subject matter. When you start out on any piece of reading, you make lots of small decisions – how to do it, when and where – that affect the way you work. We are now going to think about some of these decisions, so that you can reflect on whether your current strategies are appropriate for serious study.

3.1 Place

Where and when did you read the Collee article? Were you lying in bed, sitting at a desk, having a bath, on a bus or what? Any of these might be a good time and place – but pause now to reflect on how well your choice worked for you.

A ctivity Break   Were you able to maintain a reasonable period of steady concentration? Did you have the necessary materials to hand – for example, pen, paper and dictionary? Do you need a surface to write on as you read? Do you need to keep moving to different places to read, or are you best-off establishing a regular spot?

Your responses to these questions may have a significant impact on how effectively you read.

3.2 Speed

How quickly did you read the Collee article? (See your answer to Question 3 on page 25.) The issue of 'reading speed' is a persistent worry for students. There always seems to be much more to read than you have time for, so you feel a tremendous pressure to read quickly. It is surprising how much you can pick up by pushing yourself through a few pages at speed.

Scanning first sentences

If you need just a quick impression of what a piece is about, it can be useful to read quickly through the first sentence of every paragraph and pick out a key word or phrase in each one.

Doing this for the first part of the Collee article, I came up with:

- most people have experienced
- cause difficult to determine
- food poisoning a misnomer
- this article – bacterial infections
- disease not inevitable on contact
- factors tipping the balance
- large dose – illness more likely
- store food at high or low temp.
- differences between individuals
- some bacteria produce toxins
- botulinal toxin affects nerves.

I would say that this list gives me a fair picture of what the article is about. But it doesn't save me the job of reading the article properly. I couldn't find out what Collee is saying about food poisoning by looking at this list; it's just a rough guide to the contents of the article.

However, this list might:

- help me to decide whether I want to go ahead and read the article properly
- put me in the right frame of mind to understand the article
- remind me afterwards of what the article is about (this is one way of making notes).

Skimming

There will be many times in your studies when you need to move even faster than this, skipping very quickly through a lot of pages to get the gist of the topics covered or to find specific information. This is *skimming*. It is an important skill, and one that you can use in many ways. To practise, from time to time select a few pages of a study text and give yourself five minutes to skim them. Then see how much you can write down. Although skimming enables you to get a sense of the contents, it is *not* a substitute for 'reading'. Skimming can tell you something *about* a text, but it can't enable you to *learn* what is in the text.

Reading

To learn the basic messages of a study text, you need to *follow the argument*. To do that you must slow right down, taking in the argument bit by bit, making notes as you go. It is sometimes claimed that there are 'speed reading' techniques that enable you to 'grasp' the contents of a text in a fraction of the time required by most people. But to approach a text in this way is to misunderstand the purpose of reading it.

The purpose of reading

The underlying purpose of reading is to develop your understanding of the subject:

◆ adding new *concepts* to those you already possess

◆ understanding *explanations* you have not met before

◆ building new mental *models* of how things work (or extending existing models)

◆ following the working when *techniques* are demonstrated for organizing data or carrying out calculations

◆ incorporating new *information* alongside that which you already possess.

These are all 'thinking' processes, and if you try to bypass them you are not really learning as you read. Learning is to do with changing your ideas, combining them in new ways and extending them to cover new ground. Reading a text is one way to bring about these changes.

It is not the purpose of reading to have a lot of words pass in front of your eyes. Nor is it enough simply to add a few new items to a long 'list' of information in your mind. The point of reading is to make yourself 'bring out' the baggage of ideas strewn about in the back of your mind and then help you to rethink and reorder it.

You need to allow time for your thoughts to develop as you study. Yet, as a student, you can't afford simply to work at whatever speed comes 'naturally'. When you are trying to keep abreast of a course, you often have to push yourself through a lot more pages than you would cover at a 'natural' rate. What you need is a range of study strategies that enables you to work at different speeds according to need. At one end of the scale is the lightning skim through a whole book – at the other end is the slow, painstaking study of a difficult paragraph, calculation or diagram. You need to become accustomed to working at different points on this scale depending on the circumstances. How fast you should go will depend on:

◆ what you already know about the subject
◆ how difficult you find the text
◆ whether the text consists mainly of words, or includes a lot of mathematics, diagrams or data
◆ how thoroughly you need to understand the material.

So, how long did you spend on the Collee article – and how long 'should' you have spent?

You might have spent 20 minutes on it and picked up all the main points. On the other hand, if it made you stop and think, it could easily have taken you more than half an hour. If you were also making notes, it might have taken an hour. If you read it more than once, it could have been an hour and a half.

Because of my own special interest in the Collee article (for the purposes of this book) I have now spent several hours on it. The longer I worked on it, the more interesting I found it, and the more clearly I grasped the issues involved. You had no reason to spend nearly so long, so clearly there is no 'right' amount of time to spend on the article; it depends entirely on what you are trying to achieve.

Time investment

By becoming a student you are choosing to invest your own time in developing your intellectual powers.

Sometimes, you will get a good return by investing in a very detailed reading of a small section of text – a section that is central to your current interests and needs.

At other times, you will get a good return by dipping into several texts here and there, skimming them in order to broaden your ideas.

In basic terms, *you* have to identify your current *needs* and the *options* open to you, and then distribute your time investment across these options in a way that gives you a good overall return.

This is easier said than done, of course. But a key test is to ask yourself 'Is this making me think?' and 'Am I getting a better grasp of the subject?' If the answers are 'No', then the time you are investing is being wasted and you should switch to a new activity.

As a very rough 'rule of thumb', you might like to think in these terms:

easy text: fairly familiar material	*100 or more words per minute*
moderately hard text: material you want to follow reasonably closely	*70 words per minute*
difficult text: unfamiliar subject matter, material you want to understand in depth	*40 words per minute*

These rates would give you reading times for the Collee article of 21 minutes, 31 minutes and 54 minutes respectively.

However, for many MST subjects these figures will not mean much. When diagrams, tables and calculations form the major part of a text, you may have to work very slowly over a single page, following the working closely. Indeed, sometimes you will need to come back and study the same segment two or three times. (You may find that you can then speed up as you work through similar material.)

3.3 Study spells

Apart from sheer 'speed', there is the question of how long to study for. You might expect to get through a two-page article in a single study session. A chapter of a book might have to be spread over several sessions, depending on the chapter (how long it is and how difficult) and on your own time constraints. It is important to recognize that your attention span is limited, and that you cannot expect to learn intensively for hour upon hour. It is generally better to divide up your reading into 'bite-sized' chunks, and have several study sessions during a week, rather than attempting everything in a single, long session.

On the other hand, if your reading sessions are too short, you will not have time to get properly into the 'frame of thinking' required by the text before you have to stop. You might find, say, two hours a reasonable span for a session, particularly if you are studying after a day's work. And after an hour of intensive concentration, you might need a short break, or a switch to another task. Take some time to 'observe' yourself and your reading habits. Think about what works best for you within the general contours of your life.

3.4 Targets

All this brings us back to a point made in Chapter 1: as a student, you have to become a 'reflective self-manager', making decisions about:

- your overall goals
- your immediate priorities
- whether the results you are getting are as good as you could reasonably expect.

It is easy to slip into just plodding forward from one page to the next – picking up at the start of each session where you left off last time – without any sense of where you have to get to and what you are trying to achieve. If you work this way, you'll soon be way off-target, and you'll get depressed about it. One way to help yourself manage your reading strategy is to keep a Study Diary (as suggested in the box on page 19). For a week or two, write down a few notes at the end of each study session on:

◆ the date, time and length of the study session

◆ what you studied, and how much you got through

◆ how you feel about the session

◆ what you might try to achieve in the next session.

Then you can look back over your notes to see what strategies seem to have worked best.

Key Points

To 'manage' your reading effectively, you have to:

◆ keep *defining reading tasks* for yourself and *setting targets* (for example, the number of pages to study this evening)

◆ keep *monitoring* your progress on the task you have defined

◆ keep *resetting* your targets in the light of your progress.

3.5 What if you get stuck?

At times, you will get stuck as you read. Some MST texts are just difficult. When it happens, don't just sit staring at the page, going over and over the same few sentences. Find an active way to tackle the problem.

You will not be able to understand some ideas and explanations the first time around. They will grow on you. For example, if ideas go against the grain of 'common-sense' thinking, it may take some time for new ways of thinking to develop. The penny eventually drops after several exposures. You can help the process along by trying to write down the gist of what you have read, particularly the part just before you got stuck. Your notes may be rough and ready, but the process of writing them will help you to 'get into' the text. Writing makes you 'take hold' of ideas and reframe them in your own words. It helps you to force makeshift meanings on to the subject matter, and enables you to construct a base from which to launch another assault in a day or two's time.

With some subjects there is so much information to hold in your mind at once that you can't sort it all out straightaway. You take it in a bit at a time, and then come back for more. However, you may be able to strip away some of the less important information by making notes of just the most central points. Making yourself pick out the key points should help you to find your way through to what the text is really saying.

Reading requires you to 'project' meaning on to the words in front of you. Being stuck may mean that you have lost track of the argument and can no longer see the way ahead. So, you have to find ways of reconstructing the argument in your mind. One way is to cast around for clues by looking elsewhere in the text.

◆ You can *look back* to earlier parts: check the title, the contents list and the introduction, to remind yourself what the writer claims to be discussing – or re-read some of what you have covered, to re-establish the arguments in your mind.

◆ You can *look ahead* a few pages, to see what ground is going to be covered – or glance at the conclusion, to see where the argument eventually ends up.

In MST subjects, new ideas are often built on more basic ideas which have already been introduced. If you are stuck, it may be that you have forgotten something you learned a while back. It may be that, by skimming over past notes, or more basic texts, you can quickly remind yourself of some key principles. If you are still stuck, you can look for clues in other books on the same subject. It is very useful to have one or two introductory-level science books on your shelf to dip into when you need a fresh angle on something. Or you could try phoning other students. Any alternative line of explanation may be just enough to get you past your block.

If you are still stuck, skip ahead and see if you can pick up the thread again somewhere else in the text. Or just leave the text altogether and start on another piece of work. Perhaps if you come back another time, it will all seem clearer. In any case, there is no point in just sitting there, achieving nothing.

Key Points

When you are stuck, make an active attack on the problem.

◆ Look for clues in earlier or later parts of the text.

◆ Make detailed notes on the preceding sections and the bit you find difficult.

◆ If nothing works, give up and work on something else.

4 Remembering what you read

After you had read the Collee article, what did you write down as the two or three points which 'stuck in your mind as worth remembering'? (See your answer to Question 5.) Was your response anything like mine (on page 25)? What did you say about how much you thought you would remember in two or three weeks' time (Question 6)? How much do you think you *should* have been able to remember?

For example, should you have been able to remember any of the following information?

◆ The names of the different types of micro-organism.

◆ The symptoms of infection by *Staphylococcus aureus*.

◆ How many cases of salmonella infection were reported in England in 1988.

◆ What a salmonella bacterium looks like.

I didn't try to remember any of these. If I ever needed to know any of these things, I'd go back to the article, or look them up elsewhere. If I were making a serious study of the subject, I might have a particular reason for being interested in one of these items and would make a note of it as I read. But, coming to the article 'cold', I assumed I was reading it to pick up a general idea of what food poisoning is and of the main mechanisms through which it occurs.

Facts, figures and names

Should you try to remember facts, figures and names as you read?

It depends what you're reading for. Often, the answer is 'No', you need to note only the general gist of the information. However, if it's made clear that particular facts are important, and that a detailed understanding is needed for future study, then write these facts down. But, even then, don't try to remember every last detail.

The point which stuck in *my* mind – the deadly botulinal toxin – was not an important one. It just happened to catch my imagination. This shows that, as we read, our minds will register things which happen to connect with what we already know. It also shows that ideas and images we pick up may stay with us, bobbing about in our thoughts, whether or not we choose to remember them. This is a very spontaneous and immediate kind of learning – we read things that feed directly into our thinking. But, as in my case, what we learn in this effortless way may not be necessarily what we really need to remember.

The second point I remembered – the conditions under which bacteria multiply quickly – was much more useful, as it is relevant to the general thrust of Collee's article. But it wouldn't be much use on its own. I need to be able to put together a fair amount of Collee's general argument if I am to be able to place this information in context. So, how much of the general argument *can* I remember? As I noted in my answer to Question 6, the article was rather jumbled in my mind. I'd need to write some of it down to see the overall shape of the argument.

Actually, I'm not really *sure* how much I remember. How would one know? Should you be able to sit down with a piece of paper and write out all the main points – or would it count as remembering if you found yourself explaining the difference between infections and intoxications in a casual conversation? The fundamental question is 'Has the article has made any changes to the way you think about food poisoning?' If it has, then these changes will remain with you as traces of the activity of reading the article. If you try re-reading the article at a later date, you should be able to detect these traces, in that you should find the article easier to read. You should also be able to read other texts on the same subject more easily. All this is evidence that your mind has retained some elements of the re-organization achieved as a result of the original reading.

What are you trying to remember?

Your aim is not to 'store' all the words of the text in your mind. Even Collee, re-reading his article now, would probably find things he'd forgotten having written. If the *author* cannot recall in detail all that he or she has written, why should *you* remember it in detail?

Your purpose is to pick your way through the words to find the underlying ideas – the 'bones beneath the flesh'. The words are there to help you to understand the ideas, but it is the ideas themselves which form the core of the text. These are what you should try to focus on; these are what you should try to remember. Of course, the attention you should pay to any text depends on its 'status'. Is it an essential learning text, or does it form part of your general 'reading around the subject'? With all texts, it's the core ideas that should interest you. You can pick up clues as to the core ideas by looking at the contents list and section headings, at any 'objectives' listed in the text, at any summaries or lists of key points, and at the assignment questions associated with the text.

In essence, you want to be able to 'think' using the concepts and ideas put forward in the text. When you have *understood* what you have read, you have acquired that thinking capacity. You have produced the change in your mental structures, which was the point of your reading. This change is the most important kind of 'remembering'.

The point of reading, then, is to be able to understand what you have read, and to be able to recall the key ideas and information when you need them again. However, holding it all in your mind is by no means the only way. Your memory is too limited and too unreliable to serve as the main means of storing what you have studied. You can construct a much more reliable route back to what you have read if you make notes. You may, of course, need to do some deliberate 'memorizing' just before an exam, but for the most part, understanding is more important than remembering. If you have understood and made notes, you can leave your memory to take care of itself.

Key Point

Don't worry about your memory. Just write things down. It's what you understand that counts.

5 Making notes

Did you have a pen in your hand as you read the Collee article? Reading is an active process. You have to 'construct' sense. One way to keep your mind active is to use a pen as you read.

Activity Break If you didn't make notes as you read the Collee article, go back over it again quickly and jot down a few points.

When you have some notes, answer the following questions.

1   What do you think is achieved by making notes?

2   What uses do you think you might have for these notes?

3   Where will you keep them?

4   Did making notes change your understanding of the article?

Before we look at your notes, did you make any marks on the text as you read? Did you do any underlining or highlighting the first time you read the article?

5.1 Underlining and highlighting

As I read Collee's article I made a lot of marks with a biro. I could just as well have used a highlighting pen. Sometimes, I use several colours of pen to mark for different purposes – yellow for general interest, pink for points relevant to what I'm working on, and so on. Figure 2.2 shows what paragraph 3 of the Collee article looked like after I'd worked on it.

The term 'food poisoning' is a misnomer. A range of micro-organisms, including viruses, bacteria, fungi and protozoa, can cause such infections. The diseases that these organisms cause may arise as a result of two possible mechanisms. They
① may be true infections, in which the microbe gains access to the human body and multiplies within it; or they
② may occur when a microbe multiplies in the food, producing a **toxin**, which poisons the person who eats the food. So a better term is 'food-borne infections and intoxications'.

Figure 2.2 *A paragraph of the Collee article, annotated for emphasis*

A ctivity Break Look carefully at my underlining. Compare it with yours, if you did any. Why do you think I underlined those words? Why did I use double underlining in places? (This was the only paragraph in which I used double underlining.) What are the numbers in the margin for? Why did I put boxes around two words?

I always try to underline words in a way that allows me to pick up the gist of the argument when I come back to the text by just reading those words. (Try reading out the words I underlined. Does it make sense to you?)

What about the double underlining? Collee seemed to be making some important general points in this paragraph, setting out the basis for his whole analysis, so I did some double underlining to try to highlight the main distinctions I thought he was making. First, I double underlined 'misnomer', because the whole paragraph is about 'food poisoning' being a misleading term. I then double underlined 'micro-organisms', because these are what Collee identifies as the cause of food poisoning, and because the term covers all the specific types of food poisoning described in the article. I double underlined 'two' and 'mechanisms', because these words seemed to encapsulate a key distinction. (I was signalling to myself to look out for the two mechanisms in what follows.) I then numbered the two mechanisms as I came to them. I double underlined 'infections' and 'body' as the key words for the first mechanism. I also double underlined the 'or', because it signals that Collee is shifting to the second mechanism. I then picked out 'food' and 'toxin' as the key words for the second mechanism, but as 'toxin' was already in bold type, I just double underlined 'food'. Finally, I put boxes around 'infections' and 'intoxications', because I anticipated that these might be two key categories used throughout the rest of the article. (In the event, they were not really mentioned again.) I put far fewer marks on the rest of the article, because it did not seem so densely argued.

This might seem like a lot of fuss to make about a bit of underlining – something that I did quickly, without a lot of thought at the time. After all, there are lots of other ways of underlining this paragraph, ways that might be just as good, or better. However, I wanted to demonstrate that the humble activity of underlining can be very strategic. It can be used to convey a lot of information. What is more, in the process of doing the underlining, I was making myself think about the text instead of just skimming over it. I was making myself get to grips with the key distinctions Collee was making.

You probably had excellent reasons for marking quite different words. It depends what your mind focuses on as you read. My markings are simply offered as a stimulus to set you thinking about:

◆ *how much* underlining you do
◆ *what* you choose to underline.

> ### *The value of highlighting and underlining*
>
> Do you feel like a vandal when you write on a book? I suppose it depends on whether it's your book. If it is your book, marking the text as you read is a very valuable way of:
>
> ◆ focusing your *attention* on the text
>
> ◆ making you *pick out* and *think about* the main ideas
>
> ◆ leaving a trace on the page of the *sense* you have made of the text.
>
> When you come back to a marked-up text, you can tune in very quickly to the thinking you did on first reading it.
>
> Marking the text is a way of modestly increasing your time investment as you read and getting a much increased pay-off – in terms of both what you understand at the time and what you can remember later.

Notes and bookmarks

Some people write notes in the margins as an alternative to underlining or highlighting. A quick diagram can be a good way of summarizing something. Or, if you don't want to write on the text itself, you can use those 'yellow stickies', which don't damage the page, and can be placed sticking out to serve as bookmarks at the same time. Or you could use a piece of card both as a bookmark and as a place to write formulas or other reference information.

Tues. evening starts here!

Read this far by Weds.

Example for assignment

End of chap.

Figure 2.3 *Using sticky notes as bookmarks*

If you scan back over material you have read, but haven't marked or underlined, you may find that very little has stuck in your mind. In contrast, it boosts your morale tremendously to see familiar markings, offering you direct evidence of the attention you have already given to the text, and leading you straight to the key points.

5.2 Ways of making notes

When you want to get seriously to grips with the ideas in a text and 'make them your own', there is really no alternative to written notes. For one thing, you don't want to be always hunting for books and articles you once read to see what you underlined. You need a more handy version of material that is important. Moreover, making notes forces you to 'grapple' with the ideas in the text as you read (even more so than when you underline), because you have to decide what to write down and how to put it. Whether or not your notes are particularly good, the mere activity of writing them down pushes you further into the meaning of the text.

But *what kind* of notes should you make and *how many*? What did your notes on Collee's article look like? They could have been very brief, or spread out over several pages. They could have been written as sentences, or set out as a diagram. There are many different ways of making notes. What works for you will depend on:

- the way your mind works
- the kind of text it is
- what you want to use the notes for
- the time you think is reasonable to 'invest'.

Key Point

Notes should *not* be simply a shorthand *copy* of the original text. They should be an attempt to pick out the 'bones' of the text – particularly those points in the text that are *relevant to your studies*.

You might decide that all you need for an article like Collee's is a couple of lines.

Food Poisoning: Collee G. – 1989

discusses bacteria in food/water causing infections or intoxications

This would remind you what the article is about, in case you wanted to go back to it and look something up. However, on their own, these lines will not bring back much of the content. If you need a bit more detail, you could skim back through the article and jot down some of the words you underlined. Figure 2.4 shows what I came up with.

Activity Break Carefully compare Figure 2.4 (overleaf) with your own notes. What are the main differences? Do your notes include more information than mine, or less? Does it matter? Are your notes clearer to you than mine are? Are they laid out differently? What are the advantages of your layout and of mine?

Looking just at Figure 2.4, could you understand all my abbreviations? Why did I use 'bullets'? Why did I start some lines a little way in from the margin? Why do you think I used arrows in some places?

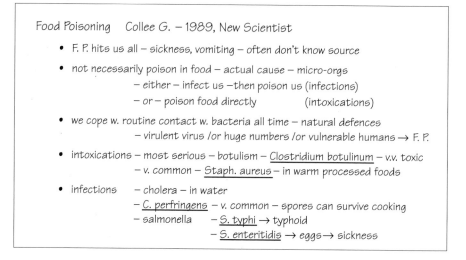

Food Poisoning   Collee G. – 1989, New Scientist

- F. P. hits us all – sickness, vomiting – often don't know source
- not necessarily poison in food – actual cause – micro-orgs
    – either – infect us –then poison us (infections)
    – or – poison food directly   (intoxications)
- we cope w. routine contact w. bacteria all time – natural defences
    – virulent virus /or huge numbers /or vulnerable humans → F. P.
- intoxications – most serious – botulism – <u>Clostridium botulinum</u> – v.v. toxic
    – v. common – <u>Staph. aureus</u> – in warm processed foods
- infections   – cholera – in water
    – <u>C. perfringens</u> – v. common – spores can survive cooking
    – salmonella   – <u>S. typhi</u> → typhoid
    – <u>S. enteritidis</u> → eggs → sickness

Figure 2.4 *A sample of notes on the article by Gerald Collee*

I hope you could see that 'F. P.' is short for 'food poisoning', 'micro-orgs' short for 'micro-organisms', and so on. Although the notes in Figure 2.4 are much shorter than Collee's article, they probably capture all the information you need for most purposes. They also make the structure of the article clear. I used a bullet for each new topic, and then set all the sub-points within that topic a little way in from the margin, so that I could see what information belongs together. I used the arrows to show that something leads to something else. So, a virulent virus leads to food poisoning, and *Salmonella typhi* leads to typhoid. You can invent any kind of symbols and abbreviations you like, so long as you will be able to remember what they mean when you come back to them. It is important to approach note-making creatively, and to lay out the notes in a way that suits the way you think.

Some people think visually, and so prefer to set their notes out as a diagram showing the main themes and their relationships to each other. I decided to try putting most of the content of the Collee article into a single 'spray diagram' (see Figure 2.5). (Various terms are used to describe diagrams of this sort – 'spider diagrams', 'mind maps' and so on – but the principles are similar.) You shouldn't normally spend your time on something as ambitious as this. I just thought it would be useful to show you just how much can be achieved with one of these diagrams. You write the topic in the middle of the page with a circle around it. You then draw a line leading out to each of the major subtopics, and lines from the subtopics to the sub-subtopics, and so on.

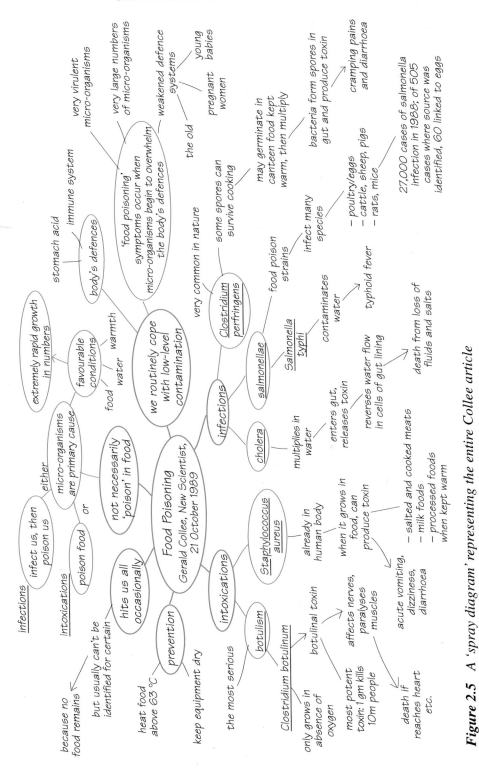

Figure 2.5 A 'spray diagram' representing the entire Collee article

Activity Break Take some time to have a close look at Figure 2.5. Move from the middle to the top left, and then work your way clockwise around the diagram. Does it help you to get a clearer idea of the contents of the Collee article? What, in particular, does it make clearer? Has anything important been left out?

Note how I have placed the points in clusters, used connecting lines to bring out the links in the argument, and included arrows to indicate direct causes. For example, you can pick any of the bacteria mentioned in the article and follow the chain of links to see what its effects are.

Does this kind of diagram work for you? Look back at your answer to Questions 4 and 6 in the Activity Break on page 25, and at my answers to the same questions on pages 25 and 26. See how much has been gained by making some notes.

Health Warning: READING IN DEPTH AND MAKING DETAILED NOTES CAN DAMAGE YOUR MORALE.

The notes in Figure 2.5 are *not* an example of what *you* should try to produce from an article like Collee's. It would be crazy to invest so much time.

The point of showing you these full notes is to demonstrate the *principles* of setting out ideas in a structured way – and to show that you can represent most of the information in a text without having to reproduce the original sentences.

It's quite striking that more than 2000 words, originally spread over several pages, can be captured fairly comprehensively in a single diagram. What is more, the diagram shows that Collee's article is a lot more tightly and consistently structured than is apparent when you read it as a string of words. Beneath the sentences and paragraphs lies a 'skeleton' of ideas.

Getting to the 'bones' of an argument

As I noted earlier, any text has just a few central ideas running through it. However, you wouldn't be able to understand these ideas properly, nor see their importance, if the writer simply stated them baldly in the fewest possible words. So, the writer puts 'flesh on the bare bones', giving examples and evidence – he or she 'talks you through' the argument, to show you how the ideas 'work'.

Once you have understood, you don't need the 'flesh' any more – you can just hold the 'bones' in your mind. Making notes is one way of picking out the bones. You should finish up with your own version of the author's key ideas, set out in a way that makes sense to *you*.

A simple diagram requires an extra investment of time, but it can help to clarify your thoughts. For example, when you can see the 'bare bones' of a piece, you will probably find it much easier to use the contents in an assignment. And, now we have done all this work on making notes, you must surely have a much better grasp of the Collee article, as well as a much better likelihood of remembering it. You should play around with various note-making methods for yourself, to find out when the gain in understanding and remembering is worth the cost in time and effort.

I'm sure that your own notes on the Collee article were quite different from any of my versions. You don't need a detailed grasp of food poisoning right now, so it wouldn't have been worth your while to invest a lot of time in close reading and elaborate note-making. At times, though, you *will* need a detailed understanding, so it is worth experimenting with different note-making styles for use on different occasions.

What are note-making skills?

Note-making is not a single 'skill', something you acquire once, for all times and occasions. It is a range of different activities, the common characteristic of which is that you are *writing for yourself* rather than an 'audience', so you don't have to worry about 'explaining' yourself.

Making notes is more 'strategy' than 'skill'. Being good at making notes involves reading texts in an active way – thinking 'What is this about?', 'What do I want to remember?', and then writing down the answers.

Note-making also requires flexibility – sometimes making detailed notes, sometimes very sketchy ones. You need to keep looking back at your notes and asking yourself 'Are they doing the job I want them to?' and 'Could I be using my time more effectively?' Think about your answers to these questions, and then adjust your approach accordingly.

5.3 What is the point of note-making?

What is achieved by making notes? What did you write down for Question 1 in the Activity Break on page 44? Here are some of my ideas.

Focusing your attention

Making notes is an excellent way of stopping your mind from wandering as you read. Mark (in Chapter 1) should have started underlining and jotting, and stopped worrying so much about what to write down. (Notes can come out any old way if necessary. Special techniques take time to develop.)

'Making' sense

As you make notes you are forcing yourself to look for *sense* in the words of the text. Furthermore, you are making yourself formulate the ideas in the text in a way that makes sense to *you.*

A form of 'external' memory

The notes you make act, in effect, as a kind of *extension to the memory capacity of your mind* – enabling you to have ready access to a far wider range of knowledge.

A symbol of progress

Notes provide you with evidence of the work you have done, so they can make an important contribution to your morale.

Preparing an assignment

Making notes which draw together what you have learned from your various study activities is a basic step in preparing for many kinds of assignment (see Chapter 9).

Pulling the course together

As you study a course, and range over a number of different topics, your mind can become cluttered with lots of disconnected bits and pieces of information. You can create some order, and make your ideas less confused and more useful, by making notes which summarize a section of the course (even if they're just a set of headings).

What note-making provides is an opportunity to develop each of the major steps of the learning spiral outlined in Chapter 1 (see page 21); it helps you to take in new information, think through novel ideas, and communicate your new understanding to others.

Making notes on notes

Sometimes, it can be useful to bring together notes you have already made to make a new, condensed version (that is, to make notes summarizing earlier notes). This can be a great help to your learning in general, because it makes your mind create orderliness at a higher level in your thinking – not 'perfect' orderliness, perhaps not something you'd like to show to other people – but a lot better than no order at all.

Notes of this kind can be especially useful as part of your revision for an exam (see Chapter 10). It is also a good idea to try to pull things together at other stages of a course – for example, when you have finished one topic and are about to move on to another.

Ready-made notes and formula sheets

Sometimes, you can make use of summaries, which give you just the key points. Or you may be given a revision guide at the end of a topic. These outlines help to show you the 'bones' of the subject, but they are not a substitute for making your own notes, because you miss out on the vital process of *thinking* about what the subject means to *you*. However, if you write your own notes on the same sheet, with arrows and lines linking them to the structure already provided, you can combine your insights with those of the author or your tutor.

You may also be given a formula sheet, saving you the trouble of compiling your own list of key formulas. You must, of course, practise *using* these formulas, so that you know what the terms mean. Don't just rely on having the list.

Having stressed all the positive points, it is important to add that making notes is not a panacea. You can do too much and end up making your studies tedious. The pleasure of exploring new areas of reading is one of the main things that keeps you studying. If note-making undermines that pleasure, it is counter-productive. When you read without making *any* notes, you will find that the content gradually drifts away from you – not simply because of the limits of your memory, but because new learning moves in and takes over the mental territory. But the last thing you want is to turn all your studying into a dreary chore. The art is to find the right balance.

Key Point

Making notes helps you in many different ways. Learning when and how to make notes as you study is critical to your development as a student.

5.4 What should you do with your notes?

If making notes is a way of 'extending your memory', then clearly you need to work out a system for storing them, so that you can find what you want, when you want it. As a start, get hold of some folders and some boxes, and make shelf space for storing them. Then, begin to develop a system. It is easy to end up with large piles of notes, so disorganized that you can't face trying to find what you want. When you are starting out it is hard to believe that you could ever produce enough notes to create filing problems. But you will waste a lot of the time you invest in the notes if you don't also invest some in working out a filing system.

Notebook or loose-leaf file?

Some people use a notebook for all their notes, and draw a line across the page after each study session. It can be very useful to have everything in one place and in sequence. And as you progress through the course, you build up a summary of the course contents. On the other hand, a loose-leaf folder has the advantage of flexibility – you can add pages, include assignments when you get them back from your tutor, and change the order of the pages around if it helps. But will you be disciplined enough to keep it up to date and in some sort of order?

Having stored your notes in a suitable form, how are you going to use them? You might fondly imagine that you will sit down and diligently read them through. Perhaps you will. On the other hand, there tends to be a shortage of suitable time – life, as they say, is too short. Your course will keep driving you forward; there will always be another topic to study, another assignment to complete. Going back over old notes is seldom as urgent, or as attractive, as moving on to something new. But I don't want to sell note-making short. Looking back over your notes is an important way of consolidating your understanding. It's a way of making sure that topics studied in detail months before don't slip from your mind. Even brief moments spent looking back at earlier work can be useful and may make a welcome change from the job in hand. Your notes should become more accessible and digestible than the sources from which they were derived.

You need notes that are easy to consult for a specific purpose, such as looking for material for an assignment or pulling together ideas for an exam (see Chapter 10). So, don't make mountains of notes. Make them short, succinct and well-structured. Then, they will be better for reference purposes, and they will also make it easier for you to refresh your memory about the range of topics covered in the course. When you start to revise your course, your notes should prove invaluable. And, even if you never go back to your notes, they're still useful – the process of writing them was valuable in itself.

6 Conclusion

Reading is one of the central activities in most courses of study. The purpose of reading is to make you *learn*. But learning is not a *passive* process. You don't just let ideas wash over you. Instead, you have to *make sense* of concepts, information and techniques, and then put them to *use* for your own purposes.

Key Points

Reading for study purposes is not simply a matter of passing your eyes across hundreds of words. It is *a set of practices* which you develop to enable you to *engage* with the knowledge in the text. These practices include:

◆ *defining your task* as you set out to read (setting a target)

◆ *underlining or highlighting* as you read, if appropriate

◆ *making notes*, as and when appropriate

◆ *stopping* to look forwards or backwards in the text when you lose your way

◆ *checking* other sources when you are in difficulties

◆ *monitoring* your progress from time to time

◆ *changing your approach* as necessary.

As a beginner, it is worth *experimenting* with a range of different ways of doing things, so that you have a wider base of experience to work from in developing a robust, flexible, all-round style. To read effectively, you have to be able to work out *what you are trying to achieve* and *how well you are progressing*. It is not easy to make these judgements – but they are what becoming a skilled student is all about.

CHAPTER 3

Working with diagrams

1 About this chapter

This chapter will look at how pictures and diagrams can be used to represent information and ideas. In MST subjects, we can often summarize how ideas or processes are connected much more neatly in a diagram than in words, or we can show how something looks and works by drawing a picture of it. This means that, as a student, you need to be comfortable with pictures and diagrams. You need to learn how to *read* them – how to extract information from them and interpret what they mean. And you need to learn how to *draw* pictures and diagrams of your own, so that you can capture your own ideas and interpretations on paper. So, part of this chapter deals with the reading of diagrams and part with the drawing of diagrams, although it is often difficult to separate the two activities.

The chapter is divided into three sections:

◆ what pictures and diagrams can do
◆ how pictures and diagrams can help you to study texts
◆ how pictures and diagrams can improve your assignments.

2 Seeing the world

With a heading like this one, you may be wondering if the book has suddenly turned into a travel brochure. If it had, would you carry on reading if there were no pictures of the places you could visit? I certainly wouldn't. I hesitate to use the old saying about 'one picture saves a thousand words', but if I didn't mention it you would be thinking it. Pictures or diagrams can be very evocative and thought-provoking, but they can also communicate a lot of information very quickly.

A ctivity Break

1 Try to think of three examples of pictures or diagrams you see regularly in your home.

2 Write down what these pictures or diagrams represent to you.

3 What do you use them for?

(Here are some possibilities to get you started: newspapers, television, book covers, calendars, road maps, DIY books, washing-machine instructions.)

Here are my answers.

◆ The first thing I had to hand was today's newspaper. It was full of photographs of things or events. I read a newspaper to tell me what is happening in the world, and it helps a lot to have pictures of people, places and happenings. I now know what my MP looks like. My rather hazy, abstract image has turned into a 'real person'. I feel that I can now envisage how he might react in different situations. (When I'm reading a novel, I like to make up my own picture of what the characters look like.)

◆ Next, I picked up a road map from the hall. This is a very colourful diagram that uses many types of symbols, but I find it easy to follow, using the key, and invaluable in planning my car journeys. It 'represents' how certain features of the real world relate to each other in terms of distance. So, for example, I know that the distance from Milton Keynes to Birmingham is about 110 kilometres, and that I can drive there in just over an hour.

◆ The last diagram I noted was our calendar. This represents the days of the week – 'time' in other words – and enables me and my partner to make a note of important dates, such as my mother's birthday, our next dental appointment, and when my partner's next assignment is due in (and the fact that it clashes with a trip to the cinema). I can see at a glance all the things I feel I need to know, days, even weeks, in advance.

Here are some students' answers.

◆ I wake up and look at my watch. There are 12 identical lines around the outside of a circular face. I know that these lines represent the hours of the day. The watch-face tells me that it is time to get up.

◆ We have a gas cooker in the kitchen. There are six knobs with arrows on them. Each knob has a small picture above it. These pictures tell me that the grill is the second knob from the left, or that the small ring at the back is the knob farthest to the right, and so on.

◆ My computing book tells me about aspects of my personal computer that affect how it runs and about how to improve its performance. I use the book for those reasons, but it's also helped by showing me what various bits of hardware look like. The label 'hard drive' was a grey area until I saw a picture of it. Suddenly, just by seeing that it was a cylinder of metal, I lost all the uncertainty that I used to feel when I read the words 'hard drive'.

I can see a pattern in the examples I used in my answers. I started off with pictures of real-world objects or events in a newspaper. These pictures look very much like what my eyes would see if I were there, albeit only part of the full scene. Then I chose a road map, which is a very simplified diagram of what I would see if I were looking down from a plane. The map sets out to highlight certain things – such as roads, service stations and motorway junctions – that are relevant to car journeys. Yet, although this type of diagram shows things that are actually there for my eyes to see, it does not look at all *like* what my eyes would see. The red line on the map is obviously not actually a road – you can't drive on a red line. But we think of it as a road because we know that this is what the line stands for. The map is much easier to 'read' than an aerial photograph, because it leaves out a lot of detail that I don't need, and uses standard symbols to represent the things I do need to know about. Finally, I chose a diagram of something you can't actually see, although it represents something that you know exists – a continuing sequence of days that, for convenience, are grouped together in sevens as the days of the week.

There is similar variety in the examples chosen by the students. Some of them are pictures of real objects (for example, the hard drive in the computing book). Yet others (for example, the watch-face) represent interrelationships between things (lines) and concepts (time). And lastly, there are diagrams that act as convenient symbols to convey information (the symbols on the cooker).

Another impression I get from these examples is that they are all familiar. We all understand and use certain types and styles of diagrams from an early age: for example, reading the time from a watch-face. They are also an efficient way of organizing information – for example, the calendar or the map. However, the types and uses of diagrams are rooted in cultural and/or different academic disciplines. So, a modern map looks quite different from an eighteenth-century map, and pictures of real objects are more common in biology (where things are easy to see) than in subatomic physics (where they are not so easy to see).

2.1 Types of diagrams

As there is this variety in the types of diagrams we use, we need to think more broadly about what pictures and diagrams are trying to represent. You will encounter three main types of diagrams when studying MST subjects.

1   *Pictures* or *pictorial diagrams* that attempt to represent the essential features of a part of reality – for example, diagrams of equipment, molecules or parts of a plant.

2   Diagrams that try to describe *interrelationships* between ideas, processes or concepts using words, lines and various blobs or boxes.

3   *Mathematical diagrams*, such as charts and graphs, that are mainly designed to convey mathematical relationships – for example, comparisons over time.

Figure 3.1 *Examples of pictorial diagrams. These are different representations of parts of a plant leaf. The details needn't concern you, but the diagrams differ in scale (the highest magnification, showing a single cell, is at the top), in the amount and type of information conveyed (both structure and processes are represented), and in how realistic they are (the bottom diagram is stylized for clarity)*

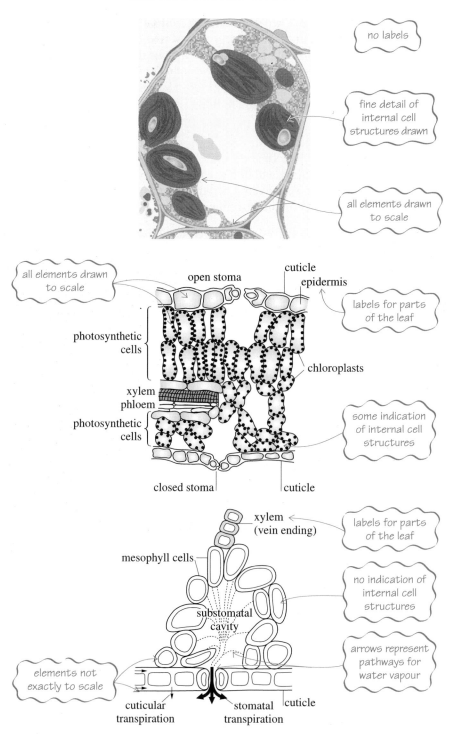

no labels

fine detail of internal cell structures drawn

all elements drawn to scale

all elements drawn to scale

open stoma

cuticle
epidermis

labels for parts of the leaf

photosynthetic cells

chloroplasts

xylem
phloem

photosynthetic cells

some indication of internal cell structures

closed stoma

cuticle

xylem (vein ending)

labels for parts of the leaf

mesophyll cells

no indication of internal cell structures

substomatal cavity

arrows represent pathways for water vapour

elements not exactly to scale

cuticular transpiration

stomatal transpiration

cuticle

Pictures, or pictorial diagrams, are a common feature of texts in MST subjects. At their simplest, they are photographs of real objects; at their most complex, they are colourful, fully labelled drawings of the inner workings of organisms or machines. The drawings of bacteria in the Collee article and the diagram of the cress seedling in Chapter 9 (Figure 9.1 on page 244) are good examples. Some other examples, with comments attached, are shown in Figure 3.1.

In nearly all cases, the purpose of the diagram is to illustrate particular features of the world around us. In some cases, the diagrams are used to make the text look pretty or appealing and don't really add anything to the understanding of the reader. And even when they're used more effectively, there is still a need to reflect on the information that is being conveyed.

◆ Is there a reference to the picture in the accompanying text?

◆ Is there a title or legend explaining what the picture is about?

◆ Are there labels on the diagram?

◆ What are the size and scale of the objects?

◆ Is the picture a simplified and stylized representation of a complex situation?

Relationship diagrams

Relationship diagrams are largely non-pictorial and aim to represent the structural or organizational features of a situation through combinations of words, lines and arrows, and a wide selection of boxes, blobs and circles. Examples of this type of diagram include the spray diagram in Chapter 2 (page 49), and the first diagram, entitled 'Some of the ways … spread', in the Collee article (page 398). Some other examples are shown in Figure 3.2. In some cases, such as flow diagrams, there may also be numbers, but these diagrams are not primarily used for mathematical relationships (which are often represented using graphs and charts – see the next section).

Relationship diagrams can be broadly divided into those that represent static relationships – for example, maps, classification trees, organization charts, circuit diagrams and influence diagrams – and those that represent a situation over a period of time – for example, flow charts, decision trees, activity sequence diagrams, algorithms and multiple-cause diagrams. You needn't worry for the moment about what these terms mean – you'll probably come across examples as you progress through your studies.

Figure 3.2 Examples of relationship diagrams. Don't be too concerned about the details of the various processes shown here – think more in terms of the variety of different approaches that are possible and the different conventions that are adopted

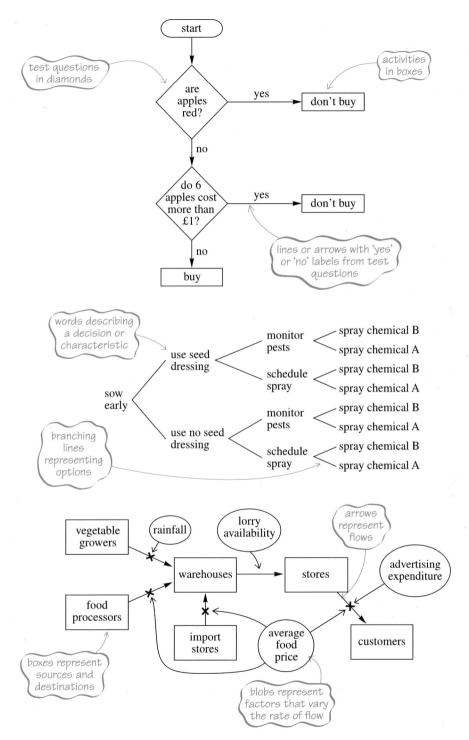

start

test questions in diamonds

activities in boxes

are apples red?

yes → don't buy

no

do 6 apples cost more than £1?

yes → don't buy

no

buy

lines or arrows with 'yes' or 'no' labels from test questions

words describing a decision or characteristic

sow early

use seed dressing

monitor pests
— spray chemical B
— spray chemical A

schedule spray
— spray chemical B
— spray chemical A

use no seed dressing

monitor pests
— spray chemical B
— spray chemical A

schedule spray
— spray chemical B
— spray chemical A

branching lines representing options

vegetable growers

rainfall

lorry availability

arrows represent flows

warehouses → stores

advertising expenditure

food processors

import stores

average food price

customers

boxes represent sources and destinations

blobs represent factors that vary the rate of flow

As with pictorial diagrams, there are questions that must be asked of relationship diagrams.

◆ Is there a reference or an explanation of the diagram in the accompanying text?

◆ Is there a title or legend explaining what type of relationship diagram it is, and what situation it represents?

◆ Is there a key to show what the lines/arrows, boxes/blobs and so on represent?

Graphs and charts

Line graphs, histograms and bar charts are diagrams that show the relationship between two different quantities. For example, in hospital, a patient's temperature is often recorded at regular intervals and plotted as a line graph. This allows medical staff to see at a glance how high the temperature is and how it is changing. You often see graphs and charts in the media summarizing unemployment figures or a company's profits over the last few months. There are two examples of these types of diagram in the Collee article – 'The longer food ...' (on page 399) and 'Numbers of bacteria ...' (on page 401) – as well as several more in this chapter.

Whatever form they take, graphs and charts are used because they summarize numerical information in a way that provides a quick, visual overview but still gives you access to large amounts of data in a condensed format. Whereas a line graph or histogram shows continuous data for all intervals, a bar chart is often used for discrete intervals – say, data from every other year – or when there is more than one value for a particular interval. (There are examples of these types of diagram in Figure 3.3.) A pie chart is simply a way of indicating the proportions of items, with the size of the slices sometimes providing yet more information (see the example on page 179). There is more information on line graphs in Section 10 of Maths Help, particularly in relation to the representation of mathematical relationships rather than just numerical information.

Graphs and charts need to be read very carefully, and the way to do this is described in Section 3.2. Figure 3.3 shows all the features of a typical line graph, histogram and bar chart.

Figure 3.3 *Examples of a line graph (top), a histogram (middle) and a bar chart (bottom). Again, you needn't worry about what data are displayed here (although you may be familiar with the values in the line graph as they're taken from the Collee article)*

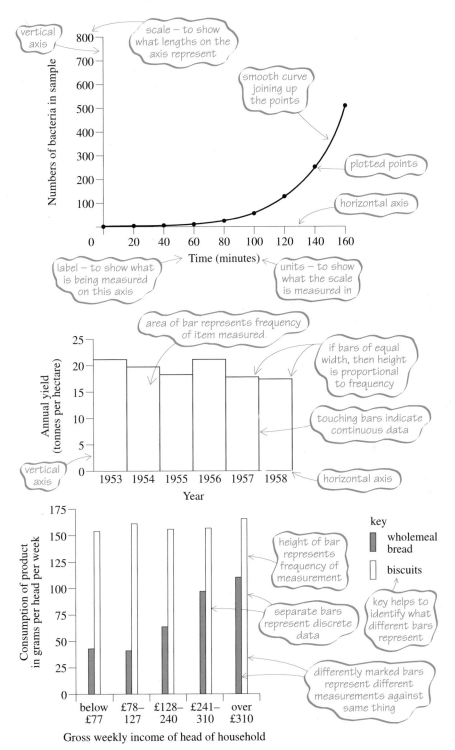

This brief outline of the types of diagrams you will meet should give you some idea of their purposes and main features. But how and when do you use them? I'll be looking at both these questions in this chapter, although the emphasis will be on relationship diagrams and graphs and charts. Before I start, I want to emphasize that whenever we *take in*, *think about* and *express* new ideas as part of our learning spiral (see Figure 1.5 on page 22), we *describe* and *represent* reality (in words, diagrams or numbers) by making *simplifications* for some *purpose*. This has to be so, because reality is so complicated. It is essential to simplify the 'real world' in order to be able to describe it or think about it.

In simplifying, we *select* certain features of a situation – the essentials – to communicate a clear message, without too much clutter obscuring the view. The view or perspective taken and the selection of features are extremely important in conveying that message. If the photograph of my MP mentioned on page 57 had been taken from 100 metres rather than 10 metres (using the same camera lens), he would probably have been indistinguishable in a crowd of people, or too small to recognize. Similarly, my calendar is great for seeing a week at a time, but my work diary has one day per page – fine for noting down all the meetings I have, but not so good for a long-term view of my workload.

In the two sections that follow, I'll be looking first at how diagrams can help your studying, and second, at how to use diagrams in your assignments. These topics equate to taking in and thinking through new ideas, and then expressing those newly formed ideas, as described in the learning spiral you met in Chapter 1.

3 Thinking through diagrams

3.1 Analysing text

Some people find it easy to use diagrams in their studies. But I realize that there are others who don't take to diagrams at all enthusiastically. If this is how *you* feel, please read what follows, as I am convinced that *everyone* can get something from using diagrams to help their thinking. However, if after working through these sections, you still believe that diagramming as an aid to studying is 'not for you', then don't force yourself into an approach that doesn't suit you. But remember that many assignments in MST subjects will either expect or even require the use of certain types of diagrams, so the skills involved in reading and using all types of diagrams are well worth developing.

Rewriting text as relationship diagrams

In Chapter 2, you were shown how a spray diagram can help with note-making (see Figure 2.5 on page 49). In this section, I want to go a little further and show how you can use diagrams to help *you* understand what someone else has written. Here, it doesn't matter how well you can draw, as long as the finished diagram makes sense to you. As you become more confident at drawing diagrams for yourself, you will be able to move on to drawing diagrams for your tutor.

At this stage, you may still have doubts about the value of diagrams for understanding situations. So, why not try using one?

---

*A**ctivity Break*** Quickly sketch one or two diagrams to convey the relationships described in Box 3.1. (If you need to, refresh your memory by looking back at Section 2.1 for ideas about the different relationship diagrams you could use.)

Box 3.1

Jane is married to Tom and they live at No. 8. Tom's sister, Dawn, lives at No. 20 and has three children: Peter, Paul and Mary. Dawn's partner, Derek, left her four years ago and moved to Scotland, and she is now living with John. John has two children of his own, Tim and Nicholas, from his marriage to Julie. Julie's father, Alf, works in the same factory as Tom's father, while Dawn's mother and Jane's mother went to school together. Alf and Millie live at No. 34. They used to live at No. 6, but moved when the children left home. Dawn has two older brothers, one of whom has moved away. Keith and Pamela are Tom's parents, but Pamela died last year. Keith now lives alone at No. 18.

The situation described in Box 3.1 is complicated and difficult to follow as text. When I gave this activity to several students, some of them produced diagrams like the one in Figure 3.4. This diagram makes the situation easier to understand, but it is still a bit complicated. However, other students eventually realized that they needed two diagrams. The first diagram (Figure 3.5) shows who is related to whom using two family trees; the second (Figure 3.6) shows who lives in which house. I certainly found that looking at these diagrams made things a lot clearer for me – in particular, in terms of the relationships between two different sets of connected things. Of course, these diagrams are just how some students chose to represent the situation, and they do not include all the information given in the box. The students selected what they thought was essential information. Someone who read this chapter suggested that I should add the arrivals and departures to Figure 3.6 (see Figure 3.7). And a few students drew Figure 3.6 as a line of boxes rather than blobs to show that the street is likely to be a 'line' of houses. You may have thought up other ways of tackling this activity, but I am sure that the process of producing a diagram improved your understanding of the situation. Whether your diagram would clearly convey the situation to other people can be tested only by trying it out – and, indeed, the comments of others can be very helpful.

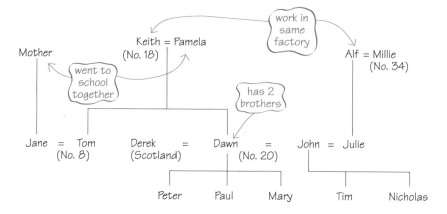

Figure 3.4 *A student's diagram showing all the relationships described in Box 3.1*

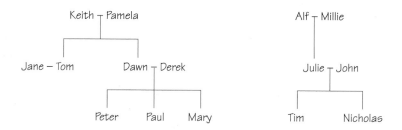

Figure 3.5 *Another student's diagram showing who is related to whom*

Figure 3.6 *Another student's diagram showing who lives where*

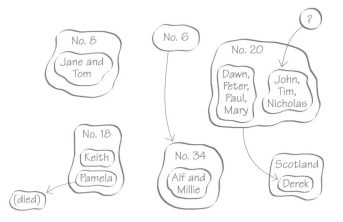

Figure 3.7 *A modified diagram showing where they all live now and where they used to live*

I hope this example has shown you the value of using diagrams rather than text to represent some relationships. Diagrams allow the relationships between parts of a situation to be seen at the same time as the parts themselves. And, whether or not your diagram makes sense to other people, it can help *you* to understand. When you can see the whole situation sketched out in front of you, then you are in a position to check (or ask someone else to check) whether all the links you have shown are logical, and whether you have included all the essential components. If the diagram does not make sense to you, then it may be that you have failed to understand the text. (Remember that these diagrams are for your personal needs and not necessarily for your tutor's eyes – that comes later in this chapter.) If your diagram makes sense to you, there is an additional bonus: it is often much easier to *remember* schematized information than strings of information. Which would you find easier to remember – the text in Box 3.1 or the diagrams the students produced?

One of the problems with written accounts is that they are 'linear'. In other words, the sentences follow one after another, in a line; they come in a given order. This is fine for accounts of events that do happen in sequence. It is not so appropriate when things are intimately connected, and do not fall into a particular order. For example, you could think of the first diagram in the Collee article (page 398) as a series of *interconnected sentences*. But these sentences have escaped from the normal convention in which one sentence follows another in order. We can see them all at the same time. In making the escape, a whole new way of thinking has opened up – a way of thinking that highlights things that are concealed when we use ordinary English. So, diagrams are not simply a way to convey meaning – they can make you aware of previously unrealized features of a situation. They help you to study more effectively. You can try this out for yourself by doing the following activity.

A *ctivity Break* Working from the Gerald Collee article, draw a relationship diagram in the form of interconnected sentences to describe how the following three factors contribute to food poisoning:

◆ numbers of bacteria eaten
◆ temperature
◆ time.

Concentrate on paragraphs 5 to 8. Start by writing down a few phrases – for example, 'large number of bacteria', 'food stored at too high a temperature' – and use arrows to indicate how they are linked. Build your diagram up step by step. Can you label the arrows? What are the final outcomes of the events you describe? Don't be concerned about the technical terms in the Collee article, simply try to use the idea of connected sentences to 'rewrite' the text and graphs.

You may find that this activity takes you as long as 20 to 40 minutes. Don't worry if you find it difficult at this stage in your studies. Have a go now, and come back to it again if you need to when you've read more of this chapter.

One student's answer is shown as Figure 3.8. This is a good attempt at rewriting the text as a relationship diagram. It includes all three factors and provides three possible outcomes – illness, diarrhoea and no illness – in the same way as Collee's second diagram (page 399). I'd prefer to see words on all the arrows, to separate 'actions' from 'outcomes' and give specific meanings to the links. For instance, I think the words 'delay of 1 or 2 days' could be added to the arrow going to 'diarrhoea may result', and 'dealt with by' to the arrow going to 'normal body defences'.

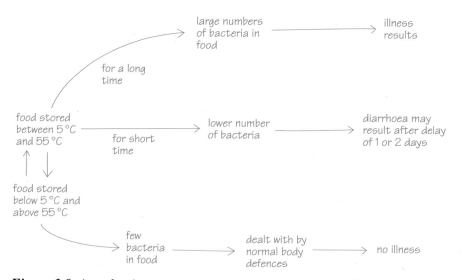

Figure 3.8 *A student's attempt at rewriting text from the Collee article as a relationship diagram*

My answer is shown as Figure 3.9. After looking at it for a while, I noticed that I had described a 'chain' of events leading from the starting points of:

◆ low numbers of bacteria

◆ more time

◆ higher temperatures

to three different end points of:

◆ no food poisoning

◆ diarrhoea

◆ death.

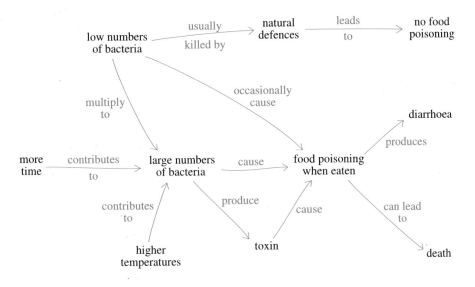

Figure 3.9 *My attempt at rewriting text from the Collee article as a relationship diagram*

This began to make me think that the words 'low', 'more' and 'higher' are imprecise – but as the article implies, there is variation in how different bacteria react to these factors. So, I decided to leave it this way. I also thought about things that were 'missing', such as the links back to diarrhoea, and to contamination of water or food by low numbers of bacteria. These links are shown in the first figure in the Collee article (page 398), but as they don't feature in paragraphs 5 to 8, I decided to leave them out. That was my choice. You may have included them, and that is fine if it helps you to understand and appreciate the information in the article.

Don't worry if your diagram is not like either of the diagrams shown here. Different people are unlikely to represent things in exactly the same way unless they are given precise instructions or they collaborate. The main point at this stage is to improve your understanding of the situation by drawing out the various components and relationships.

To illustrate this learning process yet further, I have reinterpreted the first Collee diagram as a flow diagram to show the movement of bacteria (Figure 3.10). Flow diagrams are very common in MST subjects, although you'll find that they can take several different forms: materials flow diagrams, as exemplified by diagrams of biochemical pathways or nutrient cycles in an ecosystem, activity sequence diagrams, as used in project planning, and decision sequence diagrams, such as the flow charts used in computing (see Section 2.1).

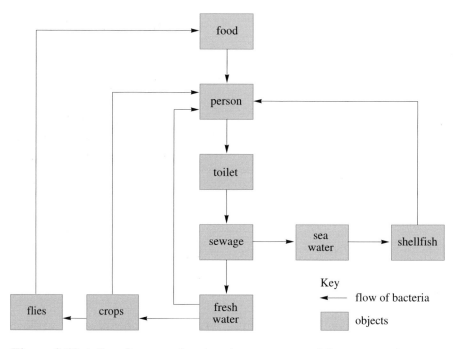

Figure 3.10 *A flow diagram showing the movement of disease-causing bacteria*

In the case of this flow diagram, the boxes represent objects and the arrows represent the transmission of bacteria from one object to another. But there is no comment on how the flow occurs. Thus bacteria present in contaminated food are eaten by people. If those people become ill, they pass the bacteria out into the toilet in their faeces. The bacteria then pass into sewage pipes, and so on. For me, drawing this flow diagram highlighted the cyclic nature of food- and water-borne diseases, which was already evident from the original diagram, but it also helped me to identify which aspects of the situation I find confusing. For example, I found it difficult to decide on the objects that were the source of the bacteria picked up by the flies. I decided to make it the crops, but it could equally have been the sewage works (which are not mentioned in the text). I feel that drawing a flow diagram has made me think harder about the situation, and has improved my chances of learning the most important points.

Key Points

Diagrams are helpful in clarifying your thinking because:

◆ they can summarize complex situations, allowing you to appreciate the complexity while seeing the individual components and the connections between those components

◆ they can give you new insights into a situation, by making you think carefully about the components and connections.

3.2 Reading diagrams

When you're studying, following the sense of a piece of text may not be straightforward. Often, you'll need to rewrite the text as notes or a diagram. Equally, some diagrams will need careful reading, and you'll have to make notes or draw other diagrams. So, how can we *read* different types of diagrams?

Activity Break Spend a few minutes looking critically at all four diagrams in the Collee article. Write down what you see as their general features. (You may want to refer back to Section 2.1.)

The first feature I noticed was that, within the four diagrams, each of the three broad categories I listed in Section 2 is represented: a relationship diagram, two mathematical diagrams and a pictorial diagram respectively.

The second feature, reflected in the first, is that none of the diagrams (or figures as they are often called in textbooks) has a number assigned to it, which makes reference to it extremely difficult (compared with most of the figures in this book). Indeed, the diagrams are not even referred to in the main body of the article, and so we have no clues about when we should break our reading of the text to read the diagrams. This is also a common shortcoming in assignments, and you should remember to avoid it.

The third feature is that two of the diagrams contain a mixture of words and pictures (the first and second). The question then is: Does this help us read the diagram and extract the relevant ideas?

Reading diagrams: questioning what they say

With each of these diagrams, and with others you are trying to read, there are several questions you can ask.

◆ What is the *purpose* of the diagram, that is, what is it aiming to tell us?

◆ How is the information *imparted*?

◆ What *assumptions* does it make about our ability to understand it?

◆ What are we expected to *remember*?

◆ How *successful* is it in doing all of the above?

A*ctivity Break* Look at the first three diagrams in the Collee article and think about the above questions. You may find this activity difficult until you have read all of this chapter, particularly the sections on graphs and charts, but have a go now and come back to it again when you have finished the chapter.

---

1 First diagram: 'Some of the ways ... can spread' (page 398).

Purpose?: The purpose is summed up by the caption or title (which should be a major function of the caption), but the diagram also appears to outline the 'paths' by which diseases are spread, as well as the ways in which they are spread. If this information were written as text, it would be a very long piece and have less impact.

How imparted?: The information is imparted through a mixture of realistic pictures, to show the sources of infection, and diagrammatic flow lines, to show the transport 'paths'.

Assumptions?: We are expected to know what the arrows mean. The arrows are not explained, as they should be, in the caption.

Remember?: That there are different sources of infection and different transport 'paths'.

How successful?: The realistic pictures create visual images that are easily recalled and can be related to the real world. A lot of information is conveyed in a small space, including the transport 'paths', the cyclical nature of the overall process and the possibilities of reinfection. The lack of a full explanation of what the arrows represent is unfortunate.

2 Second diagram: 'The longer food is left ... delayed disease' (page 399).

Purpose?: The purpose is partly stated in the caption, but it is not totally clear. I think the graph is being used to show the relationships between the three variables of time, number of bacteria and degree of illness.

How imparted?: The information is imparted by a mixture of graphical methods and pictorial representation.

Assumptions?: It is assumed that we recognize that the numbers of bacteria are increasing up the vertical axis, and that the width of the arrow is proportional to the numbers of bacteria (this is not a standard convention, so it could be confusing). We are also expected to know that the two diagonal slash lines on the horizontal axis represent a significant time gap, and that the different dotted lines represent different outcomes.

Remember?: That falling ill and the degree of illness depend on the number of bacteria eaten. This is a qualitative statement, because no quantities are given on the graph.

Successful?: I don't think this is a successful diagram, because it mixes up too many factors: number of bacteria, time and temperature. And as you'll appreciate from the Activity Break on page 68, the relationship is complex. The lack of numbers lessens the impact of the diagram, while the significance of the words and the rectangular box is unclear. The use of both solid and dotted lines is also confusing. The ideas might be put across more effectively using text or a number of different diagrams.

3   Third diagram: 'Numbers of bacteria ... three hours' (page 401).

Purpose?: To show the rapid increase in numbers of bacteria over time. This is made clear in the figure caption.

How imparted?: The information is conveyed by means of a histogram, which is an easy way of comparing a lot of continuous data when overall effect, rather than precise numbers, is what matters.

Assumptions?: That we know that the height of the columns represents the number of bacteria at given time intervals (as the columns are of equal width). This assumption is not stated explicitly in the caption.

Remember?: That because the numbers of bacteria double every 20 minutes, there is a very rapid increase in the numbers of bacteria.

Successful?: This method of representation makes an immediate visual impact and gets the main message across quickly. However, the absence of scales and labelling on the axes is unhelpful and unacceptable.

I hope that this activity and my responses have made you think a bit harder about what diagrams are trying to communicate and about how you can interpret them. But, as I have already noted, you may have to do more than just read diagrams, you may have to redraw them in some way.

Reading graphs and charts: manipulating numbers

Text is just one way of communicating information. Numbers are another way, but whether presented singly, in groups or even as tables (see Chapter 5), numbers often require a lot of work from the reader to uncover the message. A much more immediate and powerful way to present numerical information is to use graphs and charts. When you use single numbers or tables, the reader has to visualize the meaning of the numbers. Graphs and charts allow the reader to do this at a glance. To show how powerful these representations can be, look at a bar chart created from the numbers in Table 3.1 (Figure 3.11).

Table 3.1 Percentage of total notified salmonella food poisoning incidents caused by different species in selected years

Year	*Salmonella typhimurium*	*Salmonella enteritidis*	Other types of salmonella
1981	38.9	10.7	50.4
1983	51.4	11.7	36.9
1985	41.1	23.2	35.7
1987	37.3	33.4	29.3
1989	24.3	52.6	23.1
1991	19.3	63.0	17.7
1993	15.6	66.1	18.3

Source: Communicable Disease Surveillance Centre

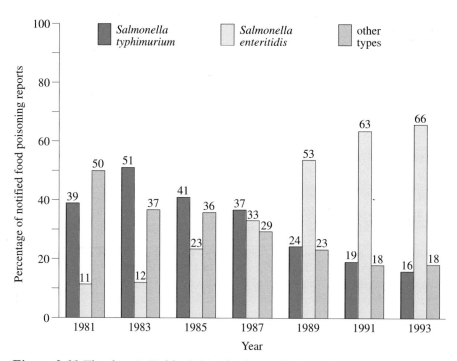

Figure 3.11 *The data in Table 3.1 in the form of a bar chart. (Although it's not standard practice, values are given next to the bars for reasons that are explained in the text)*

The bar chart in Figure 3.11 shows three bars for the first year, one bar for the percentage of food poisoning incidents caused by each of the two named types of salmonella bacteria, plus one bar for all the other types of salmonella lumped together. After a gap, there are three bars for the next year, then another three for the third year, and so on for each of the seven years selected. This type of bar chart is used to compare different sets of data and is called a *comparative bar chart*.

Activity Break   Compare the numbers in the two representations to convince yourself that the bar chart is the data from the table presented in a different way.

Look at the top row of numbers in Table 3.1. Find the figure 38.9% – which is the percentage of salmonella-related food poisoning incidents in 1981 caused by *Salmonella typhimurium*. If you 'round' this figure to the nearest whole number, it comes to 39% (some advice on rounding numbers up and down and the errors this can produce is to be found in Maths Help on pages 346 to 349). Now look at the top of the left-hand bar in Figure 3.11. Again, the figure is 39% – so this vertical bar stands for the percentage of food poisoning incidents due to *Salmonella typhimurium* in 1981. The key at the top of the chart tells you this. Now check the first figure in the next column of Table 3.1. It shows a 10.7% level of food poisoning incidents. This rounds to 11. On top of the second bar in Figure 3.11 you will see 11. Quickly check all the numbers in the table to convince yourself that they are the same as the numbers in the chart. Make sure you agree that the key at the top of the chart agrees with the headings in the table.

Now look at the table and see if you can detect any clear patterns. Then look at the chart, scanning from left to right and back again, trying to detect patterns. I hope you agree that the trends show up more clearly in the chart than in the table. You can see that the percentage of *Salmonella enteritidis* cases has risen steadily from a very low level to a very high level, whereas the percentage of incidents caused by *Salmonella typhimurium* has gradually decreased (as has the percentage of incidents caused by all other types of salmonella). This shows us what we have already learned from the table – that there have been consistent trends in the numbers of cases of certain food poisoning organisms. But the diagram brings out the message much more clearly and forcefully. This is one of the reasons for presenting data in diagrams rather than in tables. If you choose the right kind of diagram, it makes the *patterns* in the data very much clearer. Incidentally, when dealing with percentages, it often helps to draw a *percentage bar chart*, in which the bars are stacked on top of one another to make 100%. This emphasizes that you are dealing with proportions of a total rather than actual numbers.

In fact, the bar chart is not the only type of diagram we can use to display this type of data. We can also use a line graph (see Figure 3.12).

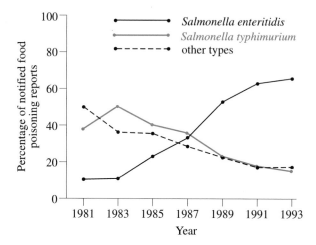

Figure 3.12 *The data in Figure 3.11 in the form of a line graph*

---

ctivity Break   Once again, try cross-checking some of the numbers from Table 3.1 to Figure 3.12, to convince yourself that we are indeed looking at the same data presented in a different way.

For instance, does 66.1% for the incidence of *Salmonella enteritidis* in 1993 occur in Figure 3.11, Figure 3.12 and Table 3.1?

If anything, the trends show up even more clearly in the line graph than in the bar chart. For example, you can see the steady rise in the proportion of *Salmonella enteritidis* incidents from 1981 at the left of the graph to 1993 at the right of the graph. And the 'blip' in the *Salmonella typhimurium* figure for 1983 is much more obvious. Indeed, the line graph is so clear and direct that you might well ask why anyone would bother with a bar chart.

The reasons for preferring a bar chart are, first, that it is not quite so abstract as the line graph, and second, that it represents the type of data involved better. When you see solid bars representing the food poisoning incidents in each year, it reminds you that the chart represents lots of real cases of people suffering. In fact, the bar chart gives you a better picture of the *overall quantity* of incidents in each year. That information is there in the line graph too, but it doesn't show up so clearly. With the line graph, the figures are condensed to a set of points, so you have to work a little harder to remind yourself of what the diagram is telling you. In addition, the numbers in Table 3.1 are discontinuous data for specific years, and so do not include all possible 12-month periods over the time covered. Although drawing lines to join up the points helps us to see trends, the lines do not represent points or years in-between.

Counting and measuring things

How numbers are used in graphs and charts depends on what the numbers are to represent.

Some things occur in a *discrete* way; the quantities change by one (or more) whole units at a time. You can't have three and a quarter eggs in a box; you have to have three or four. While the statisticians' 'average family' may contain 1.7 children, real families contain 0,1,2,3, … or more. Quantities that occur in a discrete way – the number of children in a family, the number of eggs in a box, or the weekly output of a car factory – can all be *counted*.

Other quantities occur in a *continuous* way. These quantities can change by amounts as small as (or smaller than) you can imagine. Examples include a person's weight or height, the amount of water in a tank, the temperature of that water, the amount of time spent on a journey, and so on. These quantities have to be *measured*.

Reading graphs and charts: getting started

Graphs and charts *ought* to be easy to read, since the main point of turning numbers into diagrams is to bring out their meaning more clearly. However, they are abstract representations that attempt to summarize certain aspects of the world in a condensed form. Consequently, they require a degree of mental effort on your part to bridge the gap between the formal pictures on the page and the aspects of 'reality' they represent. It is important to approach graphs and diagrams *carefully*, allowing yourself time to 'get the feel' of what you are looking at. Don't just assume you know what information a graph contains. Take a thorough look (and, if you have problems, see Section 10 of Maths Help).

The sheer visual impact of a chart or graph can make it difficult to look past the attractive layout and shading to the underlying message. So, it is a good idea to look quickly at the main headings and the axes, and then focus on a point here and there to check what you are being told. Pick on one of the bars or points on a line and tell yourself what it stands for. Scan your way around the diagram – up and down and from side to side. Similarly, examine in detail the words written around the diagram: the main headings, the key and the axes. The axes should always be labelled and should tell you what the units are (see Chapter 5 for a discussion of units). Read any small print by the diagram to make sure you don't draw the wrong conclusions. Check the scale of the axes and note where they start. Graphs and charts can be 'designed' to emphasize certain trends, as we saw in Figures 3.11 and 3.12, and this issue is highlighted by the graphs in Figure 3.13. They all show exactly the same information, but the reader may well interpret each graph differently.

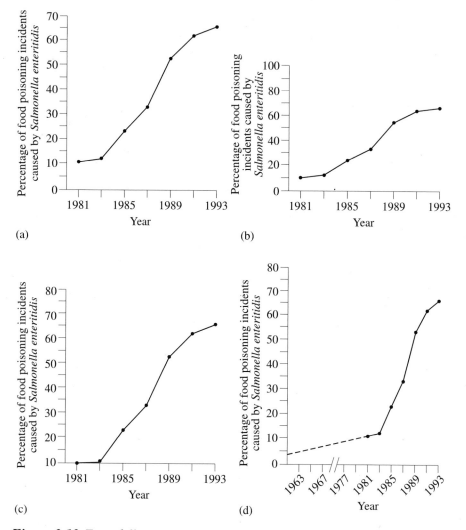

Figure 3.13 *Four different presentations of the same data*

Activity Break   Look at the graphs in Figure 3.13. What are your first impressions of the information they are trying to convey?

These graphs look, at first glance, to be completely different. However, if you examine them carefully, you will see that the numbers are exactly the same, only the vertical and horizontal scales are different. In Figure 3.13(b), the impression is given that the increase in the percentage of food poisoning incidents caused by *Salmonella enteritidis* has been very slight. Figure 3.13(a) gives the impression that the increase has been much more rapid. In Figure 3.13(c), it seems as if the rapid increase starts from a very low base, because of the use of a false zero (that is, starting with 10 at the origin). Figure 3.13(d) extends the horizontal axis and uses a break, like the one in Collee's second diagram, to give an impression of even faster rates of increase. It also extends the line back into areas where there are no specific data, thus further confusing the real trends. The lesson from the line graphs in Figure 3.13 is that you need to examine a graph very carefully before jumping to conclusions.

Reading graphs and charts: extracting information

When you are sure that you know what a chart or graph is all about, start to look for any main trends. Jot down for yourself a few conclusions that you think can be drawn. It often takes a little time before you can interpret the chart or graph properly. It is worth the effort, however, because information held in the form of a graph is highly patterned; and as our memories work by finding patterns in information and storing them, the information in graphs is easier to remember than information from a table or a text.

Graphs also make it easier to make predictions about information left out of the original table. For example, if you look along the line for *Salmonella enteritidis* in Figure 3.12, from 1989 to 1991, it suggests that the level for the year in-between (1990) is likely to be between about 53% and 63%. In other words, we can 'read off' predictions from a line plotted on a graph. But these predictions between points (called 'interpolations') must always be treated with caution. A lot depends on how the information has been gathered. In this case, because we are dealing with selected years, the line graph does not show all the variation there has been – for example, that the actual figure for 1990 is 62.6%, not much different to 1991's. You should treat predictions that go outside the range of figures (called 'extrapolations') with even more caution: for example, a prediction for 1963 – see Figure 3.13(d). You will find more about the issues surrounding interpolation and extrapolation in Maths Help on pages 382 and 383.

A final question you should ask is 'Where has the data come from, and is it shown in the most appropriate form?' Would the shape of the graph be different if we showed the actual numbers rather than percentages of reported incidents? To check this, I went back to the original source of the data and produced the graph in Figure 3.14 (overleaf). This graph is similar to Figure 3.12, but the trends have been slightly altered. Instead of a gradual decline in the percentages of cases of *Salmonella typhimurium* and the other types of salmonella, there seems to have been a more or less constant *number* of cases from year to year. And whereas Figure 3.12 implies that the proportion of *Salmonella enteritidis* incidents rises steadily over the years, Figure 3.14 suggests an extremely rapid, five-fold increase in the actual number of incidents between 1985 and 1989. So, the choice of the type of diagram has influenced the information we obtain from it.

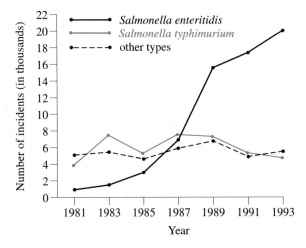

Figure 3.14 *A graph of the same data used in Figure 3.12, with incidents expressed as actual numbers rather than percentages*

Key Points

When reading charts or graphs, you should:

◆ Take time to get a 'feel' for what the chart or graph is telling you, that is, its purpose.

◆ Pick on one or two points and ensure they make sense to you.

◆ Read the scales on the axes and the words attached to them carefully to see what values the axes start at and what units they are measured in.

◆ Look for patterns, peaks and troughs, and blips.

◆ Look at the overall shape of a graph. Is it a straight line, a jagged line or a curve?

◆ Examine the sources of the data and think about how the information is presented in graphs and charts before accepting their conclusions.

4 Communicating through diagrams

So far in this chapter we have been looking at how you can improve your understanding of other people's texts and diagrams. I have shown you some study techniques that you can use to 'translate' text into diagrams and diagrams into meaningful text. However, this discussion has been focused on what you can do for yourself. At some point, you'll have to produce assignments that require, or will be enhanced by, the use of diagrams. One of the first decisions you'll face is whether to use an existing diagram or develop one of your own.

4.1 Using diagrams from course materials or other sources

Using diagrams from the course materials or other sources in assignments is a good idea. Properly used, they will help you to express yourself concisely and gain the maximum advantage from any word limit. They also offer you an opportunity both to deepen your learning about a subject and to demonstrate your ability to analyse and express that new understanding to another person.

To show how a diagram can make your ideas come alive, I'll demonstrate what might be done using the first diagram from the Collee article (page 398). Let's imagine that you have been asked to write an assignment on the factors involved in the spread of food- or water-borne diseases and consider the options available.

Option 1: Don't use the diagram at all

*A*ctivity Break   It is quite possible to write a good answer to the question without using the diagram. What do you think are the advantages and disadvantages of not using the diagram?

If you are someone who is not a 'diagrams person', then not using the diagram would save you struggling with something that makes you feel uncomfortable.

For those who do feel able to use diagrams, this particular diagram is quite complex to draw as it uses realistic images. You could redraw the diagram, with words replacing the drawings (see Figure 3.15 overleaf), but in many cases a realistic diagram will be required, in which case you'll need to think about Option 2.

In terms of the advantages, it is generally agreed that diagrams save words, so using the diagram leaves you extra words with which to gain marks elsewhere. I would also argue that diagrams can express a situation very powerfully and clearly, but you may want to wait until you have examined the options below before deciding whether you agree with me. (Of course, if you're specifically asked for one or more diagrams, then Option 1 isn't an option!)

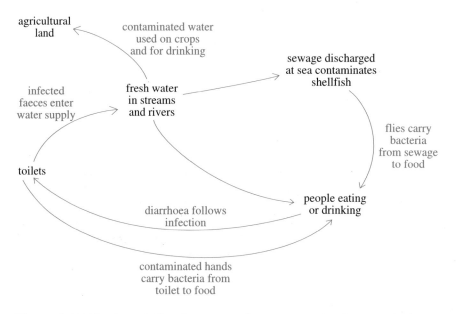

Figure 3.15 *The first Collee diagram redrawn using words instead of pictures*

Option 2: Copying out diagrams

I am trying to encourage you to use diagrams, but there is a pitfall associated with this option. This option is one that many students do use, so it's worth exploring why it is not a particularly good idea. The following is a slight parody of the sort of written assignment I have in mind. The text reads something like this:

'There are many ways in which diseases can be spread, see Figure 1.'

There then follows 'Figure 1' which is a direct copy of the diagram from the source book, after which there is no further explanation or application. The answer simply continues on to another aspect of the question, leaving the diagram 'hanging' there by itself.

Let's consider this issue in terms of diagrams being useful for learning and for expressing our thoughts. In terms of learning, simply copying the diagram from the course book doesn't achieve very much; there is no indication that you've understood the diagram, or that you've used it to help you understand the situation. In terms of expressing your thoughts, simply copying the diagram is not a great deal of use either, because it doesn't express *your* thoughts or views on the subject.

However, sometimes you will need to draw a pictorial diagram, either from a real-life specimen or by copying a printed diagram. Don't attempt to draw every minute detail: it would take far too long. Decide which features are important and draw them as well as you can. Use a pencil and have an eraser handy. Once you are satisfied with your diagram, label it clearly. For some purposes you may have to ink in the lines once you're happy with the diagram.

Option 3: Linking the diagrams to a case

This can be a very useful option. Rather than just using the diagram as a general example, you could pick on one or more specific diseases and discuss how they relate to the general picture. By doing this, you have undertaken some specific new learning and demonstrated that you have applied that new knowledge or understanding in a creative way. In this example, the diagram is not an appendage to the discussion, hanging out on a 'limb', but has been used as part of the central 'body' of the assignment.

Option 4: Challenging and adapting diagrams

In this option, we take a diagram from the source material and either adapt it or challenge what it is trying to tell the reader. This is fine and indicates a thinking approach to the assignment. There is one golden rule: 'State clearly that this is what you are doing!' This is important for two reasons: first, the courtesy of acknowledging your sources, even if you have significantly adapted the diagram, and second, to demonstrate that you have studied the material carefully and produced a new analysis, not just plucked it out of the air.

An example of this is shown overleaf in Figures 3.16(a) and 3.16(b). I have split Figure 3.15 into two, treating food- and water-borne diseases separately. I might do this to discuss the different ways in which the spread of diseases could be prevented. As it happens, my new diagrams seem to show that the water-borne route is much simpler than the food-borne route, and I could go on to discuss why this might be so.

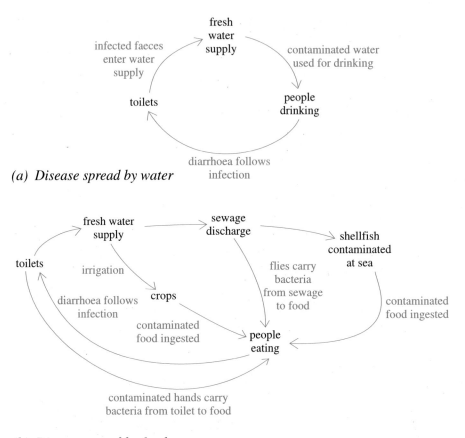

(a) Disease spread by water

(b) Disease spread by food

Figure 3.16 *Figure 3.15 split into two separate diagrams*

4.2 Using diagrams of your own choice and design

This option is the most challenging and most rewarding, as it clearly shows that you have explored and analysed the source material and reworked it for yourself. In many cases, the source material may not contain any diagrams, simply text or numbers, perhaps expressed as a table. Alternatively, you may have had to make some specific observations or undertake an experiment to produce your own data. In this case, you may be expected to produce a diagram to enhance or improve your assignment. Specific advice on drawing your own graphs is given in Maths Help on pages 371 to 385. If you use a computer, you will also be aware of how easy it can be to produce graphs and charts from sets of data (see Chapter 7).

The difficult part is selecting the most appropriate graph or chart to use. This depends mostly on the type of data you're using, but it also depends on your purpose in drawing the diagram.

◆ Discrete data – that is, things that can be counted – are best presented as a bar chart.

◆ Continuous data – that is, things that can be measured – can be presented as a line graph, as a bar chart or as a histogram. The choice will be influenced by the number of data and whether a mathematical relationship is involved.

◆ If the data are expressed as percentages rather than actual numbers, choose a histogram, a (percentage) bar chart or a pie chart.

◆ When you want to show the frequency of something, or compare similar sets of data, choose a bar chart or a histogram.

◆ If you are showing a mathematical relationship, or a causal link between two factors, a line graph is best.

This list of pointers is not exhaustive, but it should be sufficient to help you get started in selecting and producing charts and graphs.

Hints and Tips

If you feel able to use diagrams, and you believe their use is relevant, then:

◆ Keep diagrams simple – don't try to squeeze in too much information.

◆ Give diagrams a title.

◆ Label and clearly indicate the scale of charts and graphs or the arrows on relationship diagrams.

◆ Always refer to diagrams from the text – don't leave them 'hanging' in isolation.

◆ Don't simply copy a diagram from a book. Link it to a real situation – either by including details on the diagram at appropriate points or by referring to specific aspects of the diagram in the accompanying text.

◆ If your diagram is similar to, or is an adaptation of, a standard form of diagramming, acknowledge the fact. If symbols are used in a way that differs from accepted conventions, acknowledge this too.

◆ Use the diagram to challenge your thinking – follow it through, as it may prompt you to consider important issues you might otherwise not address. Use the diagram to make your analysis more rigorous.

- ◆ If you choose to adapt or challenge the diagram, that's all right. But do justify your approach, and state that your alteration is intentional.

- ◆ Check the diagram with someone not involved in the situation. If they understand it, it is probably useful.

- ◆ If you choose the most appropriate kind of chart or graph, it makes the patterns in the data much clearer and more obvious than tables can.

- ◆ Quote the source of the data used.

5 Where do you go from here?

This chapter has given you a good many tips about what is useful and what things to avoid. These tips are just the beginning of the practical 'know-how' you'll develop once you've begun your MST study. Some of the skills you'll learn will be specific to the particular subjects you're studying – biologists have different diagrammatic 'tools of the trade' from mathematicians, computer enthusiasts and physicists. Other, more general skills will be central to actually studying and to reflecting on what you are learning.

However your skill with diagrams develops, you'll always have to select the best method of conveying information for the job in hand. If you can use or adapt one of the more standard forms of diagramming mentioned in this chapter – relationship diagrams, for example – then it is wise to do so. But remember that there are conventions to follow that ensure that what you produce will be fully understood by others – especially your tutor.

I hope that what I've said will encourage you to be adventurous and draw your own diagrams; when you do so, remember that your aim is to express important information clearly, which means that the basic 'dos and don'ts' I've outlined are particularly important. But diagrams aren't just helpful for expressing information; at the same time, they can stimulate further learning or enquiry. And what's more, the diagrams we use for exploring ideas and situations are valuable in helping us express those ideas. I've always found diagrams essential to learning and to communicating; I hope your experience will convince you of the same.

CHAPTER 4

Learning and using mathematics

1 Introduction

Your first experience of mathematics was probably using numbers in everyday situations: for example, counting, measuring, and dealing with money. After that, you probably discovered that numbers could be used to work out all sorts of problems, and that looking at shapes and their properties had lots of practical applications too. Mathematics can be used to help solve many different problems – from everyday examples, such as working out your water bill or estimating the time you need to allow for a journey, to very complicated scientific and technological projects, such as sending astronauts to the moon. Although you will meet other ways of investigating problems during your studies, maths does play a very important part in tackling problems in many aspects of life. It is an essential tool for scientists and technologists, so learning about new mathematical ideas and how they can be used is very important for MST students.

Activity Break   Can you think of examples where you have used (or could use) maths in some everyday situations, such as travel, leisure, cookery or in your home?

How do you think maths could be used in economics, architecture, politics, medicine or the study of the environment?

Here are a few examples to start you thinking.

Home	World
• Planning my spending and budget.	• Working out the inflation rate or tax rate.
• Scaling up recipes from four to six people	• Predicting the outcome of an election.
• Finding the quickest route between two places.	• Deciding which is the most effective drug for an illness, or how much of a drug should be used.
• Working out how much paint I need for the decorating.	• Investigating the safety aspects of a building.
• Finding a best buy.	• Predicting the effects of pollution.
• Working out the cost of a holiday from a brochure.	• Working out the cheapest routes for supplying shops from warehouses.

How can mathematics help with these problems?

Most mathematical investigations can be described in terms of the cycle shown in Figure 4.1.

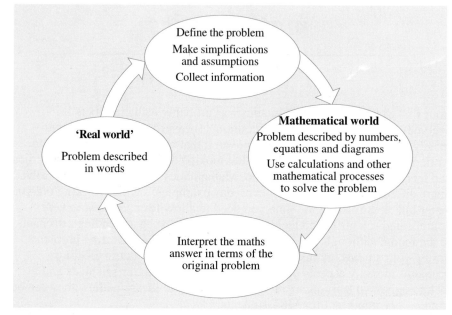

Figure 4.1

To see how the cycle works, consider the following problem.

You have agreed to organize a minibus trip to the Science Museum in London for your fellow students on the course. They would like to arrive there at about 11 a.m.

The *'real-world'* problem is: 'What time should you arrange to pick everyone up?' The key question is: 'How long will the journey take?' The journey time will depend on traffic conditions, so it is difficult to be precise. However, a precise time is not needed; a rough idea of the time will do.

First, *define the problem.* From a map, the distance from your town to London is 150 miles. The problem is easier to solve mathematically if some simplifications and assumptions are made.

1   Overall, the minibus travels at about 45 miles per hour.

2   Allow 30 minutes to park and walk to the museum.

Then, *go into the 'mathematical world'.*

Using these facts and assumptions, the pick-up time can now be calculated.

The minibus can travel 45 miles in one hour.

So, the time taken to travel 150 miles $= \dfrac{150}{45}$ hours

$$= 3\tfrac{1}{3} \text{ hours}$$

$$= 3 \text{ hours } 20 \text{ minutes.}$$

Hence, the time for the journey and parking = 3 hours 50 minutes.

Therefore, the pick-up time should be 7:10 a.m. (or 0710 hours).

Now, *interpret the mathematical answer.* From past experience, you know that some people in the group always arrive late. So, a sensible pick-up time would be 7 a.m. – allowing extra time for the latecomers to arrive. If some students protest that this is too early, you might have to work around the problem-solving cycle again, changing your assumptions about the parking time or the speed at which the minibus can travel. Note that the answer you get depends on the assumptions made and the data used. If these are wrong or inaccurate, the answer may not be reliable. For example, the traffic flow in London may make the average speed much slower than has been assumed here. So, leaving at 7 a.m. may not be early enough.

The cycle in Figure 4.1 can be used to find solutions to many different kinds of problem, although several trips around the cycle may be needed for complicated investigations, as assumptions are modified and the original problem redefined. Investigating problems in this way, however, does require certain skills and mathematical techniques. As an MST student, you will often use mathematics to investigate problems, so it is important that you develop the skills involved in studying new mathematical concepts and applying those ideas in practical situations. You will need to be able to:

◆ read mathematics and understand the language and notation

◆ choose and apply mathematical techniques, and decide on the next step to take

◆ decide whether an answer is reasonable or sufficient

◆ sort out what to do when you get stuck

◆ reflect on what you have learned and on how it fits in with what you already know

◆ write down your own mathematics.

This chapter will help you with these skills. The next two sections – 'Reading maths' and 'Practising maths' – are particularly useful if you are learning maths as part of a course. They contain practical advice on understanding maths texts, using worked examples and tackling exercises. The final two sections – 'Tackling mathematical problems' and 'Expressing yourself mathematically' – will be useful both as part of your studies and when you are using maths in a practical situation.

All the sections of this chapter use examples to illustrate ideas. If you would like extra help with the mathematical techniques involved, please refer to Maths Help towards the back of this book. The page references are marked in the text like this: see Maths Help on pages 00 to 00.

2 Reading maths

You have already met a lot of general strategies for reading and understanding scientific texts in Chapter 2. These techniques – scanning, active reading and making notes – work just as well when you are studying maths. To see how, suppose Sushma has decided to study the 'Approximations and uncertainties' section of Maths Help on pages 346 to 352. To get an overall idea of the main points, and as a guide to how much time and effort she will have to spend on it, Sushma uses about five minutes of her lunch hour to skim through the section. Here are her comments, with the main points that I would like you to note about Sushma's notes written in 'clouds'.

> Main idea of section

It's about rounding numbers off. I know how to round numbers to the nearest 10, 100 etc. and to decimal places, so I should be able to get through that first section fairly quickly. Allow 30 mins.

> Assess your knowledge and the time it will take
> This will help you to plan your study time

> Clear objectives for studying: errors, significant figures and the differences between them

The section on errors is new. I'll have to spend quite a lot of time on that. And I've not heard of significant figures before.

I need to find out the difference between the sig. figs and the decimal places. Why do we need these different ways of rounding?

> Questions to think about and search out the answers

At her next study session, Sushma plans to study the section in detail. Following the advice in Chapter 2, she works through the examples, makes notes and tries some exercises on her own. To keep her learning active, she asks questions of her own and makes notes of her answers.

◆ How does this fit in with what I already know?

You use the same '5 or more' rule for all the different ways of rounding, but significant figures allow you to deal with very big or very small numbers more easily.

◆ Have I seen or used anything similar to this before?

Yes, I know how to round to the nearest 10, 100 and so on – this just extends those ideas.

◆ Can I relate it to some everyday experience or practical example?

Yes, it's a bit like estimating how much my shopping bill will be, before I have to pay.

◆ Where could these ideas be used?

A lot of the numbers in the media are rounded off. You could use these ideas whenever you need a rough idea of the size of a number and aren't too fussy about its actual value (for example, in estimating answers to calculations).

These kinds of questions work well for most topics. Try using them! They challenge you to take a broader view of the topic and deepen your overall understanding. Another important question to ask is 'What would happen if …?' Try changing some of the initial assumptions or values. You need to explore where the ideas apply and think about their limitations. For example, Sushma might ask 'What would happen if you rounded *down* when the next digit is 5, instead of rounding up?' or 'What would happen if people sometimes rounded down and sometimes rounded up?'

You can see that the general skills you are developing for tackling scientific texts will help you to make sense of a mathematical topic as well. Experiment with different approaches until you find those that work well for you.

But if you compare a piece of mathematical writing with a scientific article, you will notice that the language used and the style of writing are slightly different. Although both kinds of writing are written in sentences and can be read aloud, maths language tends to be more condensed, with more notation and abbreviations. Before you can make sense of the mathematical ideas, you have to understand this language. Imagine a story written in a foreign language using a alphabet different from your own. First, you would have to master the alphabet, then the vocabulary and grammar, and finally, you could try to understand the story. You would expect all this to take a lot of time and effort. You have to spend time learning a language before you can understand ideas expressed in that language, and still longer before you are sufficiently fluent to be able to think in the language.

2.1 Learning the language

Here are some ideas to help you to get to grips with maths language.

Making an MST dictionary

You should be introduced to new notation as you need it, and you should be given plenty of opportunity to practise using it. To help you to remember the language and check meanings quickly, try using a small notebook to make yourself a maths (or MST) dictionary (Figure 4.2). You can use it to store new words and abbreviations alphabetically. Preparing definitions in your own words or diagrams will help you to remember them. Remember, an example may illustrate an idea more clearly than words ever can. For example, how would you explain the square root of a number? Recording symbols in your dictionary is a little more tricky. Try including a section at the back of your dictionary divided into separate topics: Numbers, Geometry, Statistics and so on. Then store each new symbol in the appropriate section. Remember to write down how to say the symbol as well as any specific meanings. You'll find your dictionary useful when you read pages 121 to 130 of Chapter 5 which explain the meaning and pronunciation of some of the symbols and abbreviations frequently used in maths and science. A separate section for formulas is also a good idea.

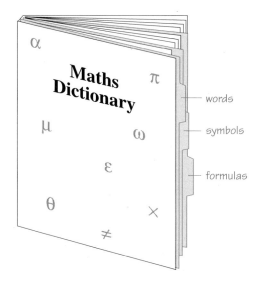

Figure 4.2

Practising using new language

Make an effort to include new vocabulary when you are discussing maths. Practise new notation as you work, making sure that you can read it properly (either in your head or aloud) as you write it down. For example, if you have written 3^2, say to yourself 'three squared', not 'three with a little two at the top'. Note that some mathematical expressions do not quite follow the left to right, top to bottom conventions used in reading English. For example: $\dfrac{2}{3} + \dfrac{4}{5}$ is read 'two thirds plus four fifths' (see Maths Help on page 317).

Noting differences in how words are used

Maths, like other subjects, has a specialized vocabulary. You will meet a lot of new words that describe particular properties or processes – for example, 'radius' or 'circumference' (see Maths Help on page 386).

Maths has borrowed quite a lot of English words too, but often these words have a very specific meaning in maths – for example, 'power', 'odd' or 'root'. Borrowed words are sometimes combined to describe particular mathematical ideas as well (for example, 'the highest common factor of two numbers'). These words and expressions can be baffling if you use the English interpretation instead of reading them mathematically. So, it is important to spend some time making sure you understand these words in a mathematical context. And remember that the same word may have more than one interpretation in mathematical language. For example, 'solution' can mean 'answer', as in 'the solution is 4', or it can mean a complete piece of work, explaining how you worked out the result and including the final answer. In this chapter, the latter meaning is used.

2.2 Learning to read mathematical texts

When people are writing maths, they tend to use a lot of notation. This includes abbreviations (such as d. p. or sig. fig.), special symbols (such as > or $\simeq$), and letters from different alphabets (such as π, α or β). Providing you understand the notation, it can help you to express ideas in a clear and concise way, making it easier to visualize the problem and understand and work with the ideas. As an example, imagine what life would have been like before the decimal number system was adopted. (For instance, think about working out your shopping bill using only Roman numerals.) So, good notation can save time and effort, and that's one reason mathematicians use it a lot.

However, since mathematical writing is concise, you do need to read each sentence slowly and carefully, checking that you understand every word and symbol. Then think about the whole meaning. You might have to look up work you've done earlier, or check the meaning of some special notation. In mathematics, the argument follows on, line after line, in a logical way, leading you down a very straight and narrow path to the conclusion. Of course, when you tackle your own mathematics, there isn't a well-marked path: you are free to go in whatever direction you like, including down complete dead-ends and into huge pits of unfathomable calculations. So, to help you keep on the right lines in your own work, you need to understand both *how* the individual steps work in a piece of maths and *why* they were taken.

To illustrate key ideas, you often see worked examples in course materials. It's important that you understand these examples, as you can use them to check on your understanding as well as models for your own solutions. The ideas overleaf will help you to follow worked examples.

2.3 Understanding how the steps work

To understand what is happening, you need to relate the steps in the example to what you already know. You can do this by writing notes and explanations on the text (providing it's your own!) and by drawing diagrams. For example, consider this newspaper extract.

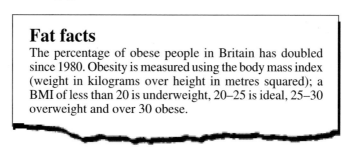

Fat facts

The percentage of obese people in Britain has doubled since 1980. Obesity is measured using the body mass index (weight in kilograms over height in metres squared); a BMI of less than 20 is underweight, 20–25 is ideal, 25–30 overweight and over 30 obese.

Source: *The Independent*, 23 November 1995, p. 4.

The extract made me wonder whether I was overweight, so I worked out my body mass index. Here is my calculation with comments written on it to help you understand it.

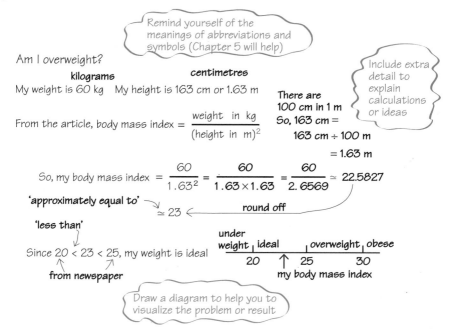

When you are tackling any mathematics, it is important that you build up internal 'pictures' of the problem in your mind; diagrams, physical models or practical examples can help you to do this. For example, I find it difficult to visualize three-dimensional problems, so I almost always resort to building a structure out of pencils, boxes, straws or anything else I can find. Sometimes, you may find a particular mathematical step difficult to understand. Studying the rest of the example, and then going back, can help. This technique is like following a street map – it sometimes helps to work backwards from where you want to go.

2.4 Understanding why the steps have been taken

Now, read through the solution again. Could you explain to a friend why these steps were taken? Compare your explanation with the comments below.

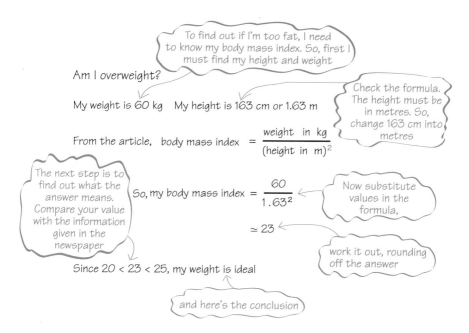

By the way, did you note that the newspaper extract uses the terms 'mass' and 'weight' in a way that implies they mean the same thing? Strictly speaking, the kilogram is a measure of mass, not weight. However, since most people use the term 'weight' in everyday life, where a scientist would talk of 'mass', I've stuck with it for this example. (The specialized vocabulary used in MST subjects is discussed in more detail in Chapter 9.)

When you are studying any worked example in mathematics, try covering it up and just moving down a line at a time. Can you predict what the next step will be? Is it the same as the next step in the solution? If not, why not?

You might have included an extra step or adopted a different way of investigating the problem. There are sometimes different but equally valid ways of tackling problems. If your method does not lead to an answer, can you see why the printed solution took the steps it did?

You can use this technique when you are writing down your own solutions too. Imagine that you have a shadow, one that asks 'Why are you doing that?' at every step. If you can't come up with a convincing answer, you might be going off the rails in your solution. A good test of your understanding is to see if you can explain the ideas to someone else. A fellow student who has been trained to ask a lot of questions is the best candidate!

The important point is that you understand why each step has been taken. You'll also have to follow certain conventions in writing out a solution of this type. For example, I wrote $\dfrac{60}{1.63^2}$ in my solution to the body mass index calculation, and ignored the units involved. Some courses – particularly courses in science subjects – insist that you always include the units in a calculation of this sort. So, in this case I would have written $\dfrac{60 \text{ kg}}{(1.63 \text{ m})^2}$ and the answer as 23 kilograms per metres squared. The golden rule is always to follow the conventions specified by the course you're studying.

This section has discussed some of the strategies you can use to understand mathematical texts. Reading and constructing tables, charts and graphs are also important for scientists, technologists and mathematicians. Chapters 3 and 5 and Maths Help (pages 371 to 385) will help you with these skills.

Key Points

◆ Skim through a new section of work before you start to study it in detail. Identify the main ideas and assess how familiar you are with the topic. This will enable you to plan your study time more effectively, and suggest clear objectives and questions for your studying.

◆ Read actively: ask questions and work through examples. Study worked examples to find out what steps have been taken and how they work.

◆ Make notes – in the form of a diagram, a table or a list of statements. It is a good idea to include examples that illustrate difficult points.

◆ Maths has its own language, with its own symbols, notation, grammar and vocabulary. You need to understand the language in order to follow mathematical arguments and describe your own solutions and investigations.

◆ As with any other language you learn, it takes time, effort and lots of practice to read maths fluently and with understanding. Creating your own maths dictionary will help.

3 Practising maths

3.1 Why practise?

If you want to be able to use maths to investigate problems or develop new ideas, just reading about it is not enough. You have to practise doing mathematics as well. As you read through a piece of mathematics, it's easy to be lulled into a false sense of security. You think you understand it, but the real test is whether you could apply it to a different problem. Would you recognize where you could use the ideas and what steps to take?

As well as checking your understanding and progress, practising has other benefits too. By working through different problems, you learn how the new ideas fit in with what you already know. Practice helps you to see patterns in different problems and gives you a feel for which technique to use and where. You might also discover similarities or links with other topics which give you a better understanding of mathematics as a whole. The more practice you do, the more familiar you become with the ideas, and the easier it becomes to remember and apply them in the future. You discover where the ideas can be used, where they can't and what their limitations are.

As you practise and become more fluent with the techniques, your confidence in your mathematical ability will grow. Managing to sort out what to do when you get stuck on a worked example helps you to develop problem-solving strategies, and gives you the confidence to persevere in tackling more complicated problems. Feeling confident and being positive are important. You should be able to say to yourself: 'I know this is difficult, and I don't understand it yet; but I've worked out difficult problems before, so I'm sure I'll be able to sort this out soon.' Thinking positively helps you to keep going. Perhaps you'll have another go later, instead of getting demoralized and giving up.

For MST students, the main purpose of practising maths is to acquire a set of skills for solving problems. If you look back at the 'Am I overweight?' example on page 94, and consider all the individual skills required to answer the question, you will come up with an impressive list for such a relatively small problem:

- measuring height and weight accurately
- converting units
- substituting values into a formula
- using a calculator
- rounding answers.

If you hadn't worked on these skills before, not only would you be unable to recognize that these skills are needed, but you would also have to spend a lot of time sorting them out in the middle of the problem. By practising maths as you go along, you become aware of the techniques that can be used to solve problems and develop the expertise necessary to apply them. This makes you feel confident and results in happy and successful problem solving later on!

3.2 How to practise

You can practise maths in a number of different ways.

Discussion

You might like to discuss new ideas, problems or questions that have occurred to you with other students or your tutor. Discussion helps everyone. If you are stuck on a problem, talking about it helps to clarify your thoughts and can provide the missing clue you need to get going again. Explaining an idea is an excellent way of deepening your understanding and fixing the ideas in your mind. You might even be forced to think about some new aspect of the problem that you had not considered previously.

Relating it to everyday experiences

For example, you could practise your interpretation skills by looking at graphs or charts in newspapers and magazines. Or, if you're working on areas and volumes, you could try working out the amount of earth needed to fill your hanging basket or the amount of water in your fish tank.

Working through examples in the text

Many maths textbooks use a similar format: a topic is introduced and explained, some worked examples are provided, and you are then invited to try some examples for yourself. This is how the Maths Help Section is organized in this book. Additional examples are often similar to the ones in the text, although they may illustrate extra points that link the work with your previous studies or extend the main text. You may also be asked to carry out some practical activities or to think about some general discussion points. Whatever form the questions take, they are usually clearly defined and have been included to help you to understand the main ideas and check on your progress. It is important that you try to work through these examples. The next part of this section will show you how to tackle worked examples.

Key Points

- If you want to be able to use maths to solve problems or understand new ideas, you will have to practise doing maths as well as reading about it.

- You can practise maths by doing examples and discussing ideas.

- Working through examples as you read gives you confidence and helps you to see how the techniques work and how they fit in with what you already know.

- Practice gives you skills that you can use to solve complicated problems.

3.3 Using examples

There are many occasions when you may want to practise doing maths by working through some examples; for example, when you are studying a new topic, reviewing a recent study session, or checking on a particular topic related to your current work.

Working through one or two new questions from a recent piece of work will remind you of the main ideas and form a useful warm-up exercise at the start of your next study session. Frequent revision helps to keep ideas and techniques at the front of your mind. And you can use examples from past exam papers, as well as those in your course books and notes, to help you revise for exams (see Chapter 10).

As part of your studying, you will have to decide how many examples to tackle and which ones to attempt. You will have to consider how much time you have available for studying that particular topic and how confident you feel about using the ideas involved. Sometimes, it will be obvious from the material that you are expected to work through all the examples. If only a few examples are included, it is wise to tackle as many as you can. For example, suppose you wanted to use Maths Help to find out how to write numbers in scientific notation (see pages 359 to 364). As there are only a few examples in this section, you should try to work through them all. If you are working from material with a good selection of questions – say, a textbook – then you can be more selective. You don't necessarily have to work through them all, and you may not have enough time to do so anyway. If, after trying a few of the early examples, you feel confident that you understand the topic, move on and try some more challenging questions. You could try working out every other question or even every third question. The missed questions can be used for revision later on. Aim to pick a range of problems that will both build up your confidence and expertise and fit into the time available.

Although you will be the only person to see most of your practice examples, it is worth keeping a neat and ordered record of your work. You may want to refer to it later on, either as part of your revision or to discuss it with someone else. If you practise writing out full solutions (including the question), your work will be much easier to understand in a few months time. Section 5 of this chapter – 'Expressing yourself mathematically' – will help you with this process. Take care to label the questions accurately and to arrange them in order, so that you can find particular topics quickly and easily.

At some point, you will almost certainly come across questions that you can't work out. The next few pages will give you some ideas on what to do if you get stuck. Some questions are divided into several parts that can be tackled separately. So, if you get stuck on the first part, do read on; you may still be able to tackle the remaining parts of the question. If the answer to one section is provided in the question, you can use it in the other parts of the question, even though you have not managed to establish the result for yourself.

When you have finished your solution, check that it is reasonable and that you have answered the question precisely as asked and with an appropriate amount of explanation. Here are some ways in which to check your solutions.

◆ Make an estimate of the answer before you start (see Chapter 5, page 133).

◆ Check that your answer is sensible given the context of the problem. Some answers – for example, 'The distance between the Earth and the Moon is 2.6 cm' – are clearly not right. With most problems, you should have a fairly good idea of the sort of answer to expect. In the 'Am I overweight?' example on page 94, I was expecting an answer of about 25 – perhaps anything between 10 and 40. If I had ended up with an answer of 0.04 or 380, I would have checked my calculation.

◆ Try using a different technique to either work out the answer or check the result. For example, you can check a subtraction by adding your answer to the number you have subtracted. If this gives you back the original number, your calculation was correct.

◆ Check the final form of your answer. Read through the question again carefully to ensure that you have included your solutions to each part of the question and that your answers are in the correct form. For example, if the question says 'Give your answer correct to 3 significant figures', try not to leave it as 765.432! (See Maths Help on pages 349 to 352 for more information about the use of significant figures.)

When you are working with calculators or computers, checking is more important, not less so. Try a rough calculation by hand with simplified numbers, or consider a simplified version of the problem. For example, if you were working on a traffic-flow problem, you might consider a case in which there is a single car on the road. Consider extreme cases as well. What happens when you use very small or very large values? For example, if you were looking at the temperature of a pot of tea as it cooled, you would expect that after a long time the temperature would be close to that of the surroundings. Does a computer model give you the same answer as common-sense thinking?

Is there a time when you should 'give up'?

If you have made a determined effort to work out a question, tried all the available strategies and are still stuck – then stop. Be realistic about the time you have available. If you spend a long time on one particular example, you may disrupt your study timetable and fall behind with important parts of the course. It would be better to jot down a note to ask your tutor for help and move on to the next question or section. Sometimes, by reading on, you get a better overall view of the problem, and this enables you to go back and solve the problem later anyway. Of course, if you are able to contact your tutor directly, then do so. A quick hint may be all that you need to get going again.

Giving up on a problem need not be an admission of defeat or the result of a lack of moral fibre. It may just mean that you are someone who organizes their time sensibly and refuses to become obsessed. So, be realistic! One aim of your studying is to become an independent learner, someone able to sort out their own problems, and this requires a certain amount of effort on your part. On the other hand, you also want to be able to understand all the key parts of the course, despite working to a fairly tight schedule. It's up to you to balance your work so that you achieve both aims.

Using answers

Answers to examples are often included, either in a section at the end of the chapter or book or immediately after the examples themselves. If they are on the same page as the examples, you might find it difficult to resist looking at them, especially if you are struggling. Use a piece of paper or card to cover up the answers and move it down, line by line, as you work your way through the questions.

If you are totally baffled by a question, and none of the strategies in Section 4 has worked, you can resort to looking at the answer and trying to work backwards from it. This isn't cheating. It can help you to work out the missing link in your solution and improve your understanding in that way. If you feel confident that you now understand what's going on, test yourself by trying some more examples *without* using the answers. If you don't feel confident, or if you find yourself using the answers again, then you'll need to have another look at the main text or discuss the ideas involved with someone else. Sometimes, a different textbook at the same level will explain the topic in a slightly different way or use more illuminating examples to help you to understand. You could also try working through a few simpler examples or ask your tutor for help. A few extra practice questions or another textbook may help you plug the gaps in your understanding and give you enough confidence to be able to tackle the rest of the topic. So, do ask for help if you need it.

When you have finished a question or group of questions, compare your answers with the answers given in the course materials. There are three possibilities.

◆ Your answers agree. Give yourself a pat on the back and move on to the next question or piece of work. If all the working is shown in the solution, compare it with yours to make sure that you have included a similar amount of detail.

◆ Your answers agree, but you have worked them out another way. In this case, you should read through the given answer carefully, checking that you understand the solution. It may suggest a method that you could use in another problem or a neater or quicker way of solving the problem.

◆ Your answers disagree. First, check through the given solution and compare it with your own to see if you can spot any mistakes. Then, see if the answer has just been written in a different form. If the problem involves measurements, check that you have used the same units (Chapter 5 has more to say about this). It is also worth double-checking the question. Are you sure that you have answered the same question? Misreading values or misinterpreting the overall problem will result in a different answer, even if all your mathematical ideas are correct (see 'Learning from your mistakes' overleaf).

If you have difficulty, understanding the solution, or if you still think that your answer is correct even though it differs from the one given, then make a note to ask your tutor for help. This situation might indicate a misunderstanding on your part or possibly a misprint in the course materials: either way, your tutor will want to know about it.

Learning from your mistakes

If you find a mistake in your solution, try to assess how serious the error is and what you can learn from it. Some mistakes are careless errors on things you know you understand (mistakes with simple arithmetic often fall into this category). If you know you are susceptible to this kind of mistake, make an effort to write out your solutions slowly and carefully, including all the steps. Hasty shortcuts have a lot to answer for! When you have finished your solution, check that your answer does at least seem reasonable, and then work through your steps again. Follow the advice given on page 100 about checking your answers to the letter!

Other mistakes can be more serious. You may have used an inappropriate technique or misunderstood some key idea. Once you have identified where you went wrong, see if you can work out why. You may need to ask someone for help at this point. Then, check your understanding by trying some more examples, plenty of them, until you feel confident. Finally, don't be disheartened if you make mistakes. Everyone does. It's much better to make mistakes and learn from them than never to try. If you are on a course and you hardly ever make mistakes or get stuck, the course is probably too easy for you. Expect to make mistakes and to get stuck. Just relax and try to enjoy learning from the experience.

---

*A**ctivity Break*** The following problem was given to two students. If you eat a third of a pizza and your friend eats a quarter, how much of the pizza is left?

Their calculations are show below; both contain mistakes. Try to find the mistakes and decide whether they represent careless slips or serious misunderstandings. Can you provide a correct solution? (Refer to Maths Help on pages 317 to 329 if you need to.)

Student A

$$\text{Amount of pizza eaten} \quad = \frac{1}{5} + \frac{1}{4} = \frac{4}{20} + \frac{5}{20} = \frac{8}{20} = \frac{4}{5}$$

Hence, the answer is $\dfrac{4}{5}$ ✗

Student B

$$\text{Fraction of pizza eaten} \quad = \frac{1}{3} + \frac{1}{4} = \frac{1+1}{3+4} = \frac{2}{7}$$

So, $\dfrac{2}{7}$ of the pizza has been eaten and $\dfrac{5}{7}$ of the pizza is left. ✗

The correct solution is:

$$\text{Fraction of pizza eaten} = \frac{1}{3} + \frac{1}{4} = \frac{4}{12} + \frac{3}{12} = \frac{7}{12}$$

$$\text{Hence, the fraction of pizza left} = 1 - \frac{7}{12} = \frac{5}{12}$$

Here are my comments on the students' solutions:

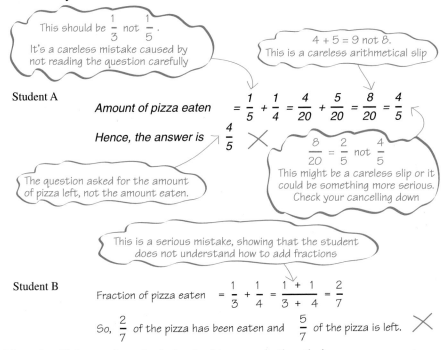

Student A

This should be $\frac{1}{3}$ not $\frac{1}{5}$. It's a careless mistake caused by not reading the question carefully

$4 + 5 = 9$ not 8. This is a careless arithmetical slip

Amount of pizza eaten $= \frac{1}{5} + \frac{1}{4} = \frac{4}{20} + \frac{5}{20} = \frac{8}{20} = \frac{4}{5}$

Hence, the answer is $\frac{4}{5}$ ✗

The question asked for the amount of pizza left, not the amount eaten.

$\frac{8}{20} = \frac{2}{5}$ not $\frac{4}{5}$. This might be a careless slip or it could be something more serious. Check your cancelling down

This is a serious mistake, showing that the student does not understand how to add fractions

Student B

Fraction of pizza eaten $= \frac{1}{3} + \frac{1}{4} = \frac{1 + 1}{3 + 4} = \frac{2}{7}$

So, $\frac{2}{7}$ *of the pizza has been eaten and* $\frac{5}{7}$ *of the pizza is left.* ✗

Note that if the students had checked to see whether their answers were reasonable, they might have spotted their mistakes. Both people eat at least a quarter of the pizza, so together they must have eaten more than half the pizza. So, there must be less than half of it left. Both students calculated that over half the pizza remained.

Key Points

♦ Try a variety of examples and check your answers with those given in the text. Make a note of any answers you don't understand and ask for help.

♦ Using the answers to help you work out problems isn't cheating. Cheating is pretending that you understand the work when you don't.

♦ Everyone makes mistakes and gets stuck, and these are often the occasions on which the best learning takes place.

Well, that's the theory. Try the following activity to test these ideas in practice.

A ctivity Break To see how you can apply the techniques in the last two sections, try working through the 'Approximations and uncertainties' section of Maths Help (on pages 346 to 352). Plan your studying by skimming the section, and then work through in detail.

If you are already familiar with some parts of this section, try a few examples to remind yourself of the main ideas, but work through the examples in new parts carefully and thoroughly. (Or try another section of Maths Help if you already feel confident with this topic.)

4 Tackling mathematical problems

During your MST studies, you will probably meet two main types of mathematical problem. The first kind are well-defined: the problems are clearly stated and contain all the information you need to sort them out. These problems include the examples in Maths Help and those described as worked examples in Section 3 of this chapter. Studying similar examples and relevant sections of the course materials can help with these questions.

The second kind are practical problems and they, at least at first, may not be clearly defined. For example, suppose you had been asked to advise on the best route to London for the minibus trip on page 88. Here, the problem is not clear; what does 'best' actually mean? Does it mean the cheapest, the quickest, the safest, the most scenic, or a combination of these factors? Do you need to consider some other aspects? So, the first step in tackling a practical problem is often to clarify the situation and decide on the key questions. Then, there may be several different, but equally appropriate, ways of tackling the problem; a practical or experimental approach may work just as well as a mathematical one. The next task is often deciding what information you need and then finding it for yourself. So, the strategy of looking at the question and asking 'Have I used every bit of relevant information in this question?' is no longer appropriate. Finally, when you arrive at a result, the important question is often not 'Is this answer *right*?', but 'Is this answer *good enough*?' So, tackling real-life problems can be a lot more involved than working through examples in the course materials.

However, the strategies you use to tackle both types of problem are similar. This section will help you to get started on a problem, suggest how you can keep yourself going, and advise you on what to do when you get stuck. So that you can see how these different ideas work, consider the following practical problem.

A friend has asked you to help redesign his garden. He would like a large lawn and a good-sized herb garden, as he is a keen cook. Can you advise on the amount of turf to buy and on how much space should be used for the herb garden?

What was your reaction as you read through this problem? If it was 'Oh help, I don't even know where to start!', do read on. One aim of this section is to show you how general strategies can be applied in particular cases. In what follows, I'm going to explore useful strategies by outlining approaches that work well in many problem situations. The key features of these general approaches will be highlighted in **bold type**.

Then, I shall apply these general strategies to the garden problem, either by running through the approach for you, or by asking you to try using the strategies for yourself. These sections are written in italics like this, so that you can distinguish the specific 'garden example' from the general principles.

When you first read through this section, concentrate on the garden problem and get an overall feel for the different techniques involved. Then, when you are tackling your own investigations in the future, you can dip back into this section, concentrating on the more general questions and approaches (written in bold type) and on how they can be used in your particular problem. The ideas discussed here can help you with many different kinds of problem, so do try them out!

4.1 Getting started on a problem

First, you need to be sure that you **understand the problem.** Read through the whole question to get an overall picture and to assess your familiarity with this type of problem. Then, read it again to sort out the key questions. Are you sure you know what you are being asked to find or do? If not, you may find drawing a diagram helps, or you could try thinking about a few special cases. Could you describe the problem to a friend in your own words? Can you explain precisely what you *want* to find out?

Then, **concentrate on the details.** Sort out the facts you have been given. Not all the facts may be relevant, but do note down any that might be at this stage. In a practical situation, you may also have to decide what extra information you need. Checking up on new notation, vocabulary or ideas may also play a part in sorting out the information you have been given. **Summarize what you know.**

If you feel that you still don't really understand the problem, try discussing it with someone else. If the problem is not clearly defined, think about what extra information you need and then go back to the person who set the problem and discuss it in detail.

*A**ctivity Break** Read through the garden problem again. The details are rather sketchy. What extra information would you like? Make a list of questions.*

You will need to discuss the garden design in some detail; there just isn't enough information for you to give any useful advice yet. Some questions you might ask are: What is the shape of the garden and its measurements? How many herbs are to be planted? Does the herb garden have a particular design? Do the herbs have to be planted in a particular part of the garden – perhaps in the sun or the shade? Are any other features, such as a vegetable plot or a patio, to be included in the garden?

If you find starting a problem difficult, you could summarize your work so far by writing down what you know and what you want to find out. This process can help you to concentrate your thoughts on the task ahead and overcome the depressing feeling of staring at a blank page, wondering what to do next.

Let's suppose that the comments on the garden problem that emerge from your discussion with your friend allow you to make two lists.

I know:

1   That the garden is a rectangle measuring 30 metres by 20 metres.

2   That the herb garden is to be planted along part of the south-facing, 20-metre garden wall. So that all the herbs can be reached easily, it will be rectangular in shape and 1 metre wide. The herb garden will be made from small triangular and square beds arranged in a lattice design like this:

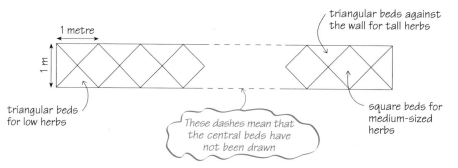

triangular beds against
the wall for tall herbs

1 metre

1 m

triangular beds
for low herbs

These dashes mean that the central beds have not been drawn

square beds for
medium-sized
herbs

3   That 40 herb beds are required.

4   That no other features are required in the garden.

I want:

1   To work out the size of the herb garden.

2   To calculate the amount of turf needed for the lawn.

When you are confident that you understand the problem, the next task is ...

4.2 Breaking the problem down into manageable steps

Concentrating on one small part of the problem at a time can make the investigation seem less overwhelming. Some success with one bit can be very encouraging – it's proof that you are making progress. This helps you to keep going and gives your confidence a boost.

How would you break the garden problem down into smaller steps?

There are two main problems: how big must the herb garden be to accommodate all the herbs, and how big is the lawn? The lawn size will depend on the size of the herb garden, so sort out the herb garden first.

Another useful technique is to **work back from what you want to find out**. Try thinking about what the steps before the answer might be. What do you need to know in order to work out the final answer?

To find the size of the herb garden, you need to work out its length. The length will depend on the number of herb beds required. So, if you could spot a relationship (or pattern) between the length of the herb garden and the number of beds, you could work out the size of the herb garden. So, your first task is to discover this relationship.

4.3 Thinking about the maths you can use

In order to solve a problem, you have to bridge the gap between what you know and what you want to find out. If the problem is straightforward, you can sometimes see what techniques are appropriate straightaway. But what do you do if you can't see the way ahead? Here are some ideas for you to try.

Building on what you already know

Use your experience: have you seen this type of problem before? If you have, you may be able to use a similar method to solve it this time. Think about the differences between the old problem and the new problem. You may need to modify your method or use another technique to set the problem in a familiar form. Practice examples often use similar techniques to the worked examples in the text, so looking back at your notes or the text for a similar or simpler example may help.

Have you seen any other problems similar to the herb garden problem? The area of the lawn looks a bit like calculating the areas of rectangles and squares (see Maths Help on pages 388 to 392). Of course, you may not have seen anything like the herb border problem before.

Trying to solve a simpler problem first

Changing some feature of the problem – for example, using smaller or simpler numbers – often helps you to see underlying patterns or processes. Having solved the simpler problem, you can then return to the original problem with fresh insights. Patterns are often easier to spot if you **consider special cases systematically** and record your results in a table. Continue looking at individual cases until you can see a pattern developing. Note that looking at specific cases helps you to get a feel for what is involved.

---

*A*ctivity Break The herb garden problem can be simplified by considering a series of borders – one 1 metre long, one 2 metres long and one 3 metres long – and counting up the number of herb beds in each border. Can you continue the following table for borders up to 6 metres long?

Border	Length of border (metres)	Number of beds
	1	4
	2	7
	3	?

Can you spot a pattern in the number of beds? Use the pattern to work out the length of the border you would need for 40 beds.

Check your table against the one on page 109. You could continue drawing diagrams of the border until you draw one that contains 40 beds. But there is a quicker way. If you look at the number of beds, you can see that there are three more beds for each extra metre in the length of the border. So, the pattern can be continued like this:

Length in metres:	5	6	7	8	9	10	11	12	13
Number of beds:	16	19	22	25	28	31	34	37	40

Here's the information we want

Hence, for 40 beds, the herb garden should be 13 metres long.

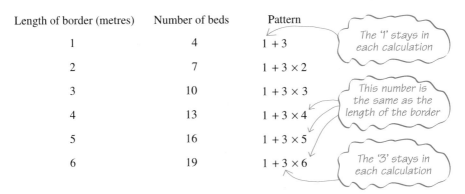

Length of border (metres)	Number of beds	Pattern
1	4	$1 + 3$
2	7	$1 + 3 \times 2$
3	10	$1 + 3 \times 3$
4	13	$1 + 3 \times 4$
5	16	$1 + 3 \times 5$
6	19	$1 + 3 \times 6$

The '1' stays in each calculation

This number is the same as the length of the border

The '3' stays in each calculation

So, the overall pattern can be expressed in general terms:

Number of beds = 1 + 3 × (length of border)

In this case, looking at a few special examples helped to sort out a more complicated problem. It also gave you a greater understanding of the underlying pattern and allowed you to extend the problem in a useful way. Note that although this table may be sufficient to convince yourself that the overall pattern between the length of the border and the number of beds does hold, a rigorous mathematical proof would take a bit more work.

Drawing a diagram

If you've read Chapter 3, you'll appreciate that a large, clear diagram can often help you to visualize a problem and may also suggest a way of tackling it. Diagrams are particularly useful for problems involving shapes, but they can be used in many other problems as well. It often helps to add extra lines to your diagram to make shapes look more familiar. For example, complicated shapes can be broken down into shapes like squares, rectangles or circles that are easier to work with. Note that a beautifully drawn and accurate diagram is not always necessary; in most cases, a quick sketch will do.

A ctivity Break You have already seen how diagrams make the herb border problem easier to understand. Can you draw another diagram to help you work out the amount of turf needed for the lawn?

Here is a diagram of the garden:

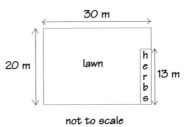

not to scale

As you know how to find the area of a rectangle (see Maths Help on page 390), the shape can be split into two rectangles, A and B.

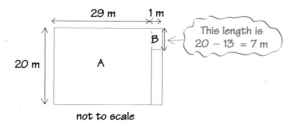

not to scale

Area of a rectangle = length × width

All the lengths are measures in metres, so the area will be measured in square metres (written m^2).

Area of rectangle A = 29 × 20 = 580 m^2

Area of rectangle B = 1 × 7 = 7 m^2

Hence, the total area of lawn = 580 + 7 = 587 m^2.

So, you would have to order 587 m^2 of turf.

4.4 Reflecting on the problem and learning from it

When you are satisfied with your solution, spend a few minutes thinking about how you solved it. For example …

◆ Did you use any special methods which could be used with other problems?

Drawing up the table for the borders helped a lot with this problem, and a similarly organized and thorough approach could be used elsewhere.

◆ Would you approach any part of the problem differently if you were asked to solve it again?

Can you think of a different way of calculating the area of the lawn? One way would be to work out the area of the whole garden and the area of the herb garden separately. Then, you could find the amount of space left in the garden after the area for the herbs has been removed:

Area of whole garden = 30 × 20 = 600 m^2

Herb area = 1 × 13 = 13 m^2

Hence, lawn area = 600 − 13 = 587 m^2

This result agrees with the previous answer.

You may prefer to use the second way of calculating the lawn area as it seems to be quicker.

◆ Can you think of any extensions to the problem? Can you suggest how to tackle these new problems?

Thinking about ways of solving extra problems will increase your experience of mathematics as well as developing your mathematical thinking. Being able to work out the next step to take and suggesting which new ideas to explore are an important part of any research project.

For example, the garden problem could be extended to include a flower border around all four walls of the garden. Or you could consider different lattice patterns or shapes for the herb garden.

Try some more adventurous designs ... How many beds in these patterns?

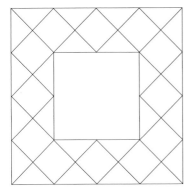

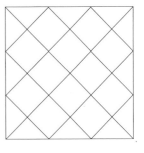

Thinking about your approach and about what you have learned will help you to tackle problems in the future, so it's worth spending some time on this sort of reflection. Learning from experience is a skill that you probably use a lot in your everyday life already. For example, if you're doing the washing, you only put your bright red socks in with the white shirts once before learning that it's not a good idea. A bit of thought will also reveal that dark blue trousers and white socks are probably not a good mix either. So, a few minutes' reflection can help with all sorts of situations, including mathematical ones.

This section has outlined some of the mathematical techniques you can try if you get stuck with a problem. Other ideas can help too. If you are still stuck:

◆ Have a break! If you are tired and unable to concentrate, any studying is difficult. Coming back to the problem a few minutes, hours or days later, feeling alert and refreshed, may make the problem much easier to sort out.

◆ Try explaining your problem to a sympathetic but questioning friend. You may find that this clarifies your thoughts enough to show you a way ahead.

Key Points

♦ Read the problem carefully. Try to sort out clearly what you already know and what you want to find out. Discuss the problem with someone else if you are stuck.

♦ Break the problem down into a series of smaller steps, if you can.

♦ Use your past experience. Have you seen a similar problem before? Can you use some other techniques?

♦ Look at simpler problems first, to check that you understand the problem and to help you to spot patterns and processes.

♦ Drawing a large, clear diagram may help you to visualize the problem. Include additional information and extra lines if they make things clearer.

♦ Check that your final result is sensible in the context of the problem.

♦ Think back over the problem and its solution. Make a note of any ideas that you could use to solve other problems.

5 Expressing yourself mathematically

An important part of any branch of MST is telling other people about your ideas. Writing down your work demonstrates your understanding. It also provides a permanent record of your discoveries and thoughts, and allows other people to share them. This section concentrates on writing good mathematics in the form of individual solutions to small mathematical problems. Chapter 9, 'Writing and assignments', explains the principles of good writing in MST subjects in general, paying particular attention to the use of words (as opposed to symbols and equations) in essays and reports. With some types of written work, especially those where text and mathematics are used together, you will need to use ideas from both these sources.

Giving the answer to a mathematical problem is not enough. You must be able to demonstrate how you have arrived at the answer. The reader will be expecting a logical, accurate and detailed account that is easy to follow and understand. Although a few numbers scribbled down may be enough to convince you of the answer, other people will expect to see all your working, neatly laid out.

Explaining your work carefully helps you as well as your reader. It gives you an opportunity to practise using new language and encourages you to think logically and express yourself clearly. There are long-term benefits too. When you revise your work, it is much easier to follow a set of clearly explained solutions than a jumble of calculations. Showing your working is particularly important in assignments and exams. Marking schemes often allocate 'method marks', so if your method is clear and appropriate you will earn some marks even if the final answer is incorrect. If you just write down the wrong answer, you will get no marks. So, practising writing mathematics is time well spent.

> ### Key Points
>
> ◆ Explaining how you worked out the result is just as important as your final answer.
>
> ◆ You need to be able to express your ideas mathematically, and this means using standard notation and appropriate language.

Writing good mathematics, whether on its own or as part of a scientific essay, takes time and practice. When you are working on a problem, you will do quite a lot of writing anyway: jotting down ideas, trying a few special cases, making mistakes and stumbling down false trails. The skill you need to develop is changing all this hard work into a concise, coherent and logical report. Start by building on the writing skills you already possess. Try to:

◆ write in sentences

◆ use correct vocabulary and notation

◆ include enough explanation for your reader to understand your work

◆ make sure your sentences follow on from each other in a logical way.

The best way to see what is involved in writing good maths is to have a go yourself.

---

*A*ctivity Break A mail order book company holds a sale offering all stock at 20% off marked prices. Postage and packing costs £2.95 for the complete order. Explain how to work out the total bill (including postage and packing) for three books marked at £7.99, £8.50 and £10.99.

Now have a look at the solution below.

$$7.99 + 8.50 + 10.99 = 27.48 \times 0.2 = 5.496$$
$$= 5.50 - 27.48$$
$$= 21.98 + 2.95$$
$$= 24.93$$

The answer is correct, but the solution is badly written. The calculation has not been explained and this makes it difficult to understand. You have to refer back to the question to make any sense of the answer. And the notation has been used incorrectly. Overleaf is the same calculation with my comments.

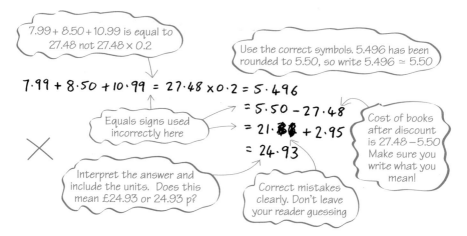

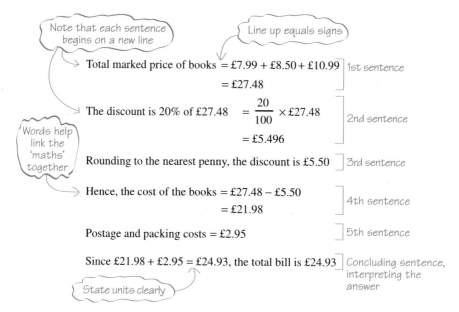

A better way of writing out the calculation is shown below. Note how this calculation is written in sentences that explain the working out. The words make it easy to read and follow and help to link the steps together. If you read this version out aloud, it makes sense and flows well.

Now, look back at your own work. Which of these two accounts is it most like? Can you improve it?

You may be thinking 'Isn't the second version very slow; a lot of writing for a simple problem?' Like most people, once you can see how to do a problem, you probably think more quickly than you can write. The first version probably represents what the writer thought quite well, but that isn't the point. One purpose of writing it down is to explain the calculation to someone else, so the second version is more appropriate.

If you are working on a complicated problem, it is sometimes difficult to decide just how much detail to include. Including too much slows your reader down; too little, and you may lose the reader. You can sometimes get an idea by looking at examples in the text or by using your tutor's examples as models. If you are doing an exercise or an assignment, it helps to remember what the task is trying to test. If you have just learned how to work out percentages and are doing some work on that topic, you should give your solutions in detail. If you have been working them out for years and need to work one out as part of another process, you may not need to write out much more than the answer. You can check on the detail in your own work by asking yourself 'Will I be able to understand this work in six months?' If the answer is likely to be 'No', you should include more detail.

With some problems, you may have used your calculator or computer for much of the work. Your tutor will want to know which software packages you have used and what information, formulas and data were involved. As well as including your results and conclusions, you may need to include print-outs or sketches of graphical screen displays. If you do use a graphics presentation package, do make sure all your graphs and diagrams are properly labelled, including the units on the axes (see Chapter 3). If necessary, special mathematical symbols can be added neatly by hand.

Hints and Tips

◆ *Let it flow.* Write in sentences, using words like 'so', 'hence' and 'therefore' to link the steps together. You can also use symbols such as ⇒ (implies that) and ∴ (therefore) to make your meaning clear. Try reading your maths aloud to check that it makes sense and flows well.

◆ *Explain yourself.* Include enough detail so that your reader can follow your work easily. Explain what you are doing as you go along: 'Substituting $x = 4$ ...'; 'Using the computer package ...'; 'The calculator displayed the following graph ...'; and so on. These sorts of phrases help the reader to follow your argument. Explain any symbols you introduce, and include the units of measurement where appropriate. 'Let w be the width of the field in metres' is a sentence the reader would prefer to see before he or she spends half an hour trying to puzzle out what the 'w' represents in a page of dense mathematics.

◆ *Use symbols and notation correctly.* Note that '=' means 'is equal to' and should be used only when two expressions have the same value. It should not be used to connect the steps of your solution together.

◆ *Don't drown in data.* Consider using tables, graphs or charts to summarize data, reveal trends and guide your reader to the key points (see Chapter 3).

◆ *Remember what it's for.* Give answers to an appropriate degree of precision and include the units in which they are measured. Finish with a concluding sentence that explains your answer in terms of the original problem.

6 Conclusion

This chapter has suggested various ideas to help you develop the skills you need for studying and using mathematics. All these skills take time and practice to develop, so don't be disheartened if your first attempts at reading, writing or problem solving are far from perfect. Your tutors and fellow students will be able to help you along. Just try the different ideas and work out which ones help you to learn and work best for you. Finally, the 'agony column' that follows addresses a few of the common problems experienced by new students of mathematics. As you read through these comments, you'll appreciate something of the common problems that others have experienced in learning and using mathematics. You'll realize that 'you are not alone'; experiencing problems and finding your way through them is an essential part of learning.

Agony column

The course is going too fast. I hardly ever manage to fully understand one topic before I have to rush on to the next.

This is a common feeling. In maths, you often find that topic B depends on topic A, which in turn depends upon P and Q, and so on. But that's not how some people learn maths. Often, they learn just enough about A to get started on B. Then, something in B casts light on a bit of A they didn't understand first time round. So, they go back to A with a new perspective and that helps tie up some loose ends in P and Q. So, don't worry if you don't manage to understand everything immediately. However, if you feel that you are missing key ideas, have a chat to your tutor. You may need a bit of extra help or to change your study timetable or techniques.

When I see a page full of numbers and symbols, my mind goes blank and I start to panic.

First, try to get your feelings under control. Put down your pen. Take a few, deep breaths and try to relax. Then, talk to yourself positively, identifying small steps that you feel confident enough to tackle. For example: 'I can sort out these symbols by looking in my MST dictionary' (see page 91). 'Then, I'll try to untangle that first line.' 'I can try some of the ideas on pages 104 to 112, or I'll make a note of the difficulty and ask my tutor ...'

The ideas for getting to grips with mathematical language on pages 91 to 93 of this chapter and pages 118 to 123 of Chapter 5 may also help.

When I get an answer, I'm not sure if it's right or if I've used the correct techniques. How can I check my own work?

There are often several methods you can use to solve a problem – all equally valid. Confidence that your method works comes with lots of practice and experience with using different techniques. Have a look at the suggestions on page 100 about checking your final answer.

I can't remember the maths I did a fortnight ago.

It's not necessary to remember everything you have studied first time around. Few people do. The important skills are knowing where to look up topics and then being able to apply the techniques again. So, if your memory is not as good as you'd like, it's important to organize your notes systematically so that you can find information quickly (see Chapter 2). But if you can remember some topics, life is a lot easier. Think how tiresome it would be to look up the names of numbers every time you wanted to count! To help you to remember, read actively, make notes and practise regularly (see pages 90 to 98). Reflecting on your progress and allowing yourself time to review new ideas will also help. Key topics that are worth remembering are often studied several times throughout a course. Each time, remembering them becomes easier as the topics become more familiar.

I get bogged down with the maths in the Physics course I'm doing. Everyone else seems to sail through.

Try to stop comparing your work with others' work. What is important is how you feel about your progress, not theirs. Although you feel that no one else has problems, this is certain to be untrue. You may just not notice their problems, or your opinion may be influenced by one or two people who happen to be very good. Or you may be more conscientious and care more about your progress. Try discussing the work. If others are having problems, you know that you're not alone, and you may be able to sort things out together. If they're not, they may be able to help you. (You can return the favour when it's time to study your pet topic.) If you're concerned about your progress, talk to your tutor who will be able to either reassure you or provide you with the help you need. The advice in this chapter should help.

I can follow the examples in the book, but I can't work out the questions in the exercises for myself.

It sounds like you need a bit more practice. Study and question the examples in the text to see how the steps work and why they were taken (see pages 94 to 96). Working through a few simpler examples first, or discussing the problems with a fellow student, may help you to see the way forward. Have a look at the ideas on tackling mathematical problems at the top of page 112.

CHAPTER 5

Working with numbers and symbols

1 Introduction: learning the language

You come across numbers and symbols every day. For instance, you find numbers on timetables, food packets and till receipts. Symbols appear on road signs, weather charts and dials for washing machines and cookers. Why aren't words used instead? I can think of at least three reasons.

Numbers and symbols summarize information in small, neat chunks.

'11:45' takes up much less space than 'eleven forty-five'.

Symbols have exact meanings, which are widely accepted as standard.

My washing machine has a spiral symbol for 'spin'. Operating a friend's machine is a little easier if it has the same symbol.

Once you know what a symbol means, you can read it very quickly.

A road sign with a symbol indicating 'bend to left' can be read very quickly as you drive past. A sign that said 'You are approaching a sharp bend to the left' would give much the same information, but you'd probably have to stop the car to read it.

Numbers and symbols are therefore very convenient forms of communication. And they assume a particular importance in MST subjects. As was mentioned in Chapter 4, they form part of the language of mathematics. This chapter aims to make you feel more at home with this new technical language through advice about how to make sense of its new 'words' and 'letters'. Rather than expecting you to become fluent in a new language, I see this chapter as a phrase book, something to help you get started. It will be particularly helpful for students of science and technology, because it concentrates on examples of numbers and symbols that are sometimes the stumbling blocks in early study.

So, not only is the language of mathematics of enormous importance in its own right, but you'll need a basic understanding for studying science or technology. Indeed, some branches of science use mathematics as their language – to appreciate the *language* of physics, you'll need to understand the *language* of mathematics. Mathematics is a universal language, which crosses boundaries between subjects and countries. It is very powerful, and beautiful. Once you understand the ways it uses numbers and symbols, you can start to appreciate the elegance of the ideas that lie at the centre of MST subjects.

Chapter 4 ended by highlighting the importance of patience and practice; for this chapter, the same advice holds. The more you practise, the more confident you'll feel. If you feel daunted now by the prospect of numbers and symbols, keep an open mind and take things one step at a time. Take time to look at just a few symbols, try to master some of the basic aspects of working with numbers. By the end of this chapter, you won't yet be fluent in this new language, but there should be less of a temptation to skip examples of numbers and symbols.

As you read this chapter, you may need to pause occasionally to work through some sections of Maths Help. These give you a chance to *use* numbers and symbols, not just learn to recognize them. So, it's a good idea to break up your study of this chapter into smaller chunks.

Key Points

◆ Learning to use numbers and symbols is like learning a language – there are rules about when and how they are used, and how they are written.

◆ You need to practise using numbers and symbols, in order to understand what they mean and gain confidence in using them.

2 Getting used to numbers and symbols

Chapter 4 mentioned the importance of learning how to read mathematical writing carefully, checking that you understand something from each word and symbol. Here, I want to take this point further and tell you more about how some important numbers and symbols are read and written. As you will see, most of the symbols have standard meanings, whenever they are used. But sometimes the same symbol can have different meanings in different contexts – rather as the same word can have different meanings in different situations.

2.1 Reading numbers

In everyday life, you often come across numbers in the middle of ordinary writing, and you probably read them without giving them a second thought. For instance, 'there were 31 related outbreaks of food poisoning in 1988' would be said 'there were thirty-one related outbreaks of food poisoning in nineteen eighty-eight'. As you read the digits, you say them as words in your mind.

Chapter 4 mentioned that, in MST subjects, numbers are sometimes written in less familiar ways, such as decimals and powers of ten. Learning the language is so much easier if numbers are read correctly. For example, '2.1' would be said 'two point one', and '10^4' would be said 'ten to the power four' or 'ten to the four'. Once you know how to say these numbers, you'll be less tempted to skip the 'difficult bits'. MST texts often contain a mixture of words, numbers and symbols, and you have to be able to read all these different ingredients to appreciate the full meaning. Figure 5.1 gives you an example.

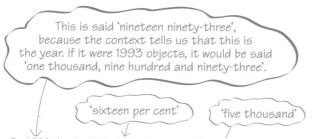

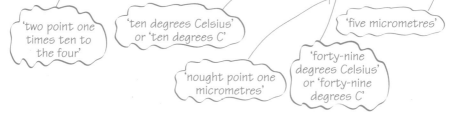

In 1993, in the UK, 16% of cases of food poisoning were diagnosed as *Salmonella typhimurium.* There were 5000 cases of this type of infection, compared with 2.1×10^4 cases of *Salmonella enteritidis.* Salmonella bacteria often infect poultry and eggs. These bacteria are tiny organisms, about 5 μm long. They grow quickly in food stored between 10 °C and 49 °C. Bacteria cannot grow without water, so eggs can be preserved by drying. Other types of food poisoning are caused by viruses, which are typically 0.1 μm long.

This is said 'nineteen ninety-three', because the context tells us that this is the year. If it were 1993 objects, it would be said 'one thousand, nine hundred and ninety-three'.

'sixteen per cent'

'five thousand'

'two point one times ten to the four'

'ten degrees Celsius' or 'ten degrees C'

'five micrometres'

'nought point one micrometres'

'forty-nine degrees Celsius' or 'forty-nine degrees C'

Figure 5.1 *How different numbers are said*

Saying decimals

Simply read the digits, starting on the left. Words that apply to numbers greater than nine are not appropriate for saying decimals. For instance:

◆ 0.27 is 'nought point two seven' not 'nought point twenty-seven'

◆ 0.135 is 'nought point one three five' not 'nought point one hundred and thirty-five'

◆ 48.02 is 'forty-eight point nought two'.

If you were to pronounce the first two numbers as 'nought point twenty-seven' and 'nought point one hundred and thirty-five', then the first number seems smaller than the second, which is not the case. (You could say 'zero' or 'oh' instead of 'nought'.)

Some numbers can appear in different forms

Numbers can be identical but be said and written differently. For example:

◆ a hundredth can be written as 1/100, 0.01 or 10^{-2}

◆ 1/100 is said 'one hundredth' or 'one over a hundred'

◆ 0.01 is said 'nought point nought one'

◆ 10^{-2} is said 'ten to the minus two'.

These different ways of writing numbers may make the meaning clearer, the calculations easier, or be quicker to write. If you are unsure about the meaning of these conventions, see Maths Help on fractions (pages 317 to 329), decimals (pages 330 to 338) and powers (pages 353 to 355).

2.2 Reading letters and symbols

In MST subjects, numbers and familiar letters of the English alphabet can be used in unfamiliar ways. Particular *symbols* are used to represent something. So, how can you tell how to read each symbol, and know what it means?

Some symbols have standard pronunciations and meanings wherever they are used. For example, 'μm' is a particular unit used to measure length and always means 'micrometres'. You pronounce 'μm' as 'mew em'. I'll have more to say about units later on.

Some symbols have an agreed meaning only within a particular context. For example, 'C' means 'carbon' in chemical notation. But 'C' means something different when used to refer to a particular temperature, like 35 °C.

Often you'll find that symbols are defined by the author where they first appear, but from then on, it's assumed that you know what they mean. So, whenever you come across a new symbol, it's worth making a note of it, with its meaning in that particular situation. You could use the MST dictionary mentioned on page 91.

So, some authors may not give the definition of a symbol with every calculation. To find the meaning, you may have to look back over a few pages – for example, the symbols could be explained in a paragraph near the beginning of the topic. In some books, the meanings of all the symbols are listed at the end of the section in which they are introduced, or in an appendix.

You don't need to memorize the meaning of every symbol you meet – you can always look them up – but as you progress, you will find that you recognize the common ones. If your course uses a formula sheet, do make sure you understand what the symbols mean! You can practise using important symbols yourself by tackling the exercises, or by reading text carefully. Perhaps you noticed the following symbols in Figure 5.1.

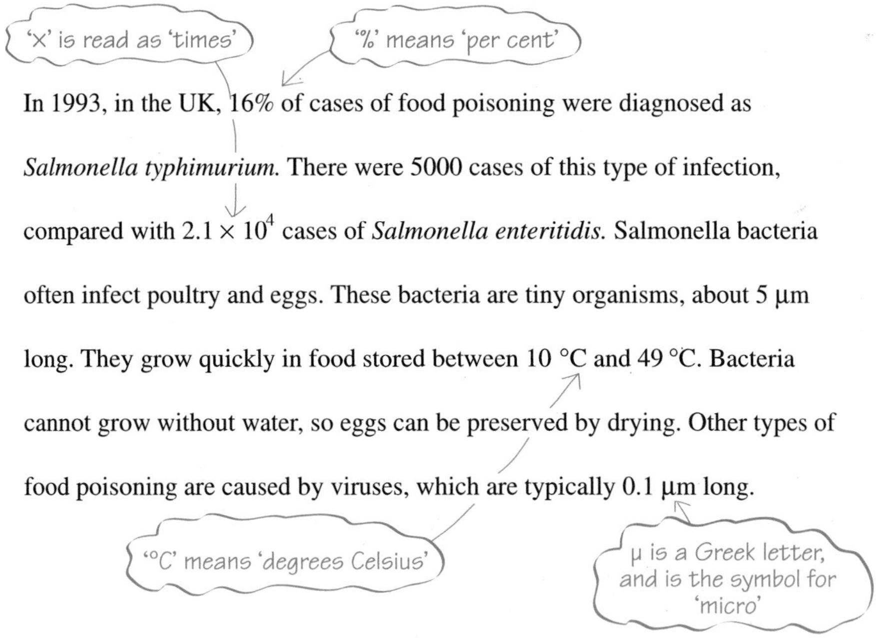

'×' is read as 'times'

'%' means 'per cent'

In 1993, in the UK, 16% of cases of food poisoning were diagnosed as

Salmonella typhimurium. There were 5000 cases of this type of infection,

compared with 2.1×10^4 cases of *Salmonella enteritidis.* Salmonella bacteria

often infect poultry and eggs. These bacteria are tiny organisms, about 5 μm

long. They grow quickly in food stored between 10 °C and 49 °C. Bacteria

cannot grow without water, so eggs can be preserved by drying. Other types of

food poisoning are caused by viruses, which are typically 0.1 μm long.

'°C' means 'degrees Celsius'

μ is a Greek letter, and is the symbol for 'micro'

Figure 5.2 *Getting used to 'reading' symbols*

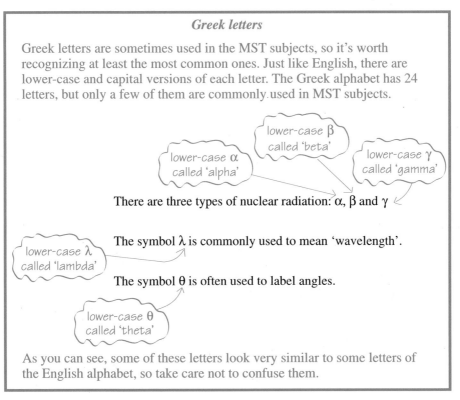

Greek letters

Greek letters are sometimes used in the MST subjects, so it's worth recognizing at least the most common ones. Just like English, there are lower-case and capital versions of each letter. The Greek alphabet has 24 letters, but only a few of them are commonly used in MST subjects.

lower-case β called 'beta'

lower-case α called 'alpha'

lower-case γ called 'gamma'

There are three types of nuclear radiation: α, β and γ

The symbol λ is commonly used to mean 'wavelength'.

lower-case λ called 'lambda'

The symbol θ is often used to label angles.

lower-case θ called 'theta'

As you can see, some of these letters look very similar to some letters of the English alphabet, so take care not to confuse them.

2.3 Writing numbers and symbols

Handwritten numbers and symbols often differ from the printed versions. It's important to write them down in such a way that someone else can understand what you have written. Here is a chance to see how well you do this.

---

*A**ctivity Break*** Copy out the information below fairly quickly in your usual handwriting.

In 1993, in the UK, 16% of cases of food poisoning were diagnosed as *Salmonella typhimurium*. There were 5000 cases of this type of infection, compared with 2.1×10^4 cases of *Salmonella enteritidis*. Salmonella bacteria often infect poultry and eggs. These bacteria are tiny organisms, about 5 μm long. They grow quickly in food stored between 10 °C and 49 °C. Bacteria cannot grow without water, so eggs can be preserved by drying. Other types of food poisoning are caused by viruses, which are typically 0.1 μm long.

This is one student's response. Obviously yours won't be identical, but this answer shows some typical difficulties. You could also ask a friend to read your version, to see how clearly you write.

> numbers not joined (unlike letters in a word)

> use underlining where print uses italics (it is difficult to write italics by hand)

> should be 'enteritidis' – watch out for unfamiliar spellings

> row of zeroes joined – a bad habit!

> superscript 4 is clearly raised, and slightly smaller than the 10

> decimal point is higher than a full stop

> handwriting unclear in places; here 'v' and 'r' look similar – a bad habit!

> handwritten Greek letter μ is different from 'u'

In 1993, in the U.K., 16% of cases of food poisoning were diagnosed as Salmonella typhimurium. There were 5000 cases of this type of infection, compared with 2.1×10^4 cases of Salmonella enteriditis. Salmonella bacteria often infect poultry and eggs. These bacteria are tiny organisms, about 5 μm long. They grow quickly in food stored between 10°C and 49°C. Bacteria cannot grow without water, so eggs can be preserved by drying. Other types of food poisoning are caused by viruses, which are typically 0.1 μm long.

Hints and Tips

Writing numbers and symbols

◆ Write clearly, especially if your normal handwriting tends to be scribbly. Slow down when you write numbers and symbols.

◆ The size and position of a number or symbol can alter its meaning. Take care, especially with raised numbers (superscripts) and lowered numbers (subscripts).

◆ Don't try to write in italics – underline the handwritten version instead.

◆ If two symbols appear similar, make sure you can tell them apart by exaggerating the differences. For example, a handwritten 'μ' needs a long tail to distinguish it from 'u'.

◆ Be careful using commas in large numbers; it's better to use spaces – for example, 72 349 501. Using commas can be confusing; if you wrote 'then add 72,349,501 and 37', this could be understood as 72 + 349 + 501 + 37, rather than 72 349 501 + 37. Use semicolons if you want to write a list of numbers, along the lines of 'add 72; 349; 501 and 37'.

Let's go back to the body mass index example introduced in Chapter 4. So far, you have seen this example printed neatly. But imagine you're a tutor who has just received the following handwritten version. As you can see, there are problems with the way this is written.

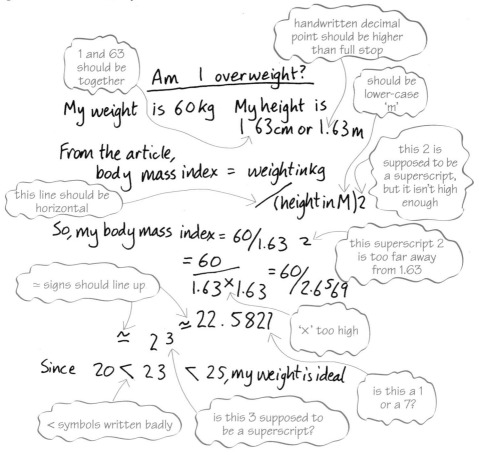

Although the symbols used here are the standard ones, the calculation doesn't make much sense because it has been written badly. The message, once again, is that you have to write symbols clearly for someone else to be able to understand them. Overleaf, the same example is written more clearly. (As in Chapter 4, I'm not including the units in the calculation, although some courses may insist on this.)

Am I overweight?

My weight is 60kg   My height is 163cm or 1.63m

From the article,

$$\text{body mass index} = \frac{\text{weight in kg}}{(\text{height in m})^2}$$

So, my body mass index $= \dfrac{60}{1.63^2} = \dfrac{60}{1.63 \times 1.63}$

$$= \frac{60}{2.6569} \simeq 22.5827$$

$$\simeq 23$$

Since $20 < 23 < 25$, my weight is ideal

This example shows that handwritten mathematical working can look different from printed mathematics. Here is the same example in a printed form.

Am I overweight?

My weight is 60 kg   My height is 163 cm or 1.63 m

From the article,   body mass index $= \dfrac{\text{weight in kg}}{(\text{height in m})^2}$

So,   my body mass index $= \dfrac{60}{1.63^2} = \dfrac{60}{1.63 \times 1.63}$

$$= \frac{60}{2.6569} \simeq 23$$

Since $20 < 23 < 25$, my weight is ideal.

When you write mathematics by hand, set out your working on the page neatly, with plenty of space between the lines. If you don't know what a symbol stands for, look it up – don't guess.

2.4 Same symbol, different meaning

I've already mentioned the potential for confusion when the same symbol has a number of meanings in different topics. Figure 5.3 shows some examples.

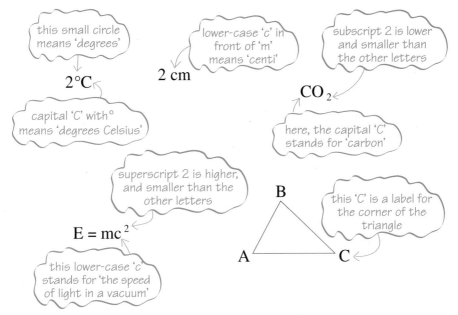

Figure 5.3 *The letter 'c' as a symbol can have different meanings*

Some of the examples in Figure 5.3 need more explanation.

2 cm   Here, the lower-case 'c' in front of the 'm' for metres represents 'centi-'. This is standard notation, so you'll meet it many times. There is more about units on pages 137 to 147.

C   The capital 'C' is used as a label at the corner of the triangle. Any letter could have been used here – there is no standard symbol, although letters of the English alphabet are usually chosen.

CO_2   Here, the capital 'C' stands for 'carbon'. This meaning only applies in chemistry (and I'll have more to say about chemical notation in the next section).

$E = mc^2$ In this equation, the lower-case 'c' represents 'the speed of light in a vacuum'. This use of the symbol 'c' is standard in physics. The complete equation would be read 'ee equals em see squared'. (In equations of this sort, the symbols are sometimes set in italic type.)

So, whenever you come across a symbol, check that you know what it means in that situation, and if you haven't come across it before, make a note of it in your MST dictionary.

2.5 Chemical symbols

Now let's consider another type of symbol that represents something particular in science: chemical symbols. You're likely to learn much more about chemical symbols as your studies progress but my main aim here, rather than teaching you chemistry, is to convince you of the usefulness of chemical notation and how it can convey meanings and relationships much better than ordinary words.

Chemists use symbols to represent substances. Substances are made up of atoms, which are the minute building blocks of matter. For instance, imagine breaking a lump of charcoal (which is essentially carbon) into two, and then splitting one of those parts, and then splitting one of those parts, and so on … Eventually, you would have an invisibly small 'chunk' of carbon, which couldn't easily be split any further. This would be a carbon atom. The original lump of charcoal consisted of a huge number of carbon atoms bonded together. Carbon is an example of an element – a simple substance which *cannot* be broken down into even simpler substances by chemical means. An element is the simplest we can get (unless we 'split the atom' by more drastic means). Each element consists of its own type of atom. All elements are coded by either one or two letters – and this code is known as the chemical symbol for a particular element. We can represent a carbon atom using the symbol C.

Oxygen is another element. Each oxygen atom can be represented by the symbol O. But oxygen gas – in air, for example – doesn't consist of single oxygen atoms. The atoms are bonded together in pairs to make molecules. A molecule is a cluster of two or more atoms, chemically bonded together.

Using chemical notation, we represent an oxygen molecule like this:

O_2 ← subscript 2 shows that there are two atoms bonded together

Air also contains carbon dioxide, but this isn't an element. Carbon dioxide consists of a combination of carbon and oxygen. When different elements combine, they form compounds. A molecule of carbon dioxide consists of one atom of carbon and two atoms of oxygen ('di-' means 'two').

So, we represent a molecule of carbon dioxide like this:

CO_2 ← here, the subscript is to the right of the 'O', so it refers to oxygen, not carbon

The notation is telling us that there are two oxygen atoms and one carbon atom in each molecule of carbon dioxide, giving a total of three atoms.

You'll have heard of water as 'aitch-two-oh', which is how the chemical notation for water is pronounced. It is written:

H_2O the subscript is to the right of the 'H', so this time it refers to hydrogen, not oxygen

The 'H' stands for hydrogen. By looking at the formula, you can tell at a glance that there are three atoms in each molecule: two hydrogen atoms (note where the subscript 2 is positioned) and one oxygen atom.

As you've seen, some chemical symbols are quite straightforward – they are simply the first letter of the name of the element written as a capital: for example, C for carbon and N for nitrogen. It's not possible to use just single capital letters for all the elements, since there are over 100 elements and only 26 letters in the alphabet. Some elements are therefore coded using two letters: for example, Cl for chlorine, Br for bromine, Ca for calcium. The first letter is written as a capital and the second letter as a lower-case letter. This avoids confusion between, for example, the element cobalt, which has the chemical symbol Co, and the compound carbon monoxide (carbon combined with oxygen) which has the chemical formula CO. Not all chemical symbols take the first letter of their English name; the symbols for sodium (Na), iron (Fe) and potassium (K) are based on their Latin names. You can now see how simple it is to code the 100 elements using chemical symbols – and all the symbols and associated elements can be looked up in any chemistry textbook or science data book.

Once you are familiar with this notation, you can start to use it. Let's see if we can make sense of a chemical equation which describes what happens when we ignite natural gas (methane, written CH_4) in a cooker or gas fire. Here are two ways in which this can be done.

methane   +   oxygen   =   carbon dioxide   +   water   *word equation*

$$CH_4 \quad + \quad 2O_2 \quad = \quad CO_2 \quad + \quad 2H_2O \qquad \text{chemical equation}$$

This tells us that when we burn methane gas (CH_4) in air, it reacts with the oxygen (O_2) from the air to form carbon dioxide (CO_2) and water (H_2O).

What information does the chemical equation give us that the word equation doesn't? The chemical equation is *balanced*, like a mathematical equation. In chemical reactions, atoms cannot vanish or appear from nowhere, so there must be as many atoms of each element on the right-hand side of the equation as there are on the left-hand side.

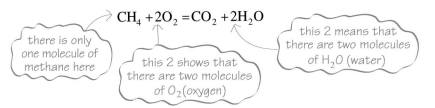

$$CH_4 + 2O_2 = CO_2 + 2H_2O$$

there is only one molecule of methane here

this 2 shows that there are two molecules of O_2 (oxygen)

this 2 means that there are two molecules of H_2O (water)

To make sure the equation balances, you need to look at the number of different atoms involved. Let's look again at the equation and count the numbers of each type of atom separately, adding up the number of each type of atom:

$$CH_4 + O_2 + O_2 = CO_2 + H_2O + H_2O$$

number of C atoms: 1   = 1

number of H atoms: 4   =   2   + 2

number of O atoms: 2 + 2   =   2 +   1 +   1

So, the equation tells us that for every molecule of methane that burns, two molecules of oxygen are used up. If there isn't enough air reaching the gas flame, there won't be enough oxygen to burn the methane completely. When this happens, poisonous carbon monoxide (CO) is formed instead of harmless carbon dioxide (CO_2). So, the chemical equation gives us a hint that a gas flame needs a good supply of air in order to burn safely. We couldn't get this information from the word equation, because it doesn't show how many molecules are reacting.

2.6 Inventing your own symbols

The great value of symbols, such as chemical notation, is that they're universally agreed. All chemistry students will recognize what the symbols C and N stand for. But useful symbols don't have to be of that type – you may want to invent your own symbols, for making private notes from texts or from lectures, as mentioned in Chapters 2 and 6. Here's a paragraph of text, followed by some notes I made using my own symbols.

> The percentage of cases of *Salmonella typhimurium* increased between 1981 and 1983, then decreased gradually over the next ten years. During this time, the percentage of cases of *Salmonella enteritidis* increased gradually, so that in 1983, there were far more cases of *S. enteritidis* than *S. typhimurium*.

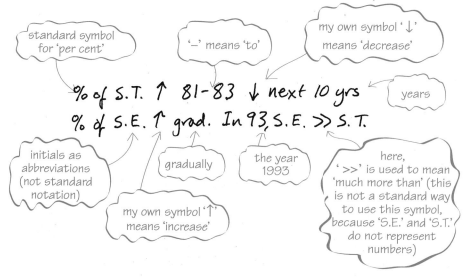

Some of these symbols have standard meanings, but anyone else would have problems working out what my notes mean. So, you should use your own symbols very sparingly in public writing (assignments, reports, exams); and when you do, it's essential that you explain what they mean – don't leave the reader guessing.

Key Points

◆ Saying numbers and symbols as you read will help you to understand them. Reading numbers and symbols often takes longer than reading words, so be prepared to slow down and read them carefully.

◆ The same number can be written in different forms – for example, 1/100 or 0.01 or 10^{-2}. Practise writing numbers in different ways, so you can recognize these variations.

◆ Take care over how you write numbers and symbols. Their size and position matter. Handwritten symbols are not identical to printed ones.

◆ The same symbol can have a different meaning in a different situation. Pay attention to details – small differences in appearance can make a big difference to the meaning. Whenever you come across a symbol, check that you know its exact meaning in that particular situation – a rough guess is unlikely to be good enough.

◆ Chemical notation is a specialized use of symbols to express ideas which are difficult to communicate in words alone.

◆ You can invent your own symbols – when you make notes, for example. If you introduce your own symbols into a piece of work that will be read by someone else, always write down what those symbols mean.

3 Developing good numerical habits

When you start to do calculations yourself, you'll need to know not just the vocabulary – what the numbers and symbols mean – but how they are combined to convey meaning. In other words, you need to know some rules of grammar.

This section explores some of the things you will need to do with numbers and symbols. Chapter 4 started you off with some of the conventions of mathematical language, encouraging you to develop particular ways of looking at mathematical problems – I could almost say it led you into good habits, mathematically speaking. In this section – and indeed for much of the remainder of this chapter – I'm going to focus on using numbers and on doing calculations, because these skills are particularly important to students of science and technology. For example, powers of ten are routinely used to record very small and very large numbers, so they are common in science. This notation allows you to compare numbers easily, and to *estimate* the results of calculations – and you already know something about the importance of estimation from Chapter 4.

3.1 Becoming familiar with powers of ten

Perhaps you're already comfortable with the idea that large numbers can be written using powers of ten – for example, 4000 can be written as 4×10^3. If not, Maths Help on page 353 and page 359 outlines the basics of powers of ten, the rules of indices (another name for 'powers') and scientific notation.

Questions such as 'How big?', 'How small?' and 'Which item is bigger?' are always cropping up in MST subjects. Answering these kinds of questions is not just about knowing the techniques required to do a calculation, it is often about getting a feel for the relative size of the numbers involved. So, a rough answer, or estimate, might be all you need.

You're certain to be used to using estimates in 'real life'. Suppose you were shopping and you estimated the bill to be about £20. An actual bill of £19 would not be a surprise, but a bill for £190 (or £1.90) would be a shock. What makes the difference is how many times one sum is different from the other:

◆ £190 is about ten times bigger than £20
◆ £1.90 is about ten times smaller than £20.

Compared with your estimate of £20, a bill of £19 would be reasonable. This is because £19 is of the *same order of magnitude* as £20 – they agree to the nearest power of ten. Similarly, we can say:

◆ £190 is *one order of magnitude* bigger than £20
◆ £1.90 is *one order of magnitude* smaller than £20.

If a number is ten times bigger than another number, then it is one order of magnitude larger. If a number is a hundred times bigger than another, then it is two orders of magnitude larger, because 100 is 10×10 or 10^2, which is ten to the power two.

A ctivity Break For each of the following pairs of numbers, decide whether they are of the same order of magnitude. If they are not, decide which number is bigger, and how many times bigger it is: 10 times, 1000 times and so on.

1	1024	3004
2	150	0.13
3	3.4×10^5	4.2×10^3
4	1.5×10^{-2}	1.1×10^2

---

1   1024 and 3004 are of same order of magnitude, because they differ by less than a factor of ten. Putting this another way, in scientific notation, the powers of ten are the same: 1.024×10^3 and 3.004×10^3.

2   150 is about 1000 times larger than 0.13, that is, three orders of magnitude larger.

3   3.4×10^5 is about 100 times larger than 4.2×10^3. You can tell by looking at the powers of ten: 5 is 2 more than 3, so 10^5 is 10^2 times 10^3. Although 4.2 is greater than 3.4, this difference is insignificant compared with the powers of ten.

4   1.1×10^2 is about 10 000 times larger than 1.5×10^{-2}. Again, you can tell by looking at the powers of ten: 2 is 4 plus –2, so 10^2 is 10^4 times 10^{-2}. Keep an eye on *negative signs* in powers of ten – they make a huge difference.

Powers of imagination

You will often come across large powers of ten in MST. To make sure you're using the convention sensibly, it's helpful to imagine the numbers involved – but this isn't always easy. Let's imagine ten things – say, ten people. This could be a short queue for a bus. Now try to imagine a hundred people, or even a thousand people. A typical coach holds about 40 people, so a hundred people is about two and a half coach loads. A thousand people would fill 25 coaches. Once we get to ten thousand people, which is 10^4, a mental picture of the number is more difficult. Ten thousand people would fill 250 coaches – and I can just about imagine that. But 10^8 people is much more difficult to visualize. Small quantities are readily expressed in scientific notation – but again, developing a feel for what these numbers imply requires some imagination. A tenth of a second (a wink of an eye) is a short period, but it's just about within my experience. However, 10^{-12} of a second – a million millionth of a second – is not.

3.2 The value of estimation

Just as with your shopping bill, it's often useful to *estimate* the result of a calculation to check that the calculation is correct. An estimate is not the same as a wild guess; it is a rough answer based on what you know about the situation. There is no such thing as a correct estimate – different people produce slightly different estimates for the same calculation, depending on how they approximated the original data.

Estimates are supposed to be fairly quick to calculate, so you only need to work to 1 or 2 significant figures for most purposes. (If you are not sure what is meant by 'significant figures', see Maths Help on page 349.) Once you have the estimate, you can calculate the accurate answer, then round this to

1 significant figure so you can check it against the estimate. If they agree to this level of accuracy, then you're on the right track! The difference between the estimate and the result of the detailed calculation lies in the number of significant figures you can rely on.

A **ctivity Break** Suppose you see this calculation in a textbook:

$$\frac{3.98 \times 54.2}{103.7}$$

Without using a calculator, is the answer:

(a) about 200?

(b) about 20?

(c) about 2?

(d) about 0.2?

If you thought 'about 2' was closest to the results then you were correct: the right answer is Answer (c).

Let's look at this calculation more closely, and see how to estimate the answer.

First of all, round all of the numbers to 1 significant figure

so $3.98 = 4$ to 1 sig. fig.

       $54.2 = 50$ to 1 sig. fig.

       $103.7 = 100$ to 1 sig. fig.

So, a rough calculation is: $\dfrac{4 \times 50}{100}$

Now you can cancel down to get an estimate: $\dfrac{4 \times \overset{1}{\cancel{50}}}{_2\cancel{100}} = 2$

If I use my calculator for the same calculation, the result displayed is 2.080 192 864 If you round the result to 1 significant figure, this gives 2, so it agrees with the estimate. So, the result of the calculation is sensible – though I still have to decide how many significant figures to quote in the final answer.

Because the original numbers are given to 3 or 4 significant figures, the answer should be quoted only to the least number of significant figures in the original data. So here, the answer should be quoted to 3 significant figures (see Maths Help on page 349).

You might write: $\dfrac{3.8 \times 54.2}{103.7} = 2.08$ (3 sig. figs)

Maths Help on page 351 gives another example of an estimate, if you want more practice.

How much arithmetic do I need to know for MST?

A common image of a professional in MST is someone spending hours doing many complicated calculations. This has some truth in it, but the very complex calculations are usually carried out by a computer. Scientists are more likely to rely on quick calculations, usually on scraps of paper or the backs of envelopes, as they discuss their results.

So, for two reasons, professionals and students of MST alike need to know how to do calculations 'by hand'.

◆ Can you believe the result from your calculator? A rough calculation with whole numbers will give you an estimate. If you know what order of magnitude of result to expect, it's easier to tell when you've pressed the wrong key or made another slip somewhere.

◆ Sometimes, a rough answer will do. Not all results need to be exact.

In practice, arithmetic with whole numbers should be enough. More complicated calculations can be done with a calculator or computer. So, it's worth spending time at this stage making sure you are confident about 'whole number' arithmetic by working through Maths Help, pages 303 to 308, without using a calculator. If you find this difficult, or you need more practice, ask your tutor, or see the books listed on page 404.

3.3 Using a calculator

Calculators are very useful tools in MST studies, so you need to develop the habit of using one. However, like all tools, calculators need to be used effectively. This means knowing *when* to use one as well as *how*.

Different kinds of calculator

There are three main types of calculator available: arithmetic, scientific and graphic. Only the scientific and graphic types are suitable for MST studies.

 Arithmetic calculators are often referred to as 'four-function', and vary from simple models, which only add, subtract, multiply and divide (the 'four functions') to those that have square root ($\sqrt{}$), percentage (%) and constant keys, and one or more memories. These calculators perform calculations as they are entered – for example, $3 + 4 \times 5 =$ will display the answer 35. They are not suitable for doing powers of ten calculations of the type you'll often meet in MST studies.

Scientific calculators have many more keys, including those needed for doing powers of ten. Apart from the number of keys, the big difference is that calculations are performed in the correct algebraic order – for example, $3 + 4 \times 5 =$ will give the answer 23 because the multiplication is done first (see Maths Help on page 304).

Graphic calculators are scientific calculators with a larger display area and can plot graphs. They have the additional advantage of showing the key presses used in a calculation, so wrong key presses can be spotted. Some also include programs for solving equations and rearranging formulas; they are, in effect, hand-held computers.

Buying a calculator

Don't buy one until you know more about your course and what you will need. Check the requirements of your course, especially if there are regulations about the use of a calculator in examinations.

Your calculator understands only mathematical language

Calculators understand a mathematical language, and this is how they must be 'talked to'. The instruction book gives you the vocabulary for your calculator – what the symbols on the keys mean. This all takes time to master, and calculator instructions are not always easy to follow. Think of a calculator as an obedient servant, but a silent one. It won't always tell you you've pressed the wrong key – but it will do exactly what you tell it.

Hints and Tips

Using your calculator correctly

- ◆ Learn how to use your calculator in stages. Start with familiar techniques, such as adding up a list of numbers. Then learn new techniques as you go along.

- ◆ Write down what you are going to calculate before you use your calculator. You can then repeat the calculation, if you suspect you've pressed the wrong key.

- ◆ Estimate the answer to a complicated calculation, using pen and paper, so that you know roughly what result to expect.

- ◆ Consult the instruction book. This will often have examples for you to try. When you first use your calculator to do a particular type of calculation, have a look at the instructions – they should show you the best way to use your calculator

- ◆ If you don't want to carry the instruction book with you, it may be worth summarizing useful key presses on a card that will fit in your pocket.

◆ If you forget how to enter a particular calculation, try a similar calculation where you know what answer to expect. For example, if you get stuck working out $7.13 \times 10^4 + 5.92 \times 10^3$, try $7 \times 10^4 + 6 \times 10^3$ first; by hand, you can work out that the answer should be about $76\,000$, or 7.6×10^4.

◆ If your calculator has a memory, pay special attention to the way it works, especially if there is more than one memory. Consult the instruction book, and practise entering numbers into the memory. Otherwise, it's easy to get confused, and lose or overwrite the contents of the memory without realizing what you're doing.

◆ Some calculations may look very similar when written down, but are entered in different ways on your calculator. For example:

	$7 \times 10^4 + 6 \times 10^3$	gives 7.6×10^4
but	$(7 + 6\,) \times 10^3$	gives 1.3×10^4
and	$7 + 6 \times 10^3$	gives 6.007×10^3
Also	$7^2 - 3^2$	gives 40
but	$(7 - 3)^2$	gives 16
and	$7^2 + (-3)^2$	gives 58

If you are not sure how to do these calculations with pen and paper, see page 304 of Maths Help, which explains the use of brackets.

Key Points

◆ Powers of ten, and scientific notation, allow you to record very large and very small numbers, and to compare them easily, once you have mastered the mathematical language.

◆ You can use powers of ten to make a quick estimate of the result of a calculation. Making an estimate is important, because it tells you what to expect.

◆ A calculator is a useful tool in MST studies. You need to learn when and how to use one. An early step is deciding what sort to buy, and this decision depends upon what you're going to use it for.

4 Working with units

4.1 Measurements need units

As you've seen earlier in this chapter, symbols are often used as shorthand in the language of the MST subjects. Many of the symbols I've mentioned are used so frequently that they have standard meanings with which you need to become familiar. This is particularly true of units, which are used in MST subjects whenever measurements are made. Whatever is measured, the result needs a unit in order to make sense. For instance, suppose I have a piece of string, and you ask me how long it is. If I reply '2', this doesn't answer your question. You need to know the units as well – is it 2 centimetres, 2 metres or 2 kilometres long?

However long the string is – 2 centimetres, 2 metres or 2 kilometres – I can record this information in a convenient shorthand form using numbers and symbols:

2 cm   2 m   2 km

two centimetres   two metres   two kilometres

So, the length of the string is written as a number followed by letters. The letters represent the units in which the length is measured. First of all, note:

- That there is a space between the number and the units. There is no space between the letters of the units unless powers are involved. For example, metres per second is written m s^{-1} rather than ms^{-1}.

- That the unit stays in its singular form, even when there are two of them – hence '2 cm' not '2 cms'.

You'll see another pattern emerging here. All three lengths have 'm' for 'metres' as part of the units, and two of them have another letter in front of the 'm'. The letters have two distinct purposes: to show *what* is being measured (metres measure length), and to show *how big or how small* the result is ('k' for 'kilo-' and 'c' for 'centi-'). The 'k' and 'c' are examples of *prefixes*, and they go in front of the letter for what is being measured ('pre-' means 'before'). So, the prefixes 'k' and 'c' tell you about the scale of the measurement – that 2 kilometres is much longer than 2 centimetres.

Suppose you come across a length of '2 mm'. What do the letters mean here? The second 'm' means 'metres, but the first 'm' is a prefix (milli-). So, '2 mm' means 'two millimetres'. The position of each 'm' shows you its meaning. When it is in front of another letter, 'm' means 'milli-' (a prefix). Otherwise, 'm' means 'metres'.

Of course, there are many more quantities that can be measured – time, temperature, energy, for example. These are all examples of physical quantities. Here, a 'physical quantity' means 'something that can be measured'. Measurements need units, so all physical quantities have a unit.

There are hundreds of different units, but scientists and technologists of all nations have agreed to use a standard system of units. Everything you could ever want to measure can be measured using a few basic units, or combinations of them. These internationally agreed units and their prefixes form the Système Internationale (International System) known as SI. The metre is the SI unit of length, and the symbol 'm' means 'metres'. So, in the world of MST subjects, all lengths are measured in metres, as opposed to inches or miles, perhaps with a prefix to show the scale of the measurement. So, the length of this page would be measured in centimetres (cm), but the distance between two towns would be measured in kilometres (km).

But what about other units, such as time? The SI unit of time is the second, 's'. Some common SI units are shown in Table 5.1. This is a small selection – enough to get you started. The full list is far too long to be included here – for more information, consult a science data book of the type mentioned in the reading list on page 404.

Table 5.1 Some common SI units

SI unit	What it measures	Symbol
kilogram	mass	kg
metre	length	m
second	time	s
joule	energy	J

Some of these SI units may look familiar; the joule (pronounced 'jool') is the SI unit of energy and has the symbol 'J'. You often come across this unit on food packet labels, and it often appears with an older, non-SI unit of energy – the calorie ('cal'). There are several other units which are often used with SI units, although not strictly part of the SI system. You will meet two of these units in this chapter: the litre, a unit of volume (symbol l), and the degree Celsius, a unit of temperature (symbol °C).

Prefixes can be used in front of any of these units. Try the following activity to see whether you can recognize the units and prefixes you've met so far.

Activity Break   Read the following statement, taken from the label on a carton of orange juice, and then write the name of each unit in full, what physical quantity it measures, and the meaning of the prefix.

> A typical serving of orange juice, 100 ml, provides 182 kJ of energy and 20 mg of vitamin C. This serving contains 0.6 g of protein and 9.4 g of sugar.

These are the units used, the quantities measured, and the meaning of the prefixes:

ml (millilitre)	measures volume	prefix 'm'
kJ (kilojoule)	measures energy	prefix 'k'
g (gram)	measures mass	no prefix
mg (milligram)	measures mass	prefix 'm'

4.2 Prefixes and powers of ten with units

Each of the examples I've mentioned so far represent a particular power of ten. For example, the prefix 'k' means 'kilo' and represents 'ten to the power three', which is a thousand. So, a unit with a 'k' in front is multiplied by a thousand:

'2 km' *is read as* 'two kilometres' *which means*
'two thousand metres'.

As another example, 'c' means 'centi-' and represents 'ten to the minus two', which is a hundredth. So, '2 cm' is 'two hundredths of a metre':

'2 cm' *is read as* 'two centimetres' *which means*
'two hundredths of a metre'.

So far, you have met the prefixes 'kilo-', 'centi-' and 'milli-'. There are others – and the common ones are shown in Table 5.2.

Table 5.2 Commonly used prefixes and powers of ten in SI

Prefix	Prefix name	Meaning	Power of ten	
G	giga-	thousand million	1 000 000 000	$= 10^9$
M	mega-	million	1 000 000	$= 10^6$
k	kilo-	thousand	1000	$= 10^3$
d	deci-	tenth	0.1	$= 10^{-1}$
c	centi-	hundredth	0.01	$= 10^{-2}$
m	milli-	thousandth	0.001	$= 10^{-3}$
μ	micro-	millionth	0.000 001	$= 10^{-6}$

Prefixes and patterns

SI prefixes follow a general pattern.

1   Capital letters are normally used for positive powers of ten. Lower-case letters are used for negative powers of ten, that is, tenths, hundredths and so on.

2   Most of the powers of ten are in multiples of 10^3, so many prefixes are a thousand times larger or smaller than the next in the series.

3   Only one prefix is used at a time.

Can you find exceptions to these rules in Table 5.2? The exception to Rule 1 is 'k' – it represents a positive power of ten, but is lower case; according to the rule, you would expect to write the symbol Kg for 'kilogram', but the correct version is kg. Note that the two exceptions to Rule 2 are 'deci-' which is 10^{-1} and 'centi-' which is 10^{-2}. There are no exceptions to Rule 3; for small masses, you'd write so many 'g' rather than 'mkg'.

So, you can replace the power of ten with the relevant SI prefix; Figure 5.4 shows the approach to take.

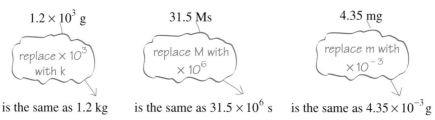

1.2×10^3 g
                  31.5 Ms
                  4.35 mg

replace $\times 10^3$ with k
    replace M with $\times 10^6$
    replace m with $\times 10^{-3}$

is the same as 1.2 kg   is the same as 31.5×10^6 s   is the same as 4.35×10^{-3} g

Figure 5.4 *Examples of replacing powers of ten with prefixes*

Tidying up powers of ten is important. A year is approximately 31.5×10^6 seconds; this is more neatly expressed as 3.15×10^7 s. You should write scientific notation as (a number between 1 and 10) × (a power of ten). So, using scientific notation means you have to learn the rules and conventions – again, this comes with practice.

Now you seen some examples, try using prefixes yourself.

ctivity Break

1 Replace each prefix with the corresponding power of ten, and tidy up the powers of ten where necessary.

    (a)   3.5 dm

    (b) 7.3×10^5 μs

    (c) 5.8×10^{-2} mg

2 Replace each power of ten with a suitable prefix (there may be more than one answer).

    (a) 5×10^6 s

    (b) 6.2×10^{-4} m

    (c) 4.92×10^4 m

---

1 (a)   3.5 dm = 3.5×10^{-1} m

    (b) 7.3×10^5 μs = $7.3 \times 10^5 \times 10^{-6}$ s = 7.3×10^{-1} s = 0.73 s

    (c) 5.8×10^{-2} mg = $5.8 \times 10^{-2} \times 10^{-3}$ g = 5.8×10^{-5} g

2 (a) 5×10^6 s = 5 Ms (another possible answer would be 5×10^3 ks)

    (b) 6.2×10^{-4} m = 0.62 mm (another possible answer would be 6.2×10^2 μm, which is 620 μm)

    (c) 4.92×10^4 m = 49.2 km

Once you are familiar with the prefixes and the powers of ten they represent, you can compare quantities more easily. For instance, 6 mg is much more than 97 µg, because 'milli-' is a thousand times larger than 'micro-'. So, it's worth memorizing the common prefixes and powers of ten – you'll meet them frequently in your studies.

4.3 Estimating quantities with units

To help get a feel for units, it's helpful to apply them to everyday quantities. Try to picture the length of a metre (about the length of a long stride), the mass of one kilogram (a bag of sugar) and the duration of a second (about one heartbeat at rest).

---

*A*ctivity Break

Estimate:

1   The volume of liquid in a teaspoon in millilitres, to the nearest millilitre.

2   The mass of a litre carton of fruit juice in kilograms.

3   The volume of a pint of milk in millilitres.

---

1   5 ml.

2   About 1 kg.

3   About half a litre, 500 ml. (In fact, one pint is 568 ml.)

This type of common-sense estimation is useful in MST subjects. Suppose you are calculating the volume of water needed for an experiment, and you expect to use about half a beaker. If your calculation gave 200 millilitres, that would be reasonable. But if you made a mistake, and worked it out as 200 *litres,* you would realize something was wrong: this is the volume of 200 cartons of fruit juice – enough to fill a bath tub!

You will come across all sorts of measurements in your MST studies. To develop a 'feel' for their relative magnitudes, it helps to refer to a number line. Figure 5.5 summarizes some measurements on three number lines for mass, length and time. You don't need to memorize these, but they give you some idea of the size of various quantities. Note that the number lines are written as powers of ten. (If you are unfamiliar with number lines, see Maths Help on page 309.)

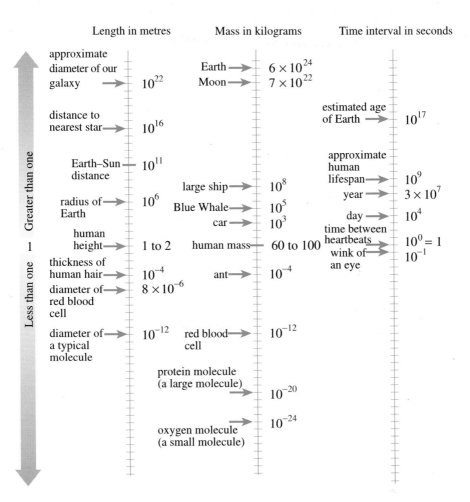

Figure 5.5 *Number lines for length, mass and time. (For help with the notation, refer to Maths Help on page 359. For example, do you know what 10^0 is?)*

A ctivity Break You can use the kilogram number line in Figure 5.5 to compare masses. Try a couple of estimates yourself. (Write the answer to the nearest power of ten.)

1 How many cars would it take to make up the mass of a Blue Whale?

2 How many Moon masses would it take to make up the mass of the Earth?

1   From the number line, a Blue Whale has a mass of about 10^5 kg and a car
    has a mass of about 10^3 kg. $10^5 \div 10^3 = 10^2 = 100$. So, 100 cars would have
    about the same mass as a whale.

2   The Earth has a mass of about 6×10^{24} kg and the Moon's mass is about $7 \times$
    10^{22} kg. Since this is only an estimate, we can ignore the '6' and '7' and
    concentrate on the powers of ten. $10^{24} \div 10^{22} = 10^2 = 100$.   So, 100 Moons
    would have about the same mass as the Earth.

4.4 Using units in calculations

Now you have been introduced to units and prefixes, let's see how they can be
used in calculations. When you calculate a quantity from a formula, you can
work out the units of that quantity by putting the units into the formula,
alongside the numbers. To see how this works, let's consider the units of
volume in more detail.

Suppose you want to calculate the volume of a carton
of fruit juice. Let's say the box is 16.7 cm tall, 10 cm
long and 6 cm wide. You can find its volume by
multiplying these three numbers together:

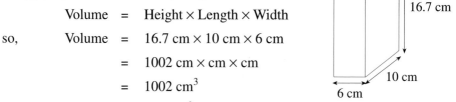

$$\text{Volume} \quad = \quad \text{Height} \times \text{Length} \times \text{Width}$$

so, $$\text{Volume} \quad = \quad 16.7 \text{ cm} \times 10 \text{ cm} \times 6 \text{ cm}$$

$$= \quad 1002 \text{ cm} \times \text{cm} \times \text{cm}$$

$$= \quad 1002 \text{ cm}^3$$

The answer isn't exactly 1000 cm³, because the original measurements were
given to 3 significant figures at most. So, you should round the result to 1000 cm³.

Note that the answer is in centimetres cubed, because we multiplied three
quantities measured in centimetres.

In any formula, the units on the left-hand side must be the same as the units on
the right-hand side. In this case, the left-hand side has the units of volume, and
the units on the right-hand side, three lengths multiplied together, combine to
give the units of volume. If we had used 'ten seconds' as the width of the box,
the units would not have balanced in this way. This is an obvious mistake, but
the principle applies to all equations involving units, however complicated.

But you don't have to measure volume in centimetres cubed. There are several
other units of volume. The carton holds one litre of fruit juice. So, let's do a
calculation to see how many centimetres cubed there are in one litre (written 1 l).
(Be careful when you read or write these units, because the symbol for litre – l
– can look a lot like the number one – 1.)

By definition, one litre is the same as a decimetre cubed. Imagine a cube which has all its sides one decimetre (1 dm) long. 1 dm is the same as 10 cm, so we can do this calculation:

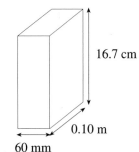

1 dm = 10 cm

$$1\,l \quad = \quad 1\ dm^3$$

$$= \quad 1\ dm \times 1\ dm \times 1\ dm$$

$$= \quad 10\ cm \times 10\ cm \times 10\ cm$$

$$= \quad 1000\ cm^3$$

1 dm = 10 cm

1 dm = 10 cm

This shows that one litre is the same as 1000 cm^3. One litre is also 1000 millilitres, so 1 millilitre (1 ml) is the same as one centimetre cubed (1 cm^3). It is also true that there are a thousand litres in one metre cubed (1000 l = 1 m^3).

So, there are several different ways to describe a volume of one litre (the amount of fruit juice in a carton):

One litre = 1 l = 1000 ml = 1000 cm^3 = 1 dm^3 = 0.001 m^3

However you write it, there is still the same volume of fruit juice. But you'd have a problem if you tried to calculate the volume of the fruit juice box using the same lengths, written with different prefixes:

Height 16.7 cm

Length 0.10 m

Width   60 mm

16.7 cm

0.10 m

60 mm

There is nothing wrong with these measurements (for instance, the width of 0.10 m is the same as 10 cm), but see what happens when you use them to calculate the volume:

	Volume	=	Height	×	Length	×	Width
so	Volume	=	16.7 cm	×	0.10 m	×	60 mm
		=	100.2 cm × m × mm				
		=	100.2 ?				

Here, you cannot write down a neat unit for volume, like cm^3, because of the mixture of prefixes used in the calculation. Unless you invent a new, jumbled unit called the 'centimetre-times-metre-times-millimetre', you have a big problem!

Even worse, if you had been in a hurry, and you hadn't shown all of the working, it would be easy to write 'cm^3' after the '100.2', which would constitute an *incorrect* answer.

What this illustrates is the importance of always using SI units with consistent prefixes. If the calculation just involves lengths, say, then you must make sure that all of the lengths are calculated in identical units. Convert the original measurements, where necessary. But, don't forget to convert the corresponding numbers as well! For instance, 20 cm is the same as 0.2 m. This will guarantee that the final answer will be in a consistent SI unit, rather than a jumble.

When you need to do a calculation with letters or symbols instead of words, the same rules apply. You replace the letter with a number and the corresponding unit. (Sometimes, the units are written to the right of the numbers, rather than included in the calculation.) For example:

Question

Find the volume of a box with height 16.7 cm, width 10 cm and breadth 6 cm using the formula V = HLW, where V is the volume, H is the height, L is the length and W is the width.

Answer

In this case, H = 16.7 cm, L = 10 cm and W = 6 cm, so we can find the volume V as follows.

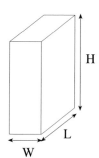

$$V \quad = \quad HLW$$

$$V \quad = \quad 16.7 \text{ cm} \times 10 \text{ cm} \times 6 \text{ cm}$$

$$= \quad 1002 \text{ cm}^3$$

Here, the units of HLW are cm × cm × cm = cm^3, so the volume is 1002 cm^3, which can be rounded to 1000 cm^3.

If the calculation is more complicated – perhaps involving mass, length and time – then you must be even more careful with the units. Remember that the golden rule is to convert all units to SI. If the original data are in SI, then the answer will be too.

As you have seen, you shouldn't mix prefixes. If in doubt, convert to units without prefixes – for example, use 'm' rather than 'cm'.

Hints and Tips
Using units in formulas

◆ Make sure you know what each letter represents. Write it down in words.

◆ When you substitute a value for a letter, make sure you know what the units are. State what you are substituting for what.

◆ When you quote the answer, write it out as a sentence that responds to the question. 'V = 1002' is *not* the answer to the question 'What is the volume?' The answer is 'The volume is 1002 cm³.'

◆ Check the units of the answer by putting the original units into the equation.

Key Points

◆ SI units use standard symbols which have two purposes: to show what is being measured (the unit) and the scale of the measurement, which is the power of ten (the prefix).

◆ Always use SI units. Don't mix different prefixes in the same calculation.

◆ Check the results of your calculations by confirming that the quantities are in the correct units. This is in addition to estimating the numerical result of the calculation.

◆ The units must balance in any equation involving physical quantities. This is a useful way to check the units of the result.

5 Numbers in tables

There are many situations that arise, both in everyday life and in your studies, where numbers appear in quantity rather than singly. For example, a bank statement, a supermarket bill, a train timetable, the results of an opinion poll in a newspaper, will all contain sets of numbers. In this and the other chapters of this book, you will find examples of sets of numbers displayed as tables, charts and graphs. This section aims to help you to read tables and present your own results as a table.

5.1 Reading tables

Tables are used to convey key information. So, how can you get the most from your reading of them? There is one golden rule that applies.

Decide what you want to want to find out about the set of numbers.

For example, in the case of a supermarket bill you may want to know the total or you may wish to check the price of a particular item. In this case, you would look at the bottom of the bill for the total or look for the row containing the item. With a train timetable, you don't try to absorb all the times of all the trains – you just look at the rows (your departure point and destination) and columns (the time you want to travel) that are relevant. As with the supermarket bill or the train timetable, the only way to make sense of scientific data is to ask questions. What is being conveyed? What do I want to find out?

Reading a table: asking questions

Chapter 3 contains advice on reading diagrams, and in a similar way, there are appropriate ways of reading tables. Table 5.3 shows the various components of a typical table that you need to look at in detail.

Table 5.3 **Percentage of total notified food poisoning incidents caused by different species in selected years** *title*

Year	Salmonella typhimurium	Salmonella enteritidis	Other types of salmonella
1981	38.9	10.7	50.4
1983	51.4	11.7	36.9
1985	41.1	23.2	35.7
1987	37.3	33.4	29.3
1989	24.3	52.6	23.1
1991	19.3	63.0	17.7
1993	15.6	66.1	18.3

column heading

all data in this row are for 1983

this is a cell containing the entry 33.4

Source: Communicable Disease Surveillance Centre *source of data*

all data in this column are for Salmonella typhimurium

(You may recognize that the information in Table 5.3 comes from Chapter 3, where it was also presented graphically.)

In general, the following questions will help you to read a table.

1 *What is the table about?*

The title should tell you; titles are always particularly important.

2 *Where has the information come from?*

The source should be stated.

3 *What do the columns and rows represent?*

Choose a single cell, and see what that entry means. The information in the cell has the properties of its row and its column. For example, in Table 5.3 the highlighted cell relates to the year 1987 (row) and *Salmonella enteritidis* (column). Always check the units – these may be given in the headings or by each number. Sometimes, the title may give you a clue.

4 *What do you want to know?*

This will depend on your reasons for reading the table. Perhaps you want to look up a single piece of information, or maybe you are looking for overall patterns. You may want to plot a graph from the data in the table, to help you spot a trend. See Chapter 3, page 76, and Maths Help on page 376 for more advice about plotting graphs.

5   *What are you expected to remember?*

Tables often contain a lot of information – you probably don't need to remember any of it. Generally, it's the overall trend that's important, not the individual values.

*A**ctivity Break** Study Table 5.3 closely and answer the following questions.

1   (a) Where has the information in the table come from?

    (b) What do the rows represent?

    (c) What does the number in the highlighted cell represent? Write this information as a sentence.

2   Calculate the sum of the numbers in each row. Explain your answer.

3   What are the highest and lowest entries in the table? What does each of these entries represent?

4   What was the percentage of incidents caused by *Salmonella typhimurium* in 1989?

5   Which type of salmonella showed the biggest percentage change in incidents over a two-year period? And over which period was this?

1   (a) The source is the Communicable Disease Surveillance Centre.

    (b) The rows represent years.

    (c) In 1987, 33.4% of total notified salmonella food-poisoning cases were caused by *Salmonella enteritidis*.

2   The sum of the numbers in each row means the entries in each row of the body of the table, excluding the row headings (the years). Adding the percentage incidents for each year gives 100. The percentages add up to 100% for each year because all types of salmonella are included, that is, 100% of them.

    You can tell that the numbers are percentages by reading the title, which also tells you that these numbers are percentages of the total incidents caused by salmonella. So, you would expect all types of salmonella to be included. The column headings show that data for two specific types of salmonella are given, and all other types are included in the third column.

3   The highest entry is 66.1 in the last row. This is the percentage of salmonella incidents due to *Salmonella enteritidis* in 1993. The lowest entry is 10.7, showing that only 10.7% of incidents in 1981 were caused by *Salmonella enteritidis*. You can tell that these entries are due to *Salmonella enteritidis* because they are in the column with that heading.

4   The percentage of incidents caused by *Salmonella typhimurium* in 1989 is found by looking across the row headed 1989 to the column headed *Salmonella typhimurium*. The answer is 24.3%.

5   The biggest percentage change is found by looking down the columns and subtracting in pairs. To speed this up you can round the numbers and reject those that are obviously small. The biggest change I found was in the incidents caused by other types of salmonella between 1981 and 1983; a drop of 13.5%.

Tables therefore use yet another kind of specialized language. They have to be read as a series of shorthand 'sentences', rather like some of the diagrams you encountered in Chapter 3. To make sense of each entry, you need to read sections of the table like sentences, as we saw in Question 1(c) above. Once you are satisfied that you know what each cell represents, you can start to use the information in the table.

Hints and Tips

How to read tables

◆   Decide what you want to know. Read the title.

◆   Look for the row headings and column headings, and make sure you understand what they mean and what units are being used.

◆   Find the entry, or entries, relevant to your query by looking down the columns and across the rows.

◆   Don't forget to give the units in the results you quote from the table.

5.2 Constructing tables

When you are constructing tables, you need to put yourself in the position of your reader (perhaps your tutor) and make sure that they can readily get the information they require from the table. The golden rule now is:

Decide what you want to communicate about the set of numbers.

Whenever you are writing results in a table, you need to be clear about what you're trying to get across about the set of numbers (the data) that you're working with. Let's consider a concrete example: suppose you want to construct a table to record the results of a particular experiment – one that is described in more detail later in the book. You don't have to do the experiment now, but read through the following account and try at least to picture in your mind's eye what going on – there's a more detailed description of the experiment in Chapter 8 (starting on page 218). The procedure involves making a simple pendulum and timing how long it takes for the weight to move to and fro in different circumstances. (Remember, the swing of the pendulum is one movement from one side to the other and back again – have a quick look at Figure 8.1 on page 219.)

The various steps of experiment are as follows.

1 A bunch of keys (the bob) is tied to a length of string to make a pendulum. The weight of the bob is recorded – in terms of whether a light or a heavy bunch of keys is used.

2 The length of the string is measured in centimetres.

3 The time in seconds for ten swings of this pendulum is recorded (first reading).

4 This measurement is repeated – and the time in seconds for another ten swings is noted (second reading)

5 The average time for ten swings is calculated from the two readings.

6 The average time is divided by ten to give the time in seconds for one swing (called the 'period').

7 The experiment is carried out four times in all; first with a light bob, second with a heavy bob, and (third and fourth) using two different lengths of string.

Let's suppose you record part of the results in your notebook as follows.

Light bob, string 100 cm long, first reading 21 s, second reading 19 s, average time for ten swings 20 s, period 2.0 s.

These data might make good sense to you, but nobody else could quickly see what you've found or begin to interpret what the results mean. You have to present the results in a logical way in the form of a table, so they could readily understood by someone else, your tutor perhaps.

What type of table to draw? First, we need to decide what the columns and rows will be. Each of the four experiments will have a row to itself. The column headings will be the various recorded times ('First reading', 'Second reading', 'Average for ten swings', 'Period'). We will also need columns for the bob weight and the string length. So there will be six columns altogether. Here is a first attempt at column headings.

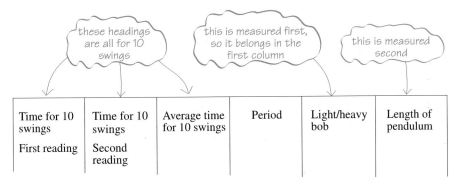

Time for 10 swings	Time for 10 swings	Average time for 10 swings	Period	Light/heavy bob	Length of pendulum
First reading	Second reading				

This can be improved. It would make more sense to have 'Light/heavy bob' and 'Length of pendulum' on the left, because these are noted first, before measuring the times. Also, we can group the three 'Time for ten swings' together. What you're doing is thinking through the best format for the table, with the data to hand. Sometimes, a particular way of presenting the results might be already given to you, but often you'll have to try different approaches and see which works best.

So, here are the improved table headings, with the results of the first experiment:

Light/heavy bob	Length of pendulum	Time for ten swings			Period
		First reading	Second reading	Average	
light	100 cm	21 s	19 s	20 s	2.0 s

Remember, there are four rows, for the four experiments. The completed table is shown below, with some typical results.

Table 5.4 Results of the pendulum experiment

Light/heavy bob	Length of pendulum (cm)	Time for ten swings (seconds)			Period (seconds)
		First reading	Second reading	Average	
light	100	21	19	20	2.0
heavy	100	20	20	20	2.0
light	50	13	15	14	1.4
light	25	12	10	11	1.1

Source: experimental data

Note that the units are given in the column heading, and that all the entries in the column have the same units. The table has a title, and the source of the data is stated.

Hints and Tips

How to construct a table

◆ Decide what the table is for. What columns will you need? What will the rows be?

◆ Plan the layout of the page. Decide how many columns and rows you'll need, allowing rows at the top and columns down the left for the headings. Turn the page around if this makes the layout better. Measure the space available for the table and divide it into rows and columns, drawing neat lines with a ruler.

◆ Write in the column and row headings, making the meanings clear and including the units where appropriate.

◆ Put the data into the table (from measurements, calculations or wherever). Don't forget to write the numbers in a suitable form (decimals, scientific notation and so on). Bear in mind both the source of the data (perhaps measured to a limited degree of accuracy) and the accuracy required (for example, if the table is to be used to plot a graph, there is no point in quoting more than 3 significant figures).

◆ If the entries are obtained by calculation, use the full accuracy available as input to the calculation. Round the numbers only to display the results.

◆ Give the table a title, and write down the source of the data.

◆ Check that you have entered the data correctly, especially if the table is a large one. Make sure that the information is in the correct columns by checking the contents of a couple of cells.

Key Points

◆ A table is a way of summarizing a large amount of information. Reading a table takes time – you need to find out what each entry means.

◆ You can use a table to communicate information. Decide how to organize the data, and organize the table accordingly. Don't forget the units!

6   Where next with mathematics?

We started the chapter by saying that the language of mathematics is beautiful. And so it is. Those who are proficient at the subject admire its logic and elegance. Perhaps you feel drawn to the subject and your confidence is growing already. But many students of science and technology see mathematics as their weak spot. If your feelings about the subject aren't positive, don't convince yourself that there's something 'in you' that stops you from 'getting on' with mathematics, forcing you to live in fear and dread of the subject. You won't be able to hide way from mathematics in your later studies. Chapters 4 and 5 have suggested a study approach that will help you break through a learning barrier – by identifying what you need to know, by applying the right approaches and techniques, and by practising.

We've mentioned several times in Chapters 4 and 5 that maths represents a new language. Learning any new language can be a struggle and difficulties are to be expected, not something to be ashamed of. Don't expect understanding to come all at once. If you persist, you will feel more and more things fitting into place. Once the basics are in place, you'll be surprised at how much confidence you'll gain.

But if you feel you're making no progress, despite your best efforts, seek help. Your tutor will be sympathetic to your problems with maths – you won't be the first student to have had such problems. Perhaps extra help can be arranged. Maths 'clinics', for example, where tutor and students work through maths exercises together, have proved enormously successful. Look out for books that will give you a chance to practise techniques – some are identified in the reading list on page 404. Once you become more skilful with maths – your knowledge of the language moving past the phrase-book stage to the conversational level – you'll find the study of all branches of MST enormously more rewarding.

CHAPTER 6

Different ways of studying

1 The diversity of study today

Thus far, we have looked mainly at working from printed texts. However, studying has always involved other activities, and in recent times the range of these activities has expanded rapidly. An effective student now needs a wider variety of skills and must be able to balance the demands of different types of studying. It is time to cast an eye over the broad range of activities which studying can now involve.

***

Activity Break   If you are returning to study after a break, what kinds of study activity do you expect to encounter (other than reading texts)?

If you are already studying, what different kinds of activities occupy your study hours?

In either case, jot down a list and add it to your Study Diary (see page 19).

***

Your answer will obviously depend on your course of studies, your circumstances and your personal preferences. To give you a point of comparison, I asked an Open University student to tell us about the activities that make up a 'typical' study week.

Pam enrolled for a Level 1 mathematics course last year. This year she is studying Level 1 technology. She lives in Hull and works shifts at a garage. She started as a sales assistant at the petrol counter, but now also works in the office on the accounts. Pam is the first person from her family to study for a degree. Thirty years ago she left school without qualifications to have a baby. At 15, she did not imagine that she would ever want to study again, and certainly not maths and technology. Pam and her school were glad to see the back of each other. Now, she has amazed her whole family, from her retired parents to her grandchildren, by passing her first course and surviving the second so far. The hours are long, the money hard to find, and sometimes she hits a difficult patch when she seems to be losing the battle. But she is determined to continue because she feels she is proving, at last, what she is really capable of. In any case, she enjoys a lot of the work. She has developed a love for her subject and an unexpected thirst for knowledge.

As a part-time student, Pam tries to fit 12 to 14 hours of study into a busy and tiring week. She works shifts, so her study times vary a lot. The technology course has several strands to it and she finds managing her time tricky. She tries to do two hours of study per day, six days a week, although sometimes she doesn't feel up to it. At other times, she can spend three or four hours studying without really noticing the time.

This is Pam's account of a 'typical' study week.

Monday: *Came in from work at 10:00 p.m. (I usually feel wide awake after work.) Read the main study text and took notes. Studied till just after midnight. (I always try to complete the section I'm working on. If I don't finish it, I tend to get confused and forget things.)*   2 hours

Tuesday: *During quiet spells at work, I did the computer-marked assessment questions for the section I read last night. (I always take the course books into work with me – although I don't often get much chance to look at them.) The next piece of work was a computer-assisted learning package, so I spent from 8:00 p.m. till 11:00 p.m. on the computer. I have to be careful not to get carried away. You can spend hours trying to 'beat the computer'. You learn a lot, but you feel very tired the next day.* $\frac{1}{2}$ hour + 3 hours

Wednesday: *Worked on a different strand of the course: did some calculations, drew some graphs and solved some problems. Studied from 10:00 a.m. till 1 p.m. (I prefer to work during the day when I can because there's no one around. It helps to be fairly fresh when you're working on problems.) I got stuck on some of the problems, so I moved on to an audio-cassette exercise for the last hour.*   3 hours

Thursday: *Attended a group tutorial from 7:00 p.m. to 9:00 p.m. It was a life-line – I sorted out what I'd been stuck on. Then spent two more hours studying at home – while my brain was still hot. I looked at the study text to check what we'd covered in the tutorial, especially the bits I'd been stuck on. Then I looked ahead to the next section, which was also discussed at the tutorial.*   2 hours (+ 2 hours of tutorial)

Friday: *Studied from 8:00 p.m. till 10:30 p.m.. Started to gear up for the assignment due next Wednesday. Went back over the block we'd just been doing and organized the notes on my computer. Just after midnight, watched a half-hour TV programme for the course (and recorded it on video).* $2\frac{1}{2}$ hours + $\frac{1}{2}$ hour

Saturday: *From 9:30 a.m. to 11:00 a.m. I reviewed recent TV programmes for an hour (recorded on video) to help me think my way into the assignment, and looked in books and newspapers for extra material. Checked back to the assignment title and jotted down a few ideas on how to answer the question.* $2\frac{1}{2}$ hours

Sunday: *Rest day – storing up strength for starting the assignment on Monday.*

When she saw all this written down, Pam was surprised to find that what she had remembered as a 'typical' week amounted to about 16 hours of study, without counting the tutorial. She said that the Tuesday computing session had gone on longer than she had meant it to, as she still had the week's reading to get through. And because an assignment was due, she was putting in extra time at the end of the week. So, perhaps the week was not quite so 'typical' after all (but then, none of them ever is). Anyway, the main point is that her study week involved a wide range of activities. Did *your* list cover a similar range?

In fact, Pam gets involved in even more study activities. When she spoke to us she had just come back from a very different kind of week at an Open University summer school held on a traditional university campus. She had spent a very intensive six days doing practical work in laboratories, working in groups to solve problems and attending lectures – keeping at it from breakfast to supper time. She said that it had been marvellous, and that she had learned more than she could have imagined in such a short time.

So, in Pam's 'typical' week, together with her week at summer school, she had experienced the following different ways of studying:

◆ reading text and making notes
◆ computer-marked assignments (CMAs)
◆ computer-aided learning (CAL)
◆ calculations, drawing graphs and solving problems
◆ audio-cassette exercises
◆ group tutorials
◆ using the computer to organize notes
◆ watching TV
◆ informal searching for assignment material
◆ practical work
◆ problem solving in groups
◆ listening to lectures
◆ tutor-marked assignments (TMAs).

So, in the space of these two weeks, Pam could remember using at least *13* different ways of studying, each of which she felt had made a valuable contribution to her learning. She said that a variety of activities made studying interesting. In particular, it allowed her to switch from one activity to another to keep her mind awake, or to provide a new way forward when she got stuck.

As was noted in Chapter 1 (on page 20), learning at higher levels is about a lot more than just remembering information. It involves taking in new ideas, *thinking* them through, and learning how to use them. A range of study activities enables you to come at these different aspects of learning from a variety of angles, and helps you to develop a well-rounded and firmly grounded understanding of the subject.

As a modern-day student, you need to be comfortable with many more ways of studying than simply working from books. In this chapter, I shall explore a variety of ways of studying, looking at what they offer and the skills and techniques they require.

I have grouped these alternative ways of studying into three broad clusters:

◆ those that make learning a *collective* activity, rather than a solitary one

◆ those that involve *listening* and *watching*, as opposed to reading

◆ those that emphasize the *'doing'* side of learning.

> ### Key Points
>
> ◆ There is now a variety of ways of studying, and each approach helps your learning in a different way.
>
> ◆ Mixed together, these approaches can make study more interesting and help you to learn in depth.
>
> ◆ To take full advantage of this variety, you need to understand the benefits of different ways of studying and develop appropriate skills.

2 Learning with other people

Although studying involves hours of private concentration, it also has a social side. Significant learning is not achieved *only* through solitary toil. We learn a lot just by talking, often without noticing it. As human beings, we survive by living in societies, and because our societies are complicated and flexible, we depend on learning enormous amounts from each other. And we do the bulk of this learning through talking to each other.

Learning by talking

Conversation gives you access to other people's thoughts and helps to clarify your own. Ideas that defeated you as you studied alone suddenly take on new meanings. Knots you have tied yourself into become loosened. As you converse, you can think in a wide-ranging and free-flowing way and achieve insights you would never arrive at on your own. Indeed, in the effort to make a point, you can even find yourself saying things you didn't know you thought! In short, *talking* helps you to *think*.

So, exchanging ideas with other people is an important way of helping yourself to learn. Equally, it plays an essential part in putting your knowledge to work after you have acquired it.

> ### *Teamwork in MST*
>
> In 'real life', mathematicians, scientists and technologists often find themselves working in teams – talking and thinking alongside people from other backgrounds. The individuals in a team have to collaborate to:
>
> ◆ define the nature of the problems to be solved
>
> ◆ pool ideas about potential solutions
>
> ◆ bring together knowledge, ideas, techniques and skills from different branches of maths, science and technology
>
> ◆ check each other's assumptions and working
>
> ◆ implement solutions.

It is a key part of your training to develop skill in communicating, whether with specialists in your area or with others outside it. It is not necessarily enough to understand something yourself; you need to be able to explain it clearly to others. Equally, you need to be able to understand what *others* say, so that you can connect their ideas with your own.

Key Points

Learning about a subject is not simply a private mental activity. It also has an important 'collective' side, because:

◆ talking with others helps you to understand your subject better

◆ you need to be able to communicate about the subject with others in order to make use of your knowledge.

2.1 How studying with others helps

Even though Pam is a 'distance student', she has no doubts about the benefits of the collective side of her studies. She described her Thursday night tutorial meetings as a 'life-line'.

A ctivity Break What do you think Pam found so valuable? Write down three benefits Pam might have gained from attending a group tutorial.

Here are the benefits Pam identified.

◆ Sometimes you read something over and over and you just can't see it – then, when the tutor says it, it's suddenly obvious.

◆ Or, you've been totally stuck on a calculation, somebody points to where you've been going wrong, and you're away again.

◆ The subject's more interesting if you have a chance to talk about it sometimes.

◆ The tutorials give you an incentive to keep up – or to catch up if you've slipped behind.

◆ You feel a lot better when you find out that other people are hitting the same problems – you realize that you're not the only one struggling.

◆ You meet some interesting people that you wouldn't get to meet otherwise.

◆ I've made a couple of friends at the tutorials. I can phone them if I have a problem during the week.

Let's look at Pam's benefits in more detail.

Getting your thoughts sorted out

Studying often seems to be a confusing mess. Sometimes, you feel you know less than when you started. Why? The problem is that you are building up new frameworks of ideas – but, at the same time, you are trying to think with those ideas. Your mind is a bit like a chaotic building site: lots of beginnings of new structures, with makeshift scaffolding and walkways around them. But the construction work has to go on. You have to keep on developing ideas and using them at the same time, even though they are part-formed and disorganized.

However, sometimes you hear your tutor, or another student, talking and a key point suddenly clicks into focus. After being baffled for days, all at once, with the right 'frame' in place, you cannot remember why you ever had a problem. You even feel vaguely stupid to have struggled for so long. *Yet that is the nature of the learning process.* You spend ages preparing the ground – exploring the nature of a problem – trying to grapple with it this way and that – developing and shifting your frame of thinking – then, as your mind still gropes for comprehension, you reach a critical point. The frame is sufficiently developed and meaning begins to flow.

A group of you can help each other in constructing new sense. Together, you can often assemble enough of a framework of understanding to push further ahead into a new topic. As you hear others trying to make sense, you glimpse new ways of approaching the subject. Meanwhile, in the process of making your own contribution, you re-work your own frames of thought – getting them better aligned and more firmly fixed – so that when you are back, studying on your own, you can come at things from a fresh angle. Eventually, your new thoughts become 'obvious'. At this point, you have achieved a major reorganization of your mental apparatus. This is 'real' learning. It is far more important than memorizing facts, figures and formulas. And it is often helped along by collective ways of studying.

Learning the language of the subject

Any subject you study has its own language. Learning to speak that language is part of the process of becoming knowledgeable about the subject. You pick up the language as you read texts and write assignments, but it is a great help to have the chance to speak it as well. As you get on 'chatting terms' with your subject, it becomes part of the way you think. As Pam said: 'The subject's more interesting if you have a chance to talk about it sometimes.' She went on to say: 'It can get tedious if you're studying on your own all the time. You need to chat about it and have a few laughs. Then you feel it's *you* that's on top, not the subject.'

Learning by example

Studying MST subjects involves learning a lot of basic techniques – such as solving equations, calibrating instruments, using a calculator, or drawing flow charts, graphs and diagrams. When you're learning how to 'do' anything, there are many ways in which you can misinterpret instructions, so it usually helps to see someone else doing it, or to have advice from an expert. As Pam noted, when you ask for help with something you're stuck on it may take only a minute to identify a mistake in your technique, and then 'you're away again'.

Learning on your own

I am emphasizing here the benefits of working alongside other students. But I hasten to add that collective study does not suit everyone. Some people choose MST subjects because they feel more comfortable with numbers, formulas and diagrams than they do with words and discussions. Some have a strong preference for working on their own, and find working in groups unappealing – even confusing. If you get on fine without contact with others, then it is obviously not 'essential'.

Keeping yourself going

As well as helping you to learn, working alongside others can help to keep you going. Pam said that having a tutorial ahead gave her an extra incentive to reach her targets; and when she slipped behind, the tutorial often helped her to catch up. Talking to others helps you to readjust your sights, work out how to cut corners and catch up with what you have missed.

Pam made a couple of friends at her tutorial group, and she contacts them when she is in difficulties. They exchange strategies for tackling the work ahead and sometimes collaborate on it. Learning does not have to be a competitive activity. You may be able to share out tasks on a project, compare outlines for a report, or cross-check findings from an experiment. Or you might collaborate in purely practical ways – for example, setting up a child-minding system. Networks of support can make the everyday challenges of study more manageable. And when you run into a crisis, as most students do from time to time (pressure at work, moving house, domestic complications and so on), these networks can make the difference between struggling on and dropping out.

Boosting your confidence

'You feel a lot better when you find out that other people are hitting the same problems – you realize that you're not the only one struggling.' Of all the benefits students claim from contact with others, this is the one most commonly cited. When you are studying alone, it is very easy to lose confidence in your abilities. You doubt your intelligence, your self-discipline, your memory, your reading skills, your powers of concentration, and your motivation. But when you contact other students, whether by meeting in a group, talking on the telephone, or sending messages by computer, you discover that everyone has the same doubts. This is one of the surest ways of boosting your confidence.

Meeting people

Finally, as Pam indicates, meeting interesting people is an end in itself. Studying often brings together people from a wide range of backgrounds who share a common interest. Sometimes, the social contact turns out to be the most rewarding part of studying.

Key Points

Working alongside others can bring many benefits.

♦ Talking with others can help you to make sense of ideas you are struggling with.

♦ It also helps you learn to 'speak the language' of the subject.

♦ Other people can often help you to iron out problems with specific techniques.

♦ Studying with a group helps to keep you to the pace of the course.

♦ When you get to know other students you can help each other out in practical ways.

♦ Sharing study worries with others boosts your confidence.

♦ Studying is a way of meeting interesting people.

2.2 Group tutorials

The terms 'tutorial', 'seminar' and 'workshop' cover a variety of ways of studying in groups. However, the use of these terms varies between teaching institutions, and here I shall simply use the term 'tutorial' to mean *any* kind of session of around one to two hours in which a tutor works with a group of between, say, 5 and 20 students. A tutor might run a tutorial as a troubleshooting session in which students ask about their problems. The tutor either works through the problems with the whole group, or divides the students into subgroups containing those with similar problems and circulates between these subgroups helping them to find solutions. Alternatively, the tutor might choose some tricky section in the study text and 'talk the class through it'. Or he or she might set some problems for the students to work on in pairs and then discuss the results with the whole class, or bring some photographs, rock samples or whatever for the group to discuss.

The main point of a tutorial is that you have access to a scarce resource – the time of an expert – in a context in which you can participate actively, alongside other students. Unlike a lecture, where you simply listen and hope you will benefit, a tutorial offers the potential of a much more direct engagement between the tutor's expertise and the learning that is currently going on in your head. But that can only happen if *you* become actively involved. You have to be ready to ask questions and be willing to participate in tackling problems and sharing your answers with the group. You also have to be ready to share tutorial time with other students and to play a constructive part in helping to solve *their* problems. Often, you will learn as much from listening carefully as your tutor deals with other students' difficulties as you will from having your own sorted out. And sometimes, you learn even more by trying to help others. So, a tutorial should be a genuinely collective process, in which the whole group pools its resources and works together to make everyone more familiar with the ideas and techniques developed in the course.

It pays to be frank with yourself about where you need help. It is tempting to ask 'safe' questions about things you almost understand already, in order not to reveal your limitations – leaving your deeper confusions to fester in secret. But your tutor needs to be directed to where your *real* difficulties lie. He or she can focus much more effectively on identifying and sorting out your problems if you are open about them. The chances are that if *you* are confused about something, others in the group will be too. If you don't understand an explanation, say so. If you let the tutor *think* you have understood when you haven't, then he or she may make later explanations too difficult for you. Don't worry about taking up tutors' time: they are paid to help you, and it's up to you to make sure the tutorial covers what *you* need.

Don't be put off by thoughts that the other students might be cleverer, or more articulate, hardworking and confident. Most of them think exactly the same about *you*. They are much less concerned about the quality of what *you* say than about what *you* think of what *they* say. Remember, too, that you have as much right to make demands on your study group as anyone else. Tutorials are part of a study package you have paid for. They have been arranged in order to help *you* learn.

> ### *Ask the 'simple' question, give the 'obvious' answer*
>
> You don't need to wait until you have a 'really important' question to ask before speaking in a tutorial. Just ask the simple question, give the obvious answer, and suggest the straightforward example. What may seem ordinary to you will often be just what the group needs – helping it to identify shared problems and sort them out. You can make a very useful contribution simply by saying, 'What do you mean by that?', 'Can you show us an example?', or 'Can you explain that again?' It is up to you and the other students to guide the tutor towards giving you what you need.

You will benefit more from your limited supply of tutorial time if you *prepare* in advance. Try to be reasonably up to date with the course work, and take the time to think about where you need help. Take a list of queries and the relevant study materials to the tutorial.

However, don't be put off attending if you have fallen behind. As Pam indicated, a tutorial is one of the best ways of catching up again. Finally, if for any reason you find that you are unable to arrive in time for the beginning of a tutorial, or have to leave before the end (which is quite common for part-time students), don't feel you have to miss the whole tutorial. Just let the tutor know about your difficulty and arrive or leave discreetly when you have to.

Hints and Tips

At tutorials:

- ◆ Arrive with a list of points you would like help with (and the relevant course texts).

- ◆ Don't worry about what other people might think of what you say. Leave them to worry about what *they* say.

- ◆ Don't be afraid to ask a *simple* question or give the *obvious* answer.

- ◆ Remember it's *your* study session, paid for out of your fees, so get the most from it.

2.3 Self-help groups

So far, I have talked as though a study group is necessarily led by a tutor. But there is no reason why you shouldn't arrange your own study group with other students. A self-help group can be of any size from two upwards. You can meet at a place and time of your choice, and set an agenda that meets your own needs. You may find a regular self-help group just as useful as tutorials, but it will take a little organizing. At least one or two members of the group will have to play a part in 'leading' it (or the leadership could be shared around the whole group on a rotating basis). Without leadership and organization, good intentions easily diffuse into indecision and general chit-chat, and people stop attending.

Hints and Tips

◆ Self-help groups are an excellent idea.

◆ They need organizing, so work out early on how to allocate the role of 'leader'.

2.4 Other forms of contact

Day schools and residential schools

One alternative to regular tutorials is to meet for a longer time less frequently. You don't have the same opportunities for developing continuing friendships and team spirit, but you spend less time and money travelling to and from meetings. The extreme case is a residential school. (Remember that Pam had just spent a week at a summer school.) Whether a residential school lasts a week or a weekend, it demands a substantial commitment of time and money on your part, so it is worth examining its purposes.

A residential school can greatly improve your general grasp of a subject by completely immersing you in it for a few days. It may also offer access to laboratories in which you can develop essential skills in observation and experimentation (see Chapter 8). In addition, there may be access to advanced computing facilities. And with large numbers of people and sufficient time, it is possible to set up group problem-solving exercises, simulations, role playing, troubleshooting workshops and the like. Finally, it is valuable to mix with a variety of tutors and pick up a wide range of knowledge and insight.

If you study mainly on your own at home, it can be hard to establish a sense of being a 'real' student. Your studies can seem like an unusual hobby tagged on to the edge of your 'normal' life. A few days at a residential school helps to put your studies in their proper place as a very important part of your life. You recognize your membership of a large body of people who share a serious interest in understanding the world better. Like Pam, many students find that a residential school is the high point of their course, transforming their approach to their studies and their understanding of the subject.

Day schools fall somewhere between a tutorial and a residential school. They are longer, larger-scale and have more resources than a tutorial, but are neither as intensive nor as costly, in time and money, as a residential school.

Learning with others 'at a distance'

So far, I have talked about face-to-face contact with students and tutors, but nowadays there are many other ways of keeping in touch.

One-to-one telephone tutorials

One obvious use for the telephone is to contact another student, or your tutor, for a quick word of advice. But the telephone can also be used more formally to provide one-to-one *telephone tutorials* for students unable to attend face-to-face tutorials. Clearly, this is not a full substitute, since the 'collective' dimension is missing. And telephone tutorials can be quite tricky. It is a drawback, for example, not being able to see each other's calculations or diagrams. Your tutor cannot see where you have gone wrong and you cannot see how the tutor gets it right.

It is easy to get side-tracked into chat on the telephone, so you need to prepare well and draw up a list of points you want to cover. Do remind your tutor who you are and what you dealt with last time, so that he or she can pick up the threads and pitch explanations and advice at the right level.

Whether it is a spontaneous call, or an arranged tutorial, telephone contact with your tutor should be used sparingly. Dealing with students sequentially, rather than in groups, gobbles up a tutor's time and can be quite draining. Since contact time with an expert is a scarce resource, use it to maximum effect.

Group telephone tutorials

Nowadays, telephoning does not have to be one-to-one. You can be linked to other students and your tutor by a 'conference call'. At one time, there were hopes that this would lead to the telephone equivalent of study groups. However, it is surprisingly difficult to emulate the ebb and flow of a tutorial when the participants cannot see each other. And since the participants cannot point, or write, they are often not quite sure what other people are going on about. It helps if everyone has the same page of text in front of them. So, when you are preparing your list of points to raise, you should note down page numbers and have the text by you during the tutorial. Group telephone tutorials are expensive and require skill and discipline, but they can play a useful role when other means of contact are impossible.

Audio-cassette 'circulars'

Another device used by some groups of 'remote' students is for one person to record course-related thoughts on to an audio-cassette and mail it to the next person on a list. That person listens to the audio-cassette and then records his or her comments and further questions before mailing it to the next individual on the list. In this way, the audio-cassette circulates the group. In effect, it generates a slow-moving 'conversation' within the group. Since the audio-cassette takes a week or two to circulate, it is hardly the answer to burning questions, but it does enable students to hear ideas and opinions from around the group.

Computer email and computer conferences

The most effective alternatives to face-to-face contact are now provided by computer networks. These ways of studying are discussed in detail in Chapter 7 (pages 191 to 192).

Key Points

◆ If you cannot attend regular face-to-face tutorials, there are various other ways of gaining the benefits of 'collective learning'.

◆ One way is to attend a residential school or day school.

◆ Or you can stay in contact 'at a distance' through various forms of modern communications technology.

3 Learning by listening and watching

When you can study print at your own time and pace, why should anyone spend time listening to people talking, or watching films or demonstrations?

Why listening and watching are important

One trouble with studying MST subjects through print alone is that what you see on the page is so neat, precise and polished – as though mathematicians, scientists and technologists have robot-like minds. This is quite misleading. Like everyone else, their thinking progresses in unpredictable leaps. It is often fuzzy, loose and haphazard; it advances by hunches, groping around for ways forward. The neat phrases and formulas you see on the printed page probably started life as scruffy scribbles, with crossings out here and fresh starts there. This is the real process of doing science. However, it would not be much help to you if the scruffy version were printed in the book. You wouldn't be able to follow it. So you see only the pristine, tidied-up version, and get little feel for the *thinking processes* that lie behind the *words* and other *symbols*.

This is why it helps to be 'talked through' the arguments and working in a text. Watching and hearing someone go over a calculation makes the underlying thought processes much clearer. You hear how the equation is 'said', and come to understand the unwritten logic behind the move from one line of calculation to the next. (It even helps to hear how the words and symbols are pronounced.) A teacher can breathe living meaning into unfamiliar and abstract expressions. You begin to see the connection between the formal, printed symbols and diagrams and active, creative thinking processes. The scientific and mathematical terms start to become a working language, one you can use to think and speak with.

3.1 Talks and lectures

For a long time, lectures were the main mode of teaching in higher education. Many lecturers spoke towards the blackboard for an hour, at the same time covering it with detailed notes. With no other source of information, your main task was to copy down these notes as accurately as possible. There was little chance of listening closely to what was said. You had to try to work out everything from your notes later on. Used this way, the lecture developed a bad reputation as a mindless, tedious and inefficient mode of learning.

Modern teaching texts can provide a much more reliable and accessible source of information than wads of scribbled notes. This means that lectures can now be used far more constructively, as a means of helping you to *understand* the concepts, theories and techniques in the texts. Far from depositing a pile of information in your head, the effect of a particularly powerful lecture might be to shake up all your thinking on a subject, so that you are no longer sure what to think. You might end up with a whole lot of new questions – but these questions could be exactly what you need to help you make more sense of your texts. Lectures like these help you to 'get inside' the subject you are studying.

Key Points

In a modern context, the lecture's strength is not as a primary information source, but as an opportunity for you:

◆ to be talked through the thought processes which lie behind formal equations and diagrams

◆ to be shown how arguments and explanations work

◆ to be shown how to apply techniques

◆ to hear how the language of the subject is used.

Getting the most out of a lecture

Listening to a lecture sets you three challenging and simultaneous tasks. You have to:

◆ *attend* to and *make sense* of a line of argument
◆ *think* about what is said
◆ *take notes* of some kind.

Of course, you can't *actually* do more than *one* of these at once. The best you can do is to switch quickly from one task to another. But in an odd way the urgency of struggling to cope with this mental juggling act is itself helpful. By putting you under pressure, lectures force you to take leaps and short cuts. You have to seize the initiative in 'making sense' of the subject and 'thinking on your feet'.

How can you juggle these three tasks? Clearly, you cannot afford to stop attending to the lecture for very long, or you will lose the drift of the argument. However, you are bound to miss *some* of what is said, because listening 'intelligently' will make you stop and think (as you make connections with ideas already in your mind). You have to find a workable trade-off between listening and thinking. This is where selective note-making helps. Deciding what to write focuses your attention on the subject and makes you think. But the notes have to be brief, or they provide a distraction in themselves. You have to weigh up quality against speed.

Effective note-making

There is no 'best' way of making notes. Some people scribble busily throughout a lecture and produce several pages; others take down a few key points set out diagrammatically. Both approaches can be effective. It depends on why you are attending the lecture, the kind of lecture it is, and the way *you* work and learn.

If lectures are your main source of information, then you probably *have* to write down a lot to be sure of getting what you need. But if the lectures are backed up by handouts and textbooks, then you may need very few notes. Equally, if a lecture is poorly delivered and packed with detailed information, you may have to write a lot just to keep track. Whereas, if the lecturer is lively and seizes your imagination with striking examples, you may learn more by concentrating on listening and writing occasional key points and topic headings. In the end, though, the main factor is you.

> ### *What sort of lecture listener are you?*
>
> Do you tend to daydream in lectures? Do you feel anxious about whether you are understanding enough? Do you feel confident that a few phrases, symbols and formulas will be enough to remind you of the points you need to hold on to? Or do you find it too difficult to decide which points are important as the lecture is in full flow? Do you worry that if you stop writing you will miss something crucial?

*A*ctivity Break Think about your past experience of lectures. What kind of notes suit your listening style?

If writing a lot helps you not to feel anxious and keeps you actively 'working', rather than letting things wash over you, then that is the right approach for you. But be aware that if you try to write everything down, you will learn very little during the lecture itself, and will have a lot of work still to do afterwards. Will you actually find time to make use of very full notes? On the other hand, if you decide you need only brief notes, how will you know what to select?

Selective note-making

The start and end of a lecture are important times for note-making. At the start, you need to make notes of the topic and the purpose of the lecture. Similarly, at the end, try to summarize the key points. So, for the first and last ten minutes you might set out to take quite full notes – allowing yourself to be more relaxed in between. You may need only a few key formulas and diagrams and the odd word or phrase to remind you of the main points. Do include any examples the lecturer gives – these will help to remind you of arguments and explanations. When a major point is made, get the whole thing down in detail so that you can make proper sense of it afterwards. Also note down any questions or comments that occur to you as you listen. After the lecture, these notes will help you to reconstruct what was going through your mind as you listened.

Styles of note-making

Selecting what to write down and positioning it on the page impose a structure on what you hear in a lecture. This structure helps you to *understand* and *remember*. Don't be stingy with your paper. Spread your notes out and use lines, arrows, brackets and boxes to emphasize divisions and links within the material. For example, you might put your own remarks and queries over to the right [or enclose them in square brackets]. Some people find it helpful to draw their notes as a big 'spray diagram', with the topic of the lecture in the centre circle and lines branching out to each subtopic (see Chapter 2, page 49).

Don't expect your lecture notes to have as much structure and clarity as the notes you make as you read. The emphasis here is on speed. A very simple but important technique is to develop your own shorthand. For example:

> Bacteria grow – v. wide range of temps:
>   salm., staph. – warm
>   list., Clost. bot. – low temp
> In genl, temps > 63 °C for 30 mins (pasteuriztn) kill pathog.
> bact. (WET)
>
> Dry heat less effect

This is short for:

> Bacteria such as salmonellae and staphylococci grow best at a relatively warm temperature, but bacteria can grow over a very wide range of temperatures. Some bacteria, such as listeriae and *Clostridium botulinum*, the cause of botulism, can grow at relatively low temperatures. In general, temperatures above that of pasteurization (63 °C for 30 minutes) kill pathogenic bacteria, provided they are wet. Dry heat is much less effective.

In my shorthand, 'v' stands for 'very', 'temps' for 'temperatures', '>' for 'greater than' or 'above', and so on. I shortened the names of the bacteria because I assumed that I could look up the full names elsewhere. I wrote 'WET' in capital letters to emphasize the contrast with dry heat.

Improving your notes after the lecture

Having invested an hour in attending a lecture, it is often worth investing a bit more time afterwards on tidying up your notes – in particular, checking that you understand them and that you have copied formulas and calculations correctly. It may help if you can do this with another student. What you get out of lectures is determined not only by what you do *during* lectures, but also by the work you put in *before* and *after*.

Hints and Tips

◆ When you attend a lecture, be clear in your mind as to *why* you are there, and *what* you want to take from it.

◆ Try to do some relevant reading before the lecture (however brief), to give yourself a good chance of making sense of it.

◆ Develop a flexible technique of listening, thinking and note-making that you can change according to the style of the lecture.

◆ Take account of your *own habits*, and work out a note-making strategy which helps you to concentrate.

◆ Don't feel you have to write down 'everything'. Listening is the main job. Pick out the main themes and key points.

◆ Check and tidy up your notes after the lecture.

3.2 Broadcasts and recordings

Many courses now make use of video and audio broadcasts and recordings. Clearly, this is a very different experience from sitting studying a book or listening to a lecture. So, what skills do you need? If you are asked to watch a programme on the life-cycle of an insect species, the performance of bridges in high winds, or experiments with subatomic particles, is it enough just to watch and listen and 'absorb'?

◆ Is there any difference between studying and casual watching or listening?

◆ What are you supposed to be able to *do* with what you learn from these programmes?

TV and video-cassettes

By combining high-quality pictures and sound, TV and video give you a sense of actually 'being there', of looking at things directly. Even when you are looking at something you could never see using natural vision, such as the magnified inside of a living human organ, you get a powerful sense that you are looking at the 'real world'. With a book or a lecture, you have to struggle to focus your attention on a sequence of words, symbols and diagrams, and then to connect these abstractions to the 'real world'. But with TV and video, all your most basic processes of experiencing the world are brought into play more or less effortlessly. Meanwhile, the 'voice-over', discussing and explaining what you are being shown, has a powerful aura of 'authenticity'. The message seems to be almost transmitted directly into your mind, with scarcely any thinking required from you. Is this learning, or is it just seeing and absorbing? Is there a difference?

It *is* learning, in the sense that you get a chance to see the world in new ways. But it is not a very profound learning unless, when you switch off, you are able to recreate that way of seeing the world for yourself. The real learning lies in *using* what you are shown in order to build on what you already know. It is the studying and thinking you do before and afterwards that turn 'viewing' into substantial 'learning'.

TV is excellent for showing you the world through an alternative frame of reference (for example, showing you how to understand the movements of objects in terms of the forces operating on them). The TV programme does all the work of holding the frame of reference in place, so things can seem 'obvious'. This can lull you into thinking that there isn't much to it. Then, when the programme ends and the frame of reference is gone, the clear understanding evaporates with it. (You can't remember where the force arrows should go, or how to add the forces together.)

At worst, TV's capacity to take on all the work of 'framing' our thoughts leads to a habit of passively accepting knowledge instead of understanding it properly for ourselves. If you want to be able to think for yourself, you have to gain some mastery of the underpinning frames of reference. You have to make some effort to 'make sense' to yourself of what you see on TV. You can do this in a variety of ways.

◆ Take down a few notes as you view.

◆ Read around the subject.

◆ Make use of what you see on the screen in your assignments. (Remember that Pam re-watched some TV programmes as a way of getting into the right 'frame of mind' for her assignment.)

TV and video are especially good at showing and explaining complicated *processes* in which there are many different aspects to be considered at the same time. You can follow a process – for example, a volcanic eruption – as it happens. What is more, you could watch a film of the eruption *and* look at an animated diagram of movements in the Earth's crust *and* examine a table of seismographic readings and ground temperatures *and* listen to a verbal explanation. TV can cut back and forth quickly between all of these sources of information, or even superimpose them on each other.

> ### *Dynamic knowledge*
>
> TV and video are particularly valuable in explaining the dynamics of processes, where writing or speech would take many words. Moreover, cross-cutting and superimposing allow many facets of a process to be explored simultaneously. Thus TV and video can develop a different kind of knowledge from 'book knowledge' – a more rounded, dynamic and multilayered understanding.

With such exciting possibilities, why have TV and video not displaced printed text? In fact, it isn't as easy as it sounds to learn from TV. Images, information and arguments are presented simultaneously to your eyes and ears, so it is hard to attend closely to any one thing, or to stop and think, or to take notes – there is just so much to think about. And when the programme is over, so much has happened that it may be difficult to pin down exactly what it was all about. Moreover, the knowledge gained has a fluid quality (an advantage during complicated explanations) and the details soon begin to recede in your memory as you go on to watch other programmes. You really need something written down as well, either printed programme notes or your own notes, to 'fix' the knowledge in a more simplified, 'encapsulated' form – something you can look at, 'operate' on yourself, and go back to to remind yourself when you need to.

TV and video excel in giving a broad, rounded understanding. Perhaps, in the future, if course assessment involves interacting directly with a screen image, this fluid, 'holistic' mode of understanding will predominate. But for now, as a student you have to translate these broad insights and use them within the more specific and detailed format of written words and symbols. TV and video tend to be used as *aids* to understanding – *not* as *primary* channels for delivering higher-level education.

Video-cassettes

Many students record TV broadcasts on to video-cassettes in order to watch them more than once and so absorb the full richness of the message. Indeed, teaching material is increasingly being recorded directly to video-cassette, rather than for broadcast. With a video-cassette, you can work at your own pace. You may want to replay the explanation of an idea that was confusing the first time around. Moving images can be stopped and replayed repeatedly, so the medium can be used interactively. For example, you might analyse a small segment of an important process (say, lava spilling out of a volcano) by replaying it several times, and answering questions about it, before moving on to hear what the 'experts' say. This could be a way of developing your skills of observation. You could replay the lava hitting a village and make detailed observations of the impact. Or, having done the 'cress-seedling' experiment in Chapter 8, you could be asked to make observations from time-lapse video-recordings of other plants growing under different conditions. This facility to 'replay' processes and study them in depth provides a powerful new way of developing insight and skills.

Radio

In education, radio tends to be used for *discussion* and *analysis*. In other words, it is used mainly as a 'verbal' medium – as an extension of text-based study, a spoken version. It can be used to bring the equivalent of a short lecture, or a discussion between 'experts', into your home. This enables you to hear the language of the textbook spoken as a living process of creating meaning. Radio is a less intense medium than TV (that is, less is happening simultaneously), so it is easier to sit with pad and pen and take notes. You can concentrate on abstract arguments without being distracted by visual images. With nothing but the words on which to focus, a debate between rival scientists can be riveting. In fact, radio encourages you to give your whole attention to exactly what the speaker is saying.

Radio is also used for 'chat'. It is less expensive and complicated to produce than TV, so it can be used more informally. Magazine programmes can keep you up to date with new developments in your field. The programme makers simply invite a researcher into a studio to comment on a recent news item regarding space exploration, genetic engineering, global warming or whatever.

Audio-cassettes

Audio-cassettes have the advantages of convenience and flexibility. They offer access to the spoken word at a time of your own choosing. You can listen on your way to work, or while you are peeling potatoes, or during a lunch break, or in bed at night. Thus they open up new areas of study time. However, when audio-cassettes are used more interactively, with stops, replays and activities, you need pen and pad and somewhere to write. You may also need your books, since audio-cassettes are very effective for 'talking you through' a section of text. Key points can be read out and discussed; you can be directed around complicated diagrams or tables of figures; and you can be 'walked through' mathematical workings. Then you can be set questions to work on with the audio-cassette switched off. In this way, an audio-cassette can be used to guide you through your studies.

Hints and Tips

◆ To gain full benefit from TV and radio broadcasts you need to prepare in advance by reading programme notes and skimming relevant sections of the course.

◆ It is hard to take notes as you watch TV, but you will learn more if you write down key points afterwards.

◆ It is easier to take notes as you listen to the radio, although some follow-up notes will help to consolidate your learning.

◆ Recording TV and radio broadcasts reduces the pressures involved in learning from these sources, as you can replay the programmes in your own time as often as you want.

◆ With audio- or video-cassettes, simply follow the instructions. Allow sufficient time to study the programmes, but guard against letting the time run away with you.

4 Learning by doing

All learning is an active process of *making* sense. However, there are elements of most MST courses where 'doing' is central. For example, laboratory work has a very long tradition in science studies at all levels. Here are three reasons why *doing* is regarded as important.

The empirical tradition

The radical break that modern science made with earlier traditions of knowledge rested on a commitment to *empirical investigation*. ('Empirical' means based on experimentation, observation and experience.) The earlier traditions rested on debate, abstract reasoning and religious teaching, but science is concerned with *testing* ideas through experimentation and meticulous observation. Thus you cannot consider yourself a 'real scientist' unless you know how to observe and experiment. Even if you don't have much opportunity to 'test' scientific ideas yourself, you need to understand the *principles* of observation and experimentation, and have at least some experience of applying those principles. You also need an understanding of the relationship between theory and reality. A scientific theory is never more than an approximation of reality. It aims to be the 'best fit' to the real world yet available, but there are always gaps. To grasp the significance of this fact, you need some experience of trying to apply a theory to the 'real world'. So, 'practical' work is fundamental to education in science and technology. (Many branches of mathematics, by contrast, work happily with abstract principles, regardless of their application to the 'real world'.)

Practical skills

As well as understanding general principles, you also need routine practical skills, such as setting up experimental apparatus, taking readings from instruments, and observing changes – along with enough 'know-how' to work out what to do when things do not turn out as expected.

Concept forming

The third reason why 'doing' is regarded as important is common to all subjects. You cannot develop new ideas only through passive listening. You have to involve yourself in *actively* making sense through doing and saying. Practical activities are a way of forcing your mind to grapple with new ideas.

Chapter 8, 'Observing and experimenting', describes some of the mental and practical approaches involved in scientific investigation. Ways of testing ideas are thought up and answers to problems are sought using practical approaches. Problem solving in MST subjects is a fundamental form of 'learning by doing', and a number of different examples appear throughout this book. In Chapter 4, for example, problem solving is portrayed as a thinking process: the application of mathematical ideas to practical problems. Three other forms of 'learning by doing' are worth a mention here.

4.1 Project work

Many courses include a project of some kind. This is an opportunity for you to study a topic of your choice in depth, working independently and building on your own interests and ideas. Carrying out a project gives you insight into the way knowledge is produced. It reminds you that knowledge doesn't just appear magically in books – it is the result of someone recognizing the importance of a particular question and setting out to find answers.

There are several stages to project work and each of them requires time and effort. One of the keys to success is to recognize the importance of each stage and to spread your time and energy across all of them. Broadly speaking, the stages are as follows.

1 *Formulating the question.* A project requires you to put together your discipline-based knowledge and your knowledge of the world and decide on a specific *question* to investigate.

2 *Planning the investigation.* You then have to work out how, in practical terms, you can pursue your inquiries: what *methods* to use, what *scale* of inquiry to attempt, what *resources* you require, and what *deadlines* you need to meet at each stage of the project. At this stage, you will often be expected to submit a project outline for approval by your tutor.

3 *Carrying out the investigation.* Having had your project outline approved by your tutor, you now have to put your plans into action, by carrying out the investigation and gathering data.

4 *Analysing the data.* You then analyse the data to see what conclusions you can draw from them.

5 *Writing a report.* And finally, you write up your project report.

Students generally approach project work with a mixture of enthusiasm and apprehension. It can be very interesting and satisfying, but it can also go badly wrong and bring your morale crashing down. The biggest pitfall is that almost everyone is too ambitious at the outset. Things always turn out to be more complicated than they seem at first, and every aspect of project work is deceptively time-consuming. To a beginner, the third stage in the list above looks like the main work. But the choice of question and the project design and planning always take a lot of thought. These early stages can easily drift on too long, and eat into time which is more scarce than you yet realize. Then stage three almost always throws up lots of unanticipated problems; sometimes quite minor ones, but enough to halt progress for a while. However, the last two stages are the ones which really catch students unawares. Working out how to treat your data and how to draw conclusions from them are major challenges. You need time to mull things over at this stage. Finally, writing your report is a lot more than producing a simple description. You have to explain the rationale for what you have done – outlining the background from which your central question arose, as well as explaining your choice of method. You then have to work out how to present your data, and how to argue the conclusions you want to draw. There is some specific advice about writing reports on page 258.

Project work teaches some extremely valuable skills – for example:

◆ how to set about an investigation
◆ how and where to find information
◆ strategic planning
◆ time management
◆ being pragmatic, and cutting corners where appropriate
◆ sorting out and making sense of real data
◆ presenting data in a way that is easy to read and understand
◆ writing clearly and concisely when you have a lot of very varied material to cover
◆ arguing from evidence to theoretical implications
◆ understanding the relationship between method and theory.

One way to help yourself to develop these skills is to keep a Project Diary. You record your thinking as the project develops: your reasons for doing things, your hopes and worries, and what you discover about your own strengths and weaknesses. A Project Diary is a specific case of the Study Diary idea discussed on page 19. As with other diaries, it will help you to reflect on your learning by recording triumphs and disasters.

You need to approach a project with care, and allow yourself time to develop the skills outlined above. But you should also see it as a great opportunity to explore your own personal interests. In spite of the time it takes and the trouble it can cause, project work is absorbing and very instructive. Years after finishing a course, your project will often be the aspect you remember most clearly and understand most thoroughly.

Hints and Tips

When you undertake a project:

◆ Don't think too big at the outset.
◆ Start early to allow plenty of time for the later stages.
◆ Keep a Project Diary.
◆ Whenever you feel doubt or despair, get in touch with your tutor or another student.

4.2 Field work

It is quite common for courses to include a field work element. For example, you might spend several days 'messing about' in and around a river, learning to look closely and to take measurements. In daily life we look past much of the detail around us. We see 'just a river'. But if you look closely, it is astonishing how many different things there are to investigate. You might measure the chemical quality of the water and its relation to activities around the river. You might observe the distribution of different types of plant and animal life. You could measure rates of water flow and estimate the energy available for hydroelectric power. In some disciplines, such as geology, biology, environmental science or production design, field work plays a particularly important role, since many aspects of the 'real world' cannot be brought into the laboratory without changing their essential nature. Field work teaches you to think practically and creatively, and develops your investigative skills.

4.3 Giving a presentation

You may be required to give a short presentation to other students at some point – on an investigation you have carried out, or an article, or a topic in a textbook. This is usually intended to take about ten to fifteen minutes, and ought to be a pretty straightforward task. However, it is easy to get over-anxious at the prospect of standing up to speak. So, here are some basic guidelines to help your presentation go well.

The most important principle is to avoid being too ambitious. In ten or fifteen minutes you are not going to be able to make more than two or three main points. Don't let anxiety push you into preparing a lot more material, or you will end up gabbling everything very fast and no one will understand a word. Begin with a brief summary of the topic and explain why it is of interest, to set the context for your audience. If you are presenting your own investigation, be sure to explain very simply what you were trying to find out and why, before launching into the detail of what you did and what you found. Keep it very simple at all times. Remember that, while you have been thinking about your subject a lot, the other students haven't, so they will need to have things spelled out carefully. Use examples and diagrams to help people see what you are getting at. Don't write out in detail what you intend to say. Just put a simple set of headings and a few 'bullet points' on an overhead projector transparency or two. Then talk your way through these notes as you show them to your audience. Speak simply and clearly, and try to make eye contact with one or two members of your audience. Remember, for everyone else your presentation it is just another session. They are not concerned about how hard you worked, or how clever you are. All they are concerned with is whether they can understand what you say.

Hints and Tips

If you have to make a presentation to other students:

◆ Don't be too ambitious – keep it short and simple.

◆ Use examples to illustrate your main points.

◆ Use overhead projector transparencies as your notes for the talk.

5 A reflective mixing of modes

I have looked at a variety of ways of studying in this chapter. Each mode requires its own skills – together they require you to become skilled in distributing your time and energy across different modes.

A ***ctivity Break*** Can you recall what different ways of studying Pam used in her 'typical' week and roughly what proportion of her time she spent on each mode?

From what you can remember, estimate what proportion of Pam's time was spent on each of the following sorts of activity:

◆ studying the course text
◆ learning with others
◆ learning by watching and listening
◆ learning by doing
◆ using a computer (see Chapter 7).

Guess first, and then look at the pie chart below (Figure 6.1). How does Pam's mixture of modes of study and the time spent on them compare with your own experience?

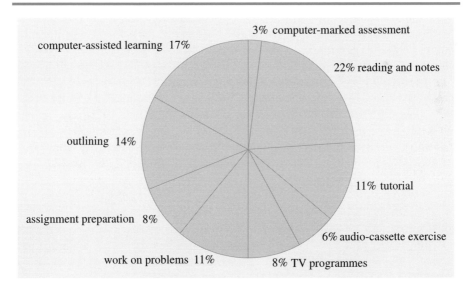

Figure 6.1

The need to manage a mixture of ways of studying takes us back to the idea of being a 'reflective self-manager' (see Chapter 1, page 16). As you plan your forthcoming studies, reflect back on what you have learned from various ways of studying and on how much time you are giving each mode. You may find that you are overemphasizing the 'mainstream' activity of reading the study text and not recognizing the contribution of some of the apparently less 'essential' activities. Or you might be allowing yourself to spend more time than you can afford on activities you enjoy. (Pam said she had to be careful not to get carried away with some of the computer work.) On the other hand, if you are enjoying something then perhaps you are learning a lot from it. You need to take the time to reflect on these questions so that you can adjust your plans to try to make the best use of the full range of study modes available to you.

Hints and Tips

Reflect back from time to time on:

◆ what you are learning from different ways of studying

◆ whether you are sharing your time effectively between the different modes of study.

CHAPTER 7

Studying with a computer

1 A basic study tool

Personal computers first appeared in the 1980s and soon became established in the mainstream of education. Generations of students have studied without a computer, but many now seem to find one virtually indispensable. Why?

In some subjects a computer has become a standard piece of equipment, just as a slide-rule or a calculator used to be. For most engineers, for example, a computer has become *an all-purpose 'tool kit'*, something you can turn to at any point in the daily routine to get a job done. It no longer makes much sense to have an engineering course which does not require access to a computer – and this is increasingly true of MST courses in general. Of course, some courses are actually *about* computing, so having a computer to work on is essential.

In fact, the use of computers has spread to students in all subjects: the humanities, business studies, art and design. Given the expense, what makes them so popular? Here are two answers.

◆ They can make you much more efficient at many of the things students have always had to do.

◆ They open up the possibility of studying in completely new ways.

As we shall see, both of these answers are true for Pam, the student we met at the start of Chapter 6. (If you haven't yet read the outline of Pam's study week, read it now on pages 155 and 156.) Pam thought she spent at least four hours a week on the computer – a lot more as an assignment approached. She rents her computer because she cannot afford to buy one, but she has no doubt that it is worth the expense. The computer helps her to study and she enjoys working on it. She feels she has gained new powers of thought and self-expression through the use of such a versatile and powerful tool.

Key Points

◆ In some fields a computer is now a standard, *all-purpose 'tool kit'*, so much 'taken for granted' that studying without one would seem very odd.

◆ In other subjects, you *can* study effectively without a computer, as generations of students have shown. Yet there are two good reasons for regarding a computer as a *basic study tool*.

– Computers can make you significantly *more efficient* at traditional study tasks.

– Computers open up completely new ways of studying.

2 Becoming more efficient

2.1 Word processing

The most widespread use of computers is for word processing. The age-old business of getting words and sentences on to paper has been transformed. How? By making it possible to make changes and move things around as much as you like without having to start all over again. Serious writing has always been a matter of putting down first thoughts and then working them up into a more polished version. It also used to involve the painstaking technical skill of forming rows of neat, legible letters with a pen. With a word processor, instead of the slow business of writing out a new draft every time you make an improvement, you just change the existing draft.

This is a great liberation. It allows you to approach writing in a more relaxed and creative way. You don't have to worry about the huge time investment involved in redrafting. You can begin as informally as you like – typing in ideas and starting a new line whenever another thought comes to you. Then, when you feel ready, you switch to shaping the bits and pieces into something more coherent. Finally, you print the piece out and it looks wonderfully neat and stylish compared with even your best handwriting. Of course, word processing does not guarantee that what you write will be intelligent or easy to understand, but it does take a lot of the drudgery out of writing, and increases the time and energy you can invest in the quality of the content.

Do you need to be able to type?

You can get by with two fingers using the 'hunt and peck' method – many people do. But you will not enjoy the full benefits of word processing until you can put words on to the screen at something approaching handwriting speed. The good news is that your computer can teach you to type. There are excellent 'typing tutor' programmes on sale, and a few weeks of regular, 20-minute sessions should have you typing as fast as you can write. At that point, you can switch to typing instead of handwriting, and your typing speed will steadily improve to well above your handwriting speed. A 'typing tutor' teaches you to 'touch type' properly, using all ten digits without looking down. Eventually, you will stop being aware of typing as such. You will just think of phrases and sentences and 'make them appear' on the computer screen. When typing becomes an unconscious, background activity you are *really* word processing.

Learning to type requires a substantial investment of time. There is no short-cut around the initial period of regular practice, and it can be frustrating and tiring at first. But if you have several years of study ahead, the investment will repay itself many times over. And, of course, you will be able to use your typing and word-processing skills in other areas of your life.

In addition to making the writing process more flexible and less tedious, word processors offer many other useful facilities, such as:

◆ correcting your spelling (this also improves your spelling by identifying persistent mistakes)

◆ giving your documents a consistent style (headings, spacing, quotations and so on)

◆ numbering your pages and producing a contents list

◆ organizing your footnotes

◆ sorting your references into alphabetical order.

All of these facilities are tremendously helpful in producing well-organized and attractive work. And it isn't *just* a matter of appearances – being able to organize your thoughts and lay your work out neatly are part of good science. Clarity of presentation aids clarity of thought, for the writer and the reader. It takes a while to learn how to use all the features of a powerful word processor, but as you become more familiar with them, you will be able to turn out increasingly well-structured scientific work.

Does the spelling checker replace the dictionary?

No. Wonderful though they are, spelling checkers have their limitations. For example, your spelling checker will not recognize most scientific words. So, when it stops at an unfamiliar word, you will need to check in a textbook or dictionary that you have spelt it correctly, and then instruct the spelling checker to add the word to its list. The spelling checker will often 'suggest' a word that is not the one you want, so think before accepting suggestions. And the spelling checker tells you nothing about the meanings of words, so you will, in any case, need a good dictionary that includes basic scientific terms.

Word processing does not mean an end to jotting on a note-pad; that is how a lot of good thinking still starts. (In fact, it often helps if you print out word-processed drafts so that you can have a proper look at them and scribble comments in the margin.) And, although word processing offers many advantages, it doesn't mean that you can use 'flash' presentation to cover up for bad science.

Word-processed junk

Although a word processor makes it a lot easier to produce text that looks good, be wary of churning out beautifully presented nonsense! You still need to *think* before you write. Don't just 'bash it in, print it out and bung it off'. The advice in Chapter 9 applies whether or not you use a word processor. Working out *what* you need to say and *how* to say it remain hard, time-consuming work and are a fundamental part of learning the subject. Word processing just helps to put the words on the page.

2.2 Organizing your notes

Closely related to word processing is something known as 'outlining' (indeed, 'outliners' are incorporated as a feature of most word processors). Outlining is a way of organizing text under headings, subheadings and sub-subheadings to produce an outline or general structure of what you have written. Figure 7.1 shows you one example. What is remarkable about outliners is that you can move the headings and subheadings as much as you like – and when you move a heading, all its subheadings and associated text move with it (unless you choose to put some of them with another heading). If you instruct the outliner to number the headings, the numbering will change automatically as you move headings around. You can also choose to see only the main headings, or just the first two levels (or whatever). This allows you to shift your focus from the overall structure to the fine detail and back again.

Activity Break   To illustrate this technique, Figure 7.1 shows some notes I made from the first three paragraphs of the Collee article on page 397. I decided to break some of the lines in two and shift some points to the right to make sub-points. This process produced Figure 7.2. Can you pick out the changes I made and do you see why I made them?

I   Food poisoning

   A   effects: diarrhoea, vomiting

   B   assumed causes: food/drink 'gone off'

II   Difficult to determine cause

   A   often no food remains

   B   can tell that food was the cause when:

      1   many people ill at same time

         (a)   eaten same food

   C   cases reported to GPs, environ. health dept

III   'Food poisoning' is misnomer

   A   caused by micro-organisms:

      1   viruses, bacteria, fungi, protozoa

      2   two mechanisms for disease:

         (a)   true infections – microbe multiplies in human body to produce toxin

         (b)   poisoning by toxin – microbe multiplies in food to produce toxin

IV   better term: 'food-borne infections and intoxications'

Figure 7.1   *A first attempt at an outline of the beginning of the Collee article*

I   Food poisoning

    1   effects:

       (a) diarrhoea, vomiting

    2   assumed causes:

       (a) food/drink 'gone off'

  A   Difficult to determine cause

       (a) often no food remains

    1   can tell that food was the cause when:

       (a) many people ill

          (i) at same time

          (ii) eaten same food

       (b) cases reported to GPs, environ. health dept

  B   'Food poisoning' is misnomer

    1   caused by micro-organisms:

       (a) viruses

       (b) bacteria

       (c) fungi

       (d) protozoa

    2   two mechanisms for disease:

       (a) true infections

          (i) microbe multiplies in human body to produce toxin

       (b) poisoning by toxin

          (i) microbe multiplies in food to produce toxin

    3   better term: 'food-borne infections and intoxications'

Figure 7.2 *A revised outline of the beginning of the Collee article*

The second version takes up a bit more space, but I find it much easier to see what the notes are about. Having just one first-level heading and two second-level headings brings out the main themes. The other changes were attempts to sort out which points belonged to which headings, to try to make the whole thing more logical. Chapter 2 talks about listing key points and making 'spray diagrams'. What I have produced here is the same kind of thing, but done with an outliner, so I can change it if I see a better way of organizing the information.

You need to play with an outliner yourself to grasp the significance of the technique. An outliner allows you to re-organize your notes as you get a clearer picture of the subject matter. Pam used hers to make summary notes after a major chunk of reading. Then, at the end of a block of work, she re-organized these notes so that they made better sense. Pam also used her outliner to sketch out assignment answers – she could even copy sections of her notes on the course text straight into her drafts (this is what she was doing on Friday evening). Pam felt that re-organizing her notes in this way had been an eye-opener: for the first time, she was aware that she was thinking strategically about linking ideas together – about how to group ideas and about how to link ideas to information and evidence.

2.3 Filing

When you have made your notes, what do you do with them? Organizing notes into files and keeping them where you can find them has always been vital to success as a student. Computers make it easy. You store documents in 'directories', which can be kept in other directories, inside yet other directories.* Notes and reports prepared on your computer do not need lots of shelf space or box files. You can set up your own filing system and keep everything on the computer's hard disk. You start with a simple filing system and make it more elaborate as you go along. The whole thing is infinitely changeable. You can create new directories whenever you like, and change the names of these directories, or the documents they contain, as your system develops.

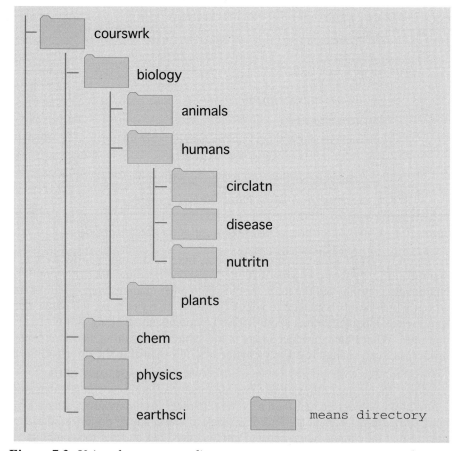

Figure 7.3 *Using the computer directory system to store your course documents*

* If you have an Apple computer, you will use 'folders' instead of 'directories', but the general principle is the same.

Figure 7.3 shows how you could create a directory called 'courswrk' to store your course documents. Inside the courswrk directory are directories for biology, chemistry, physics and earth sciences. Inside the biology directory are directories for animal, plant and human biology. And inside the human biology directory are directories for particular topics. Now you just have to decide whether to keep your outline of the Collee article in the disease directory or the nutrition directory (although you can always change your mind and move it later). You might decide to change your directories, because you have little in the circulation directory and lots in the disease directory – so you make some new directories within the disease directory, and move the contents of the circulation directory elsewhere before deleting it.*

When you want to find a document you can ask the computer to list the contents of your directories in a variety of ways (for example, according to how recent the documents are or how big). If that doesn't work, you can use 'search' facilities which hunt for documents with a particular word in their titles, or for all the documents you worked on in a particular week or month. The beauty of computer filing is that it is so easy. Each time you work on something you tell the computer to 'save it' in a convenient directory, and it is there should you ever need it. If you are having a clear-out, and decide you do not need a document, you just delete it. Filing is easy when the computer does most of the tedious and time-consuming bits.

Backing up and archiving

The golden rule in using computers is to 'save' your work and to 'back up' your documents (that is, to make extra copies). If you don't, you can easily lose what you've worked so hard to produce.

Backing up usually involves copying documents from your hard disk on to a floppy disk – just in case disaster strikes and the hard disk stops working (crashes) or is damaged in some way.

Archiving – storing important documents in an organized manner – is another aspect of good practice. You may need to retrieve an assignment that you wrote several months ago, or a set of notes you made, or some calculations you attempted. As a rule, there will always be enough memory in your computer for you to store everything you need to keep. (Remember to ensure that archived documents are identified properly, so that you can find them again.)

Sometimes, 'good housekeeping' involves throwing things away. This can be therapeutic: it reminds you of your current priorities and of how far you have moved on.

Word processing, outlining and electronic filing are new ways of doing things students have always had to do. They give you so much more power and flexibility in your work that it is worth having a computer for these facilities alone.

* To find out how to set up a filing system, use your computer's 'Help' facility or consult the manual provided with your computer.

2.4 Making tables and drawing graphs

Setting out data in tables and drawing graphs have also been routine activities for generations of MST students (see Chapter 3). Again, computers make these tasks much easier. With a 'spreadsheet' program you can produce a neat table and a beautifully drawn graph in a few minutes, once you know how. It took me under ten minutes to turn the information Pam gave me into the pie chart on page 179 (and slightly longer to work out the best way of 'importing' it from the spreadsheet into this word-processed document). It is not my purpose here to look at *how* to use spreadsheets or other software packages. You will generally be told what to do in your course of study, or you can find out from a book.* My aim is simply to describe how you can use a computer to make studying easier and more efficient.

2.5 Calculating

One tedious aspect of MST subjects used to be the sheer labour involved in doing complicated calculations (then re-doing them to check you had not made a mistake – and hunting for the mistake if the answers did not agree). You could easily find yourself spending an afternoon turning the handle of a mechanical calculating machine if you had something complicated to work out. Now a computer can do calculations for you almost instantaneously. No longer is the sight of complicated numbers or formulas something to be depressed about. Much of the repetitive, boring work, requiring constant attention to accuracy, can be handed over to the computer. You can focus your energies on working out *what* calculations need to be done, whether the results of the calculations *look sensible*, and what the results *mean*.

In fact, in the past, some types of data analysis were too complicated to attempt at all unless you were a full-time researcher. Now, a wide range of mathematical packages bring highly complex analyses within the reach of students. However, there are dangers in knowing how to 'press buttons' and 'pull levers' on powerful analytical tools without understanding what is going on. There is more to learn than just how to feed numbers in and get results out. To understand the meaning of what comes out of an analysis, you need to know what *assumptions* it makes and the *limits* of its application. Overall, though, the emphasis has shifted. Instead of being weighed down by the complexities of the mathematics and calculations, you can focus on *making use* of analytical tools to understand *other* things.

---

* There are some excellent books that explain how to use the more popular packages. These books can be quite expensive, but they will save you a lot of time. Browse through several before buying, to make sure you get one that is at the right level and covers the things you need to know.

Key Points

Many things which students have always had to do can be done more efficiently and easily using a computer.

You can use:

◆ a *word processor* to prepare reports and assignments

◆ an *outliner* to prepare and organize your notes

◆ the computer's *filing system* to store your course-related documents

◆ spreadsheets and other packages to produce *tables* and *graphs*

◆ various kinds of packages to do *calculations* for you.

Computer-induced inefficiency

In this section I have stressed the ways a computer *can* make studying easier and more efficient. But it is important to emphasize the word 'can'. When you *first* start using a computer or a new software package you will be *slowed down*. Studying will seem *harder.* You have to invest some time in getting to know how the software works and in learning how to make it do what you want. The ease and efficiency come later.

Yet however proficient you become, there will *always* be things which are done *less* efficiently on a computer. For example, the computer will draw beautiful pie charts for you, but if you want to sketch diagrams like those on page 61 you may be better off with pen and paper. You *can* do it on a computer, but it takes more time than it is worth. Similarly, if you are working on a maths problem you will generally find it much quicker to work on paper. Instead of messing about getting your software to display $\sqrt[3]{x + 3y^2}$, you can just write it down and keep your mind focused on 'doing the maths'. It is not worth putting short calculations and rough estimates on to the computer. Similarly, a few jotted notes are often better than a computer 'outline'. Working on the computer, *when you don't need to*, can be a terrible waste of time.

Modern software packages are so pretty and full of features that you could easily get carried away trying to use them all. For example, 'office' packages often include a 'calendar' facility. It looks so neat; you can enter your engagements and deadlines and have the computer 'beep' to remind you of things. But unless you work in a busy office it's doubtful whether opening the calendar program and typing in your commitments is as efficient as noting them in a diary. You don't *have* to do everything on a computer to be up-to-date and efficient.

3 New ways of studying

As well as helping with traditional study tasks, computers allow completely new ways of studying.

3.1 Computer-assisted learning (CAL)

On Tuesday evening, Pam was busy developing her number skills using a CAL program. The program tested what she could already do, showed her how to do some new things, and then gave her examples to work through. This kind of program is *interactive*, in that it asks you to do something, tells you whether you have done it right, and decides, from your response, what to ask you to do next. It can take you back to learn a point again, give you more practice, or move you on to something new. A computer is a very patient and attentive teacher. It allows you as many tries as you like, and pays immediate attention to your answers. It can also be quite challenging: for example, Pam said that she enjoyed trying to 'beat the computer'.

But learning on computers isn't always fun. A computer can be a tiresomely pedantic teacher when the program does not move you through the subject briskly enough, or fails to get to the heart of what you really want to know. If computer-assisted learning makes you feel 'controlled' – sent off hither and thither on trivial tasks – it can quickly become very boring. A teaching programme is only as good as the knowledge that goes into it and the quality of its design. Writing good CAL programs is very time-consuming and expensive. Used well, they are a powerful teaching medium, but the quality can be very variable. So, when you come across CAL, give it a good try – but if you are getting nowhere, and the work is optional, give up and devote your time to something more useful.

3.2 Modelling

Computers are particularly good at modelling complicated processes. For example, a computer simulation of the workings of a nuclear reactor can give you a better idea of its internal processes than a filmed tour of the buildings and equipment. The program can answer questions and allows you to 'intervene' in the processes involved (for example, by seeing what happens when you change the supply of nuclear fuel). Modelling can even be used to simulate 'doing an experiment', so that instead of looking for equipment and space at home, you perform a 'virtual experiment' on your computer screen.

Of course, computer modelling isn't restricted to 'pictorial' representations of 'the real world'. Mathematical modelling, for example, can be entirely abstract (a representation of complex relationships between purely hypothetical mathematical entities).

3.3 Email

If your computer is connected by a modem to a computer network, you can send electronic messages (email) to other computers linked to the network. This means you can send a message to other students, or to your tutor, at any time of the day or night. For example, if you get stuck on something, you can send off a request for help to your student friends. You can choose whether to send your message to one friend or several. If one of them happens to be 'logged on' to the network at the time you might get a reply within minutes, or it might be a few hours, or a day or so, before they pick up your message and reply. However, you can be confident that your message will reach them quickly. (And if, for any reason, your message does not get through, your computer will generally let you know.)

You might decide that you need expert advice, but you don't want to interrupt your tutor's evening by telephoning. So you send an email which your tutor can read when he or she next looks at the messages from students. You are not thwarted by phoning when people are out or the phone is engaged. Your message simply joins a queue in the other person's 'in tray'. You can 'attach' documents, diagrams or tables of data to your emails. Perhaps you could even send a section of your draft assignment to your tutor by email, and receive comments by the same route (although first you should check that this is OK with your tutor). At some stage in the future, submitting assignments and receiving feedback by email may become commonplace. For students studying by distance education, in particular, email opens up invaluable channels of rapid and reliable communication.

3.4 Computer conferencing

A computer conference is an extension of the email idea. Instead of messages being sent from one person to another, *all* messages are sent to *everyone* who is a conference member. It works like a shared notice-board. People stick up messages, and whoever reads a message and wants to reply puts their reply on the notice-board next to the original message. Several people may reply to the same message, or reply to a reply. So lots of 'conversations' spring up, and everyone in the conference can read or add messages whenever they choose.

A conference can be made up of a group of students and their tutor. So if, as you sit studying, you come across something puzzling, instead of wondering whom to ask, you just post a question on the conference notice-board and everyone else will see it. One or two of the other students might suggest answers – or might reply 'Yes, that's giving me trouble too' and add questions of their own. When your tutor reads the question, he or she may decide that it has already been answered well enough, or may feel the need to offer additional advice. This is a good thing from the tutor's point of view because things only have to be said once for the whole group, avoiding the need for lots of individual emails or telephone calls.

The tutor's answer may lead to other questions. It works like a continuing conversation, spread out over days, with people dropping in to 'listen' at any time and 'speaking' when they choose. A group can have several conferences on different topics running at the same time. There might be a conference set aside for assignments, in which students talk about plans for the next assignment or about how the last one went. The tutor can 'drop in' to find out what the students are concerned about and offer advice. Often there is a conference just for 'chat', in which people can talk about whatever they like and get to know each other. Chat conferences are very popular. You feel a lot less isolated as a student if you are a member of a friendly group, with shared interests and problems. Busy adults find it hard to make time for socializing with fellow students, but a computer conference allows you to drop in for 10 minutes any time you like.

Once group members get to know each other they can use the conference facility to talk about all kinds of things. One or two students might put past assignments into the conference for others to comment on, allowing the tutor to draw out some general points for the whole group.

The possibilities are endless – the limitation is time. With everyone able to contribute whenever they like, the number of messages can quickly become overwhelming. Agreed rules and some self-discipline are required if computer conferencing is to work well.

'Netiquette'

The 'good manners' of conferencing on the network are known as 'netiquette'. A computer conference is a kind of 'social space': shared, but not located in a specific place and time. Unlike most social spaces, it isn't influenced by people's physical attributes (their appearance, manner, confidence, gestures or accent). However, like any social space, it has to develop its own 'culture' if people are to understand each other and get along.

Conferencing and email can be used side by side. Email allows *private* communication; conferencing is *public*. You might, for example, ask your tutor something in private, but then find that the problem is widely shared. Your tutor may then ask whether you would mind copying your question into the conference so that everyone can share the answer. The tutor might even send an email asking permission to save your question on to a disk so that he or she can 'paste' it into next year's conference. Once the computer connections exist, there are countless ways in which to use them.

3.5 The Internet

We have seen how computers can link you to other people, but computer networks can also connect you to sources of information. For example, you'll certainly have heard of the Internet. It's a vast computer network – a global collection of people and computers linked by cables and telephone lines – that can put you in contact with people and sources of information from all over the world.

Although complex in technical terms, the Internet is delightfully simple to use. All you need is a personal computer with appropriate software, a modem and a telephone line. Instead of going to a library to get books, and having to wait if a book is out on loan, there are electronic 'books' in electronic libraries that you can 'download' and read on your computer screen. Similarly, it is possible to have direct access to data banks of information for research purposes.

However, the Internet raises a number of questions about copyright and payment.

The theft of intellectual property

Information technology has opened up a new world of publishing, one in which information can be distributed at high speed all over the world, in forms so flexible that anybody can 'grab it' for themselves. This raises age-old questions about the ownership of ideas and texts, but in a far more urgent form. If you released your ideas to the networked world, you would probably feel rewarded if you found yourself quoted in someone's book. But what if someone in a far-off place simply copied your work and published it? What if you wrote a brilliant essay to your tutor, and he or she secretly 'pasted' it into their next publication? Come to that, why write your own research paper if you can download one from the Internet? Processing and printing text have become so easy that we *all* have reason to be concerned about 'intellectual property rights'.

This applies to you too. It is important that you respect the copyright on information made available to *you* through electronic media. There is no harm in electronically copying a quotation to 'paste' it into your assignment, so long as you give a proper reference (see Chapter 9), but:

◆   you should not copy large chunks

◆   you must always indicate when you are quoting and give an appropriate reference

◆   if material is made available under copyright, you should never copy it for use in any context other than your studies.

A mass of information is already available on the Internet, some of it put there by institutions and some by individuals. Anyone linked up can make information available on the Internet (though there are, of course, no guarantees as to the quality of this 'free' information). There are also a number of information services available at a price, and depending on your area of interest, there may be much that you would find useful. However, you have to be able to find your way through the electronic labyrinth to the information that you need. 'Surfing the Internet' can be a time-consuming and costly business. And if you are a newcomer to an area of study, there is a lot to be said for small amounts of well-structured and carefully explained information, rather than a vast ocean of the stuff.

Yet, as the Internet develops, it will increasingly be used as a medium for *delivering* education to students – students who may be linked to the network from virtually any point on the globe. Education has always transcended national boundaries in the form of an international community of scholars.

But internationalism enters a new dimension when a student in Brazil can enrol to study a course with a tutor in Australia, 'alongside' a student in South Africa and another in Canada; all of them raising questions and discussing answers through a computer conference. No longer will you be restricted to the courses available in your own country. Before long, perhaps, you will be able to enrol with the 'Global University'.

3.6 CD-ROM

Another way of delivering information electronically is to put it on a CD-ROM. With the Internet, you have to log on, search your way to an information source, and wait for the information to be downloaded on to your computer. With a CD-ROM, you just put in your disk and the information it contains is seconds away. At its simplest, a CD-ROM is just another way of publishing text. Anything to be found in books can be put on a CD-ROM in vast quantities, the advantage being that you can find what you want very quickly. Say you had a disk containing the published works of Charles Darwin, and you were wondering where he first used the word 'evolution'. Your computer could find the place instantly. Or say you had a CD-ROM containing records of disease epidemics. You could quickly find out whether it includes information on outbreaks of food poisoning in your region, and then transfer the relevant data to a spreadsheet to construct tables and charts as described in Chapter 3.

A CD-ROM can be much more than the equivalent of a stack of books or a data bank; it can also store moving images, sounds and computer software. This takes us to the final topic in this section: multimedia.

3.7 Multimedia

A computer's extraordinary ability to handle information allows it to bring together different communication media within a single co-ordinated package. Segments of moving film, animated cartoons, soundtrack segments, text and photographs can be interwoven with 'software' to help you explore a subject. You start from a screen menu (perhaps with music, or a voice-over talking you through the program), and you point to whatever it is you want to investigate. This takes you to another screen, from which you can undertake a closer examination or move on to something new. You can explore by following your own interests.

Educational packages of this kind are already available on CD-ROM. But the possibilities do not stop there. In principle, at a given moment you could be linked to a database on the Internet, to your fellow students in a computer conference, and to laboratory equipment feeding in data from an experiment. The technical means of handling this interweaving of communication channels are still being developed, as is educational software which can make use of these amazing possibilities. However, the great artists and communicators of multimedia are, in the main, yet to be discovered. At present, the promise is exciting, but apart from games and leisure pursuits, the content sometimes leaves a lot to be desired. Compared with the simplicity of teaching through speech and print, the complexity of multimedia presents a formidable barrier to coherent, purposeful education. Yet its day will surely come.

Key Points

The extraordinary advances in computing and communications technology have produced new ways of studying.

These new ways of studying include:

◆ *computer-assisted learning* packages designed to interact with you as you study

◆ programs which *model* complex processes, allowing you to explore them in depth

◆ *email*, which enables students to communicate privately with tutors and other students

◆ *computer conferences*, which enable students and tutors to communicate collectively

◆ access to educational information from around the world through the *Internet*

◆ instant access to large quantities of information held on *CD-ROM*

◆ *multimedia* packages, which interweave a combination of these communication technologies.

4 Problems with computers

I have stressed how much computers offer you. But not every minute spent gazing at your screen is pure bliss. Computers are a great help, but they can also cause you considerable grief.

4.1 Getting started

Pam had already used computers at work, but had simply followed instructions and used them as glorified typewriters. So she felt nervous when she opened the box containing the computer. Could she put it all together properly? Would she press the wrong button and break it? How could she absorb so many pages of instructions? It took her a while to work out what plugged in where. Should she connect the printer to the 'serial' or the 'parallel' port? To her relief, she had the computer 'up and running' in an hour, but then found herself looking at a screen display which meant nothing to her. Where to begin? By the end of the evening she had made a few tentative explorations but still felt overwhelmed.

Next day, both machine and software looked more familiar (although she hadn't realized how much space the system would take up). Within a week, Pam was amazed at how much she could do with the computer. She admitted to several moments of panic, when things seemed to disappear from the screen for no reason, or words suddenly switched into italics or became smaller. There were also spells of frustration, when she couldn't work out how to do things – and a very bad evening trying to get the printer to work properly. Luckily, her daughter had been able to help her through the worst. Soon Pam could type a letter, or a report, and print it out. She still felt very hesitant, though, about trying new things. She was convinced she would do something wrong and lose everything she had written.

Yet six months later most of it seemed easy. She had lost a few bits of work on the way. But now she knew how to avoid these losses through regular saving and backing up. Now she found she was more confident about not losing work stored on her hard disk than she was about the notes scattered around the house. She had borrowed a book about the word-processing package she was using from a friend, and had started dipping into it to try new things. She found she could work out how to use most of the features she needed. In fact, she was becoming so confident and knowledgeable that she was handing out advice to work-mates and was already beginning to think of some changes they should make to the computing facilities in her office at work.

Pam's experiences are common. Computers seem complicated and temperamental until you get the gist of the logic by which they work. There is so much to learn so quickly, and it is easy to feel overwhelmed. But if you give yourself the time to *explore*, and gradually build up a sense of *control* over both machine and software, you will soon find yourself putting them to use just like any other tool. (You don't have to know everything. You just want to feel confident that you can work out how to do the basics.)

You need to learn three things:

◆ how to set up the equipment itself (the hardware)

◆ how to work with the operating system (Windows, DOS or the Macintosh interface)

◆ how to use the main features of your software packages.

The first two have the highest priority to begin with. You might spend quite a few hours in the first couple of weeks finding your way around the equipment and operating system, getting everything working and learning the basics, such as how to 'format' disks, create directories (or folders), save your work and back it up. When you are on top of the hardware and operating system you can take as long as you like exploring the delights of your software packages.

With new software, you need a burst of learning at the beginning to get yourself going. Then you can advance to the more sophisticated features a bit at a time (although there are so many features in modern packages that you are unlikely ever to know them all). It is much easier to learn about a software feature when you need it – and it helps if you can take a little time to 'play'. You need the freedom to try out different approaches – 'I wonder what happens if I choose that option …' – and time to consult the on-line help facilities or a guide book to work out what *did* happen (if it wasn't what you expected).

Computers and their software are remarkably robust and pretty logical. Most of the hardware does not break easily (although computers don't like having drinks spilt on them!). What happens on the screen almost always happens for a logical reason. You just need to work out the logic. If things 'disappear' from view, they have seldom gone for good. You will generally be able to find them by searching around. And if you get into difficulties, ask someone for help. You rarely need an expert. A friend, or a fellow student, may know enough to get you going again. If you're really stuck, try your tutor.

4.2 Crashes, hang-ups and gremlins

Even when you are well on top of your computing, problems can arise. Your machine may 'freeze' or 'hang up' from time to time (in other words, stop responding to anything you do with your keyboard or mouse). All you can do then is switch off and start again, and hope that you 'saved' your work fairly recently. It rarely means that there is a serious problem with the computer; somehow you just made demands that were incompatible, so 'confusing' the system. Just carry on as you were.

Sometimes the problem isn't a 'hang up', but some other 'gremlin' in the works.

For example, while I was making some changes to this chapter my computer started a routine 'auto save' process, then gave me a message that my hard disk was full, though I was sure there was lots of free space. The computer gave this same message in response to most of the things I tried to do. I was in danger of losing some complicated changes I had just made, and I wasn't sure I'd be able to remember them. So I resorted to cunning. I guessed that my document had become too long and too complicated and that this was causing the problem. The message I was getting was an error. I found that the software was still functioning enough to let me cut out a few pages of the document at a time, paste them into a fresh document and save this new document. When I came to the box on page 189 containing the maths, I found that the computer wouldn't let me cut it out for pasting into another document. I guessed that the equation was probably the cause of the problem, so I deleted it and things were OK again.

I saved everything, shut down the computer and started it up again. I went back to the original document, split it in half, and saved it as two documents to reduce the demands on the system's memory. I then put the equation back in, deleted the temporary documents I'd created – and just carried on. I'd lost over half an hour, but I felt good about not having to go back over the editing I'd done.

This is fairly typical. The computer behaves oddly from time to time, but the consequences are seldom disastrous. There is usually some way of rescuing the situation, particularly if you make a habit of taking a few precautions. One is to set your software to save what you are working on every 15 minutes or so. (You have to balance the amount of work you are prepared to lose against the brief interruption caused by the 'auto save'.) Another precaution is to back up your hard disk at regular intervals, so that if it 'crashes' you have a copy of most of the contents. But even if your hard disk does crash, it may still be possible to rescue a lot of the contents. And if you delete something yourself, by mistake, there are ways of getting it back. So, there is no need to be nervous, to think that anything you do might cause a disaster. You might waste a bit of time occasionally, but with modern computers and software, disasters are few and far between.

Because personal computers are so new in education, and their potential so great, this chapter has been as much a tour around the possibilities as an exploration of study skills. But then one of the broader skills of the modern student is to be able to judge when and how to use a computer. To end the chapter, here is some general advice.

Hints and Tips

◆ Watch *the time*. A computer helps you to do a lot of things more efficiently, but it also has a tendency to 'eat up time'. Keep an eye on how long you spend on different computer activities. Maintain a balance with other study activities.

◆ *Work on paper as well*. If you feel uncomfortable working straight on to a computer screen, start by jotting on paper. Keep switching between working on screen and working on paper. Print your work out regularly so that you can read it 'properly' and scribble notes.

◆ *Look for a guide book*. Consider borrowing or buying a guide book to help you with your software package.

◆ *Get help*. If you get stuck, ask for help from friends, other students or your tutor.

◆ *Keep exploring*. Don't feel you have to learn everything at once. Make time to explore a new software feature now and then.

◆ *Avoid strain*. Working long hours on a computer can cause serious strain to your eyes, hands, wrists, neck or back. Position your computer and chair properly, and take regular breaks to stretch and relax.

◆ *Learn to type*. A big investment, but very worth while.

CHAPTER 8

Observing and experimenting

1 How can you spot a scientist?

'You look just like a scientist,' remarked the taxi driver as we waited in heavy London traffic. What did he mean? I immediately tried to look more 'normal'.

*A**ctivity Break* What do you think he might have meant?
What do *you* think scientists are like?

Most of us are influenced by what we see in films and on TV. Sometimes we see scientists portrayed as mad villains; sometimes they are shown as serious-minded, humourless heroes, striving to save the world; and sometimes we see them as cheerful, quirky accomplices who provide the hero with amazing escapes from impossible situations. Whatever the slant, the core image is of a person who is quite different from 'normal' people: highly intelligent, but cut off from ordinary human impulses, very systematic, driven by a single-minded devotion to scientific progress, and prepared to place logic ahead of feelings and morals. In my experience, all this is far from the truth. Scientists are as varied as any other bunch of people and, from the outside, are pretty well indistinguishable from 'normal' people. So, are scientists in any way different? The taxi driver's next question took me to the heart of the matter.

'Tell me, what is it that scientists do?'

I mumbled a half-hearted reply. It wasn't until I had paid the fare, entered my destination, the Science Museum (so *that's* how he knew I was a scientist), and had had two cups of tea to recover my composure, that a suitably concise response came to mind.

'They study the world by observing things and doing experiments.'

On reflection, I had remembered that *this* is what is distinctive about scientists – the particular thinking skills and practical skills they develop through detailed and systematic study of the physical and natural world. In other words, if scientists are any different from other people, it is to do with their training in *observing* and *experimenting*.

It was too late to pass these thoughts on to my taxi driver – or to add that technologists also share these skills and habits of thought. If only I had thought, I could have invited him to come into the Science Museum with me, so that I could have shown him what scientists and technologists really do – their endless search for new knowledge about the world and for new ways of making practical use of that knowledge. After all, the Science Museum is a treasure trove of examples – it is full of engines, pumps, rockets and computers.

Scientists, technologists and mathematicians

Technologists are set alongside scientists in this chapter, as they are equally committed to observing and experimenting. The difference is that scientists are primarily concerned with exploring the fundamental principles underlying the way the world works; technologists are primarily concerned with exploring how scientific principles can be put to practical use. In spite of this difference, scientists and technologists develop broadly similar mental and practical skills.

Mathematicians, on the other hand, are as likely to be concerned with abstract analysis as with detailed study of the 'real world'. If you are studying maths, the relevance of this chapter will depend to a certain extent on the nature of your course.

Perhaps my taxi driver was only making conversation, perhaps he didn't really want a full-blown answer to his question. But *you*, at least, should be interested, since you too will need to develop skills in observing and experimenting. You will undoubtedly acquire a great deal of information and theory from books, videos and the like. But you will not acquire a proper understanding of either science or technology until you have become steeped both in the ways of thinking and in the practical 'tricks of the trade' necessary to investigate the world for yourself. (Look back at the paragraph on 'the empirical tradition' at the beginning of Section 4 of Chapter 6 on page 175.) These skills will be explored in this chapter. They are not an optional extra – they lie at the heart of the studies ahead of you.

Key Points

◆ The distinctive thing about scientists and technologists is their commitment to careful and systematic observing and experimenting.

◆ The mental and practical skills involved in observing and experimenting are fundamental to scientific and technological understanding.

2 Observing

'Seeing is believing.' … 'The evidence was in front of my eyes.'

We place so much faith in what we see. But in science and technology, observing involves more than simply 'looking'.

---

*A***ctivity Break** Spend a few minutes looking attentively at your immediate surroundings. You'll probably see at least a few things that you didn't expect, even if your surroundings are familiar.

That patch of wallpaper is an odd colour. … When did that crack develop? … And yet you have probably looked at these same surroundings many times before. So, the amount of information you get from looking depends on how attentively you look. Observing 'with a fresh eye' increases the *quantity* of information you pick up.

But there is more to it than sheer quantity. Say you continue looking and begin to ask yourself *questions* – for example, 'I wonder what caused that dirty patch of wallpaper?' You then look more closely and *purposefully*, and what you thought was just a dirt smear turns out to be mould. So, you start to look around and you find some other patches. You then search the room *thoroughly*, and find that there are mould patches in only one corner of the room. You begin to wonder why, with the aim of doing something about them. You have already brought some *knowledge* to bear on the problem, in recognizing mould when you saw it. Now, you need to draw on more knowledge about the conditions in which mould grows, to identify the *causes* of the mould on your wallpaper.

By this stage, you are doing much more than just casual 'looking'. You are applying some of the key principles of *scientific observation*. You are:

◆ focusing on something familiar, but looking at it with *a fresh eye* (instead of assuming that you already know what you are looking at)

◆ looking closely and paying attention to *detail*

◆ *thinking* about what you see, and asking yourself *questions*

◆ looking *purposefully* (when you start searching for mould, as against gazing around)

◆ looking *systematically* (when you make your thorough search of the room)

◆ guiding your looking according to your *existing knowledge* of the world (in this case, your knowledge about moulds and how they grow).

This kind of intelligent, purposeful, detailed and systematic looking is one of the cornerstones of science (alongside the use of other senses, such as listening and touching, of course). Science is based not just on large *quantities* of information about the world, but also on high-*quality* information, gathered and recorded with great care and skill. 'Observing' might sound a rather ordinary sort of activity, something we do all the time. But to a scientist, observing presents an intellectual and practical challenge of the highest order.

Key Points

◆ Observing in a scientific way involves much more than casual looking.

◆ Scientific observation involves attentive, thoughtful, purposeful, systematic and knowledgeable looking.

2.1 Getting to know your bird neighbours

There is so much 'world' to observe. How does one begin? Let's start with an example. Suppose you develop an interest in birds, and you want to know more about the birds living in your neighbourhood. So, you decide to focus on the birds that visit a nearby garden. On a casual stroll, you begin to get an idea of the good places to look. How will you identify the birds that you see? What times of day are best for observing them? You realize that, to make headway, your enquiry has to become more serious. You consult books to get your 'eye in', and begin to recognize the males, females and juveniles of different species. One morning, you notice five sparrows in the garden, but there are only two an hour later. A single magpie spends a long time by your flower beds not doing much in particular. Later that day, you see another magpie, behaving more purposefully, but you're not sure if it's the same individual. What are you to do with these observations? What use are they to you? What is it you want to know?

A local bird enthusiast tells you that song thrushes are less common than they used to be. The next day, your aged uncle claims that wrens are the commonest garden bird in the area because there are no blackbirds to drive them out. These claims interest you, but as far as you can tell they are made in the absence of any clear and objective *evidence*. So, you remain sceptical. You then start to wonder about which species of bird is most abundant in the area, but you feel unable to draw any conclusions from your casual observations thus far.

You decide it is time to become more systematic. Should you count the number of different species of bird that land in the garden at a particular time of day, within a particular time period? How long should the period be? Five minutes? Five hours? Do you give the same score to a bird that potters around the garden for ten minutes as you do to one that flies in, hops twice, and then flies off? What about 'returnees' – that is, birds that land, fly out and then come back again? Is that two visits or one? What if 'counting time' coincides with a thunderstorm one day? Should you delay counting until 'bird-friendly' conditions return?

There are no hard and fast answers to any of these questions. You have to *think logically and creatively* about the best way of making your measurements. You have to design a standard approach that 'makes sense' but doesn't make impossible demands on your time. At the front of your mind should be the *purpose* of your investigation. As a start, you invent sensible rules. For example, you will 'observe' for an hour each day from 12:00 noon, whatever the weather, and count the numbers of each type of bird that alight on any part of the garden during that time. You decide to count returnees as a single score because you are interested in the relative abundance of different types of bird. What started as a casual activity is now becoming something more structured and creative, something that begins to deserve the label of 'investigation'.

Bird censuses of this type have been organized by the Royal Society for the Protection of Birds for more than 25 years. The scheme is called the Big Garden Birdwatch. Every year about 20 000 young people throughout the UK watch their gardens for one hour during the last week of January. Each youngster counts the number of 'arrivals' of each species. The numbers are then added together to produce national averages. As a result, the combined data have a value that greatly exceeds that of any single observation. A 'top 20' list is published annually by the RSPB, showing the most common garden visitors throughout the UK. A year-by-year comparison of these lists gives us a reasonably reliable picture of the 'ups and downs' of whole populations of birds.

Big Garden Birdwatch

Starlings are the most common garden visitors in nearly all parts of the UK, closely followed by the house sparrow. Over the past 25 years, the numbers of recorded visits of all birds have gone down steadily, but the top ten visitors have not changed substantially. Song thrushes, however, are much less common, with about half the recorded number of visits in 1994 compared with 1979. Blackbirds are the fifth most frequent visitor and wrens the 19th – rankings they have held more or less unchanged since 1979. In 1995, coal tits entered the top ten. Evergreens are the favoured habitat of coal tits, and over the past 50 years conifer plantations have been maturing, especially in the south of England. This change in habitat availability may be one explanation for the rising numbers of coal tits.

We can see here how much more is revealed by organized, 'scientific' study. Gazing into the garden may be a relaxing pastime (and is useful for that alone), but it's not a *scientific* activity. A more systematic approach means that numbers can be recorded and trends revealed. Intriguing new questions spring to mind. What started off simply as 'sight' of the natural world has become 'insight' into the natural world.

Key Point

◆ Observing is a very creative aspect of science and technology. It involves:
  – deciding what are answerable questions
  – working out a 'sensible', practical approach
  – observing systematically.

The information gained from observing can set off interesting new trains of thought. For example, you might wonder whether the bird population of your garden is influenced by the types of food available. You might have an urge to go beyond mere 'observation' and put out different types of food. This enables you to begin investigating new sorts of questions; not just questions about *which* birds visit, but questions about *why* they visit. When you try to find out 'what happens if …', your thoughts are moving beyond simply observing towards that other great mode of scientific inquiry: experimenting.

3 Experimenting

Some years ago, a newspaper invited its readers to take part in an experiment that would 'change the world'. It published a picture of the hands of an acclaimed faith healer and asked its readers to place their hands on the picture at a particular time of day to experience the flow of 'healing power'. Readers were invited to write in with accounts of how the experience had eased their ills and 185 letters were received in response, all claiming that participants had, to varying degrees, 'felt better' after placing their hands on the picture.

A ctivity Break What conclusions would you draw from this 'experiment'? Write down a few thoughts.

This might look like an impressive number of cases 'proving' that faith healing works. But is it really a convincing experiment? Before we can answer this question, we need to look at the logic of experimenting.

3.1 Putting ideas to the test

The aim of an experiment is to see whether an idea stands up to testing in controlled conditions. Lots of people make claims along the lines that Granny's remedy never fails, or that wearing a lucky sweater gives them a better chance of success. And lots of other people fail to be impressed by such claims. What is taken to be clinching 'evidence' by one person may be completely discounted by another. So, are we simply left with conflicting opinions, or is it possible to agree ways of settling these disputes? Can tests be carried out that command wide respect?

Central to scientific thinking is the belief that it *is* possible to conduct tests that are widely accepted, provided that strict rules of testing are followed. One rule is that you have to be very clear about what you are setting out to test.

Thinking up hypotheses

If you want to carry out an experiment, it is generally because you have a 'hunch' that something plays a part in causing something else. Your hunch is based on your existing understanding of how the thing you are interested in works.

Let's look at an everyday example. One evening, you switch on the living-room light and nothing happens. What can you do? You have to fall back on your general understanding of things electric.

On the basis of past experience, you can think of four possible explanations. These competing explanations represent four hypotheses that could explain what you've observed.

A   *There has been a power cut in the area.*

B   *The bulb in the living-room light-fitting has burnt out.*

C   *A fuse has blown in your home.*

D   *Something has gone wrong with your living-room light-fitting.*

So, a hypothesis is simply an informed 'hunch' – an educated guess. When we talk of a number of these guesses, we talk of a number of hypotheses (note the spelling). Each of the hypotheses A to D suggests a different action on your part. But how can you tell which explanation is the right one? You don't have the experience or the equipment to test hypothesis D, so you decide to start with the other three. From hypothesis A, you make a prediction that if there is a power cut in the area, other houses in the street will also be without electricity. You can test this prediction by performing the simplest of experiments: you look around you. You can see from where you are sitting that lights are on in other houses. This undermines hypothesis A, so you turn to hypotheses B and C. You make a second prediction: if hypothesis B is correct, other lights in the house should still be working. You test this prediction by checking the hall light-switch and, sure enough, the light comes on. This is consistent with hypothesis B, but it's also consistent with hypothesis C. So, how can you decide between the two? Rather than bother to investigate the fuse box, you take the simpler option and develop a third prediction: if hypothesis B is correct, the light should work with a new bulb. You try it, and 'hey presto' – it works! So, hypothesis B wins this time.

What if the new bulb hadn't worked? Then, you would have predicted a burnt-out fuse in your main fuse box: hypothesis C. If the new bulb hadn't worked, and putting in a new fuse had made no difference, you would have suspected that hypothesis D was correct – that the light-fitting was faulty.

This example gives you an idea of how particular hypotheses can be checked against reality. A good hypothesis allows you to make predictions and then test them. Thinking of intelligent 'hunches' like these is an everyday occurrence. Your mind races through the various options. But when all the mental steps involved are written down, it becomes clear that careful, logical thinking is involved. Sometimes, as here, there may be alternative hypotheses, and particular findings take you towards or away from competing hypotheses. At other times, you may be testing a single hypothesis. In all cases, you develop a prediction along the lines of 'If that hypothesis was likely, I should notice …' When you test this prediction, the results either lend support to the hypothesis or reduce support for it. But a particular hypothesis is not necessarily completely undermined by contrary results. Suppose two light bulbs had blown independently in your house at the same time. You might have tried the hall light-switch and, finding that it didn't work, rejected hypothesis B and not bothered trying a new bulb. But hypothesis B could have been the right one – it isn't impossible for two bulbs to go at the same time, it's just unlikely. Logical thinking, prediction and testing of this type tell you less about 'the truth' than about the likelihood of particular hypotheses.

Results can either strengthen a particular hypothesis (the hypothesis is 'supported') or weaken it (the hypothesis is 'not supported'). If the counter evidence is particularly strong, a particular hypothesis may be thought of as 'wrong'. But it's rare for an idea to be completely destroyed by a single experimental result. And even the best experimental result never 'proves' something to be 'true' beyond all doubt.

Criteria and rules for testing hypotheses

We can return now to the faith-healing 'experiment'. We know that some people believe that faith healing works. And it seems that there is also a belief that people can be cured *en masse*, at a distance, through a newspaper photograph. The prediction that springs from this hypothesis seems to be that:

If people follow the prescribed procedure and touch the photograph, a significant amount of healing will take place.

This is very vague. What is to be included within 'healing'. What is 'a significant amount'? How much better do they have to feel? Would a couple of minutes of 'feeling good' count, or would they have to abandon long-standing medication? The 'experiment' also assumes that people are reliable judges of their own health and well-being. But would independent witnesses agree with their judgements? There is a lot of room for argument here.

The predictions from the 'power-cut' hypothesis were easy to test in an unambiguous way. It was obvious whether the light had come on when it was switched on, and whether next-door's lights were on. In contrast, the faith-healing 'experiment' makes no specific predictions about outcomes. Nor does it suggest any rules for observing the effects of the experiment. People are left to make whatever observations they choose. We are told that 185 people wrote in, but we do not know whether they were talking about dramatic recoveries from serious illnesses or 185 minor mood swings. So, we must have serious doubts about the quality of the 'observing' in this 'experiment'.

Key Points

- If an experiment is to be convincing, the hypothesis has to be open to unambiguous testing.

- Unambiguous testing requires clear rules for observing the outcome of the experiment.

Coping with alternative explanations

The weakest aspect of the faith-healing experiment is that it makes no effort to rule out alternative explanations. (Remember how looking at next-door's lights ruled out the 'power-cut' explanation.) We can easily think of other explanations for the results obtained by the newspaper's experiment. For example, you could put forward a 'psychological' hypothesis, arguing that some people are just very suggestible. If you told these people that their health would be improved by putting their hands on a picture of a bottle of pills, for example, many might report feeling better after doing so. The newspaper's experiment gives us no grounds for choosing between this 'suggestibility' hypothesis and the faith-healing hypothesis.

There is an even less exciting explanation you could turn to. This one argues that, in any very large group of people, on a given day, some will start to feel better and some will start to feel worse, *whatever* they do. If you assume that, say, 50 000 readers tried the experiment, you would expect a few hundred of them to feel better afterwards anyway (and expect another few hundred to feel worse). You could then argue that only those who felt better would be likely to be excited enough to make the effort to write to the newspaper. The rest would think 'Oh, well – it's just a bit of nonsense', and quickly forget about it. So, the 185 reports of feeling better could be nothing more than the outcome of random variations in how people feel, with only those individuals feeling better likely to write in.

The experiment could have been made a lot more convincing by putting a 'fake' photograph into half of the newspapers – perhaps a picture of the hands of a person who made no claim to special healing powers. Readers could be asked to quote a number when they wrote in, thereby revealing whether they had used the real picture or the fake. The readers with the real picture would be called the *experimental group* and the readers with the fake picture would be called the *control group*. The 'faith-healing' hypothesis predicts that most of the reports of feeling better would come from readers in the experimental group (that is, those who used the real picture). This result would *not* support either of the other two explanations: both the 'suggestibility' hypothesis and the 'random variation' hypothesis predict that roughly the same number of people in each group would report benefits. If the results supported the 'faith-healing' hypothesis, the evidence for that explanation would be much more compelling.

Using a control group often enables an experiment to cunningly anticipate the challenges posed by alternative explanations. This kind of creative 'thinking ahead' makes experimental work a very interesting intellectual challenge. Experiments often take quite a lot of time and effort. You don't want to rush into an experiment and produce results that can be accounted for just as easily by some other, unforeseen, explanation. You have to know what other ideas you are up against, and use your wits to try to rule out alternative explanations. This is why it's so important to plan experiments in advance – an effective experiment must be carefully *designed*.

Key Points

- A good experiment is designed to rule out alternative explanations of its findings.

- This often means making a prediction and testing it to produce results that are difficult to account for using any other explanations.

- One way of defending your hypothesis against alternative explanations of your findings is to include a 'control group' alongside the 'experimental group'.

In summary, then, the faith-healing experiment proved nothing. It certainly didn't change the world and, of course, it doesn't allow us to say for sure that faith healing never happens. The general lesson is that there is a lot more to designing an experiment than meets the eye. We should not accept what someone says just because he or she claims to have done an experiment. And we should examine all experiments very cautiously and critically to check that they are well-designed and test what they claim to test. We should check that sensible rules have been followed in making the observations. And we should check how the results have been interpreted to make sure that the conclusions are justified.

Key Point

Becoming a good scientist involves learning to be very cautious and fussy about how experiments are designed, executed and written up.

So, thinking 'scientifically' is not so much about having a huge mass of scientific knowledge or the ability to soak up information; it's more about a critical attitude of mind. Of course, you'll come across a lot of scientific 'knowledge' based on experiments that have been repeated many times and cross-checked by other scientists. So, I am not suggesting that you have to be deeply suspicious of every bit of science you meet. But you do need to get into the habit of asking questions and being sceptical. A critical approach is part of the mental skill of thinking scientifically.

3.2 Focusing your enquiry

Experimenting is not a neat, standard procedure – something you learn by heart. Experiments come in all shapes and sizes. They involve designing, fiddling about, hoping for the best, improvising, modelling, writing down data, interpreting, being heart-broken, being thrilled, changing your mind, thinking up new hypotheses and predictions, and (sometimes) giving up. This is true whether they are scientific experiments aimed at revealing more about the workings of the natural world, or technological experiments aimed at providing answers to human needs, from the building of a better mousetrap to an artificial human heart. Yet, as we have seen, all experiments must follow certain rules. One of these rules is that you should try to narrow down the scope of the enquiry as far as possible. Why is this so important?

Suppose that you are interested in whether a new drug ('Slimudown') offers any real help to people who want to lose weight. The way the drug works is well-established: it stops the digestion of starchy food – suggesting that 'you can eat as much as you like' and still shed the pounds. You manage to persuade four people to try using the drug for a month.

Sue is fit, 40 years old, of average weight, and exercises regularly. Ingmar, who was overweight, gave up junk food during the test period. Nazir is 70 years old and a very light eater. Norman went on holiday in the middle of the experiment. (In fact, Norman didn't take his pills for the whole month.) Each volunteer was weighed before and after the month-long test period. Table 8.1 shows the results of the experiment.

Table 8.1 The results of one month of using 'Slimudown'

	Initial weight	Final weight	Comments
Sue	59 kg	55 kg	'absolutely delighted'
Ingmar	98 kg	92 kg	'completely useless'
Nazir	47 kg	46 kg	'pleased to lose some weight'
Norman	88 kg	89 kg	'very disappointed'

*A*ctivity Break What conclusions would you draw from these results? Write down any doubts you have about this experiment.

You don't have to be a scientist to be sceptical of these data. Common sense tells you that the study doesn't reveal much. Here is the response of Jan, who claims to be 'hopeless at science'.

The four people are so totally different that it is impossible to draw any conclusions. As Sue is fit and looks after herself she will probably have made more of an effort. Ingmar gave up junk food, so he would have lost weight anyway. Nazir is already very light, and the older a person gets, the more difficult it is to lose weight. Norman went on holiday and didn't really participate in the experiment.

Jan is quite right. There are too many complications in this experiment. The participants vary in the extent to which they were 'overweight' at the start, in their fitness, eating habits, lifestyles and ages, as well as in the extent to which they participated in the experiment. Each of these factors that vary is called a 'variable'. And in this experiment, there are *too many variables*. The two variables you are really interested in are:

◆ the use of the drug (which varies from *zero use* before the experiment to *regular dosage* during the experiment)

◆ the participants' weights (as measured at the start and end of the experiment).

All the other variables are a nuisance. They simply complicate the interpretation of the results. You want to be able to link any changes in weight (or non-changes) to the use of the drug. But each of the other variables can also be used to explain your results. Ideally, you want to be able to rule them out.

Variables

Variables are factors that vary. In any real-life situation, there are lots of variables. In an experiment, you want as few variables as possible in addition to those you are investigating.

Eliminating unwanted variables

One way of removing extraneous variables is to choose participants that are as similar to each other as possible. If they are all roughly the same age, starting weight and so on, then these factors are no longer significant variables. Of course, this puts limits on the conclusions you can draw. If you show that the drug has little effect on 30-year-old women who are modestly overweight, you will need to do further experiments with other groups before you can generalize from your findings. Nevertheless, it is better to gather limited but clear-cut evidence, bit by bit, than it is to include everyone but end up unable to draw any firm conclusions.

Controlling for unwanted variables

In practice, it is difficult to eliminate every unwanted variable through the selection of participants. An alternative is to use the approach suggested for the 'faith-healing' experiment: you set up a control group. You examine your list of participants and divide them into two groups. (You'll need many more than four participants – although I haven't the space here to discuss the issues involved in deciding on an appropriate number.) Try to make sure that the two groups are very similar with regard to all the complicating variables (age, sex, weight and so on). Then, as far as comparisons between the two *groups* are concerned, these variables have been ruled out. You give one group the drug (or whatever 'treatment' you are testing) and give the other group something that looks exactly the same but has no effects (a substitute 'drug' of this sort is called a 'placebo').

The design of the experiment now represents a 'fair test'. The control group allows you to argue that any differences you find between the two groups at the end of the experiment are due to the drug. Of course, different experiments will require different types of controls. Indeed, as you'll see later, the variables may be so well-controlled in some experiments that a control group is unnecessary.

The general point is that the world is very complicated, with lots of different variables, all interacting with each other. One of the fine arts of experimenting is working out how to focus on just those variables that are of interest.

Is there a single scientific method?

It used to be fashionable to claim that science is unique because it uses a particular *scientific* method to approach all problems. This method involves putting forward a hypothesis, making predictions and then thinking up tests to test the validity of the hypothesis. A sceptical experimenter tries to falsify a hypothesis – he or she tries to prove that the thinking behind the hypothesis is wrong. Scientific ideas therefore have to be open to *falsification*.

Testing hypotheses is certainly important, as the examples in this chapter demonstrate. But is it all there is? In practice, scientists and technologists employ a whole host of working methods. Some follow the orthodox 'let's see by experiment if this hypothesis is falsifiable' approach, but observation alone is often very important – to astronomers, for example – and the work is no less 'scientific' as a result.

As you study MST subjects, you'll come to appreciate how diverse these subjects are – even within a single area, such as science. Geologists do things differently from chemists. Some theoretical scientists are unlikely to move away from their desks and computers. The process of creating hypotheses and setting up experiments is enormously important and a good place to start – that's why I'm spending most of this chapter on this subject – but, in reality, the methods of 'the sciences' come in all shapes and sizes. However, they all share certain qualities – especially rigour and reproducibility – that ensure that the results are widely accepted.

Key Points

♦ A well-designed experiment focuses in on just a few significant variables and enables other variables to be discounted.

♦ One way to rule out variables is to try to prevent them from entering the experiment. Another way is to use a control group.

You will be told a lot more about observing and experimenting in any course that requires you to do practical investigations. Our aim in this chapter is simply to set you thinking about experimental design, to show you how important it is to develop your practical skills and to give you a flavour of what's involved. To get a proper feel for experimental design and practice, you really need to 'have a go'. However much you read about it, you won't really grasp the point without actually doing some practical investigating. So, the rest of this chapter consists of three experiments for you to try for yourself.

4 Experimenting 'for real'

You might be wondering whether it's really worth the trouble of doing these experiments. After all, you have lots of other important things to do with your time, and probably a number of competing study tasks. Let me assure you that the experiments won't take much time. And you won't find them difficult or complicated. But doing them will be a great help to you in making 'real' all that I have discussed so far. They will launch you into the ways of thinking, the organizing skills and the practical habits that you will need to develop during your studies. A little practical experience goes a long way when it comes to rooting your understanding in solid reality and giving your insights a practical, strategic edge.

Of course, you needn't do all the experiments at once – perhaps you'll decide to do one or two now and the remainder further on in your studies. The choice is yours. In the language of Chapter 1, you have to be a 'reflective self-manager' and decide for yourself how to proceed.

Time requirements

◆ Experiment 1 should take less than 30 minutes to set up. You then leave it for a couple of days before spending another 15 minutes on it.

◆ Experiment 2 should take no more than 90 minutes.

◆ Experiment 3 should take about 30 minutes to set up. Then you'll need to spend a couple of minutes a day looking at what's happening over the next fortnight, and a final 15 minutes making your observations.

Assembling your apparatus

You should be able to find the things you need in your home or they'll be available at little cost from a local shop. Be inventive. Beg or borrow what you can't find.

Writing up your findings

There is an additional reason for doing Experiment 3. It raises important issues about how experiments are written up. And we'll use your experience of Experiment 3 to explore a number of writing skills in Chapter 9.

4.1 Experiment 1: Can washing powders eat dirt?

Initial question (sparking off the enquiry)

Is calling a washing powder 'biological' just a gimmick? The powder looks pretty much like ordinary washing power. And a washing machine hardly looks like the sort of place in which biological processes go on. Can we believe claims that washing powders actually digest dirt? Why not test them out?

Background information

Biological washing powders claim to contain various *enzymes*. Enzymes are agents of chemical change. The saliva in your own mouth contains an enzyme for digesting (or breaking down) certain types of food. Other parts of your digestive system produce different enzymes that digest other types of food.

The clothes we wear are stained by sweat and (I'll hold back on the details) other 'bodily substances'. So, dirt in clothes includes components that *could* be digested by enzymes (that is, broken down and dissolved in the washing water). We are going to focus on one of these components – proteins – that biological washing powders claim to digest. We are not going to experiment on the proteins within dirt itself, because they would be difficult to work with. Instead, we'll use a more convenient form of protein: the white of a hard-boiled egg. If we find that a washing powder works on 'egg protein', this will give us grounds for expecting it to work on the proteins in grubby shirt collars.

Hypothesis

I'll express my hypothesis as a prediction: *A solution of biological washing powder will digest (in effect, dissolve) egg white.*

But perhaps egg white is digested by a solution of *any* type of washing powder. To guard against this competing explanation, we'll need to set up a control using a non-biological powder.

Equipment

You need:

◆ one egg

◆ two clean jam-jars with blank labels

◆ about one tablespoon of a biological washing powder

◆ about one tablespoon of a non-biological washing powder

◆ two clean containers (for example, cereal bowls).

Do I do the experiments alone or with other students?
The choice is yours, but in general my advice would be to jump at the chance of working with other students. You may find that more than one pair of hands is useful, as is the opportunity to discuss your approach and your findings within the group.

Don't bother buying whole packets of washing powder just for this experiment. Try to borrow some from a neighbour. A concentrated washing powder will do, if it's what you use, but remember that the labelling on the package must include the word 'biological'.

Safety note

Avoid handling either type of washing powder or breathing them in. Neither is that dangerous, but allergic reactions are possible.

You should always take safety very seriously during experiments, even if nothing 'looks' threatening. Sometimes, you'll be instructed to wear goggles; sometimes, you'll be handling glass equipment; some chemicals are dangerous. Your kitchen may become your laboratory, but keep the worlds of practical science and food preparation apart. Don't eat or drink while you work. In Experiments 1 and 3, don't eat what you grow or process – no matter how tempting the idea of an egg and cress sandwich might be! Finally, remember the safety of others – don't leave solutions (for example, washing-powder solutions) 'hanging around' in cups. These instructions may strike you as 'over the top', but acquiring good habits now will make this type of good practice second nature when safety becomes crucial.

Scientific experiments tend to deal with complicated relationships, subtle processes and small changes, so it is very easy to get the 'wrong' result. Yet scientific knowledge advances only if people can repeat each other's experiments and get the exactly the same results. If you can't even agree about the results of your experiments, you've little chance of agreeing about what those experiments mean. So, it is often extremely important that an experiment is carried out as a very precise sequence of steps, and that the details of the sequence are written down carefully, so that other people can repeat it exactly. This sequence is known as the 'method' of the experiment.

Key Points

◆ The reliability of science rests on the ability of scientists to repeat each other's experiments.

◆ This means that an experiment has to follow a precise sequence of steps (or 'method').

◆ The method is written down so that anyone can repeat the experiment.

Three useful tips

◆ Read through the whole procedure before you start. This helps you to work out how each step fits into the whole sequence.

◆ Tick off the steps as you complete them to ensure that nothing is left out.

◆ If you have difficulty with terms like 'cm^3', or with any of the other number work and calculations in these experiments, consult the Maths Help section at the end of the book.

Method

1   Hard-boil the egg for at least 10 minutes.

2   When the egg has cooled, remove the shell and cut the egg into slices no more than about half a centimetre thick. Remove the egg yolk, so that you are left with slices of egg white. Cut these slices into six or so small cubes with sides no more than about half a centimetre long.

3   Place a tablespoon of biological washing powder into one of the jam-jars and write 'Biological' on the label. Place a tablespoon of non-biological washing powder into the other jam-jar and write 'Non-biological' on the label.

4   Add about eight tablespoons of warm water (about 120 cm^3) to each jam-jar and swirl the jars around to help dissolve the powder. (Don't expect all the powder to dissolve yet.)

5   Select six cubes of egg white of about the same size.

6   Using a spoon, place three cubes of egg white into the solution in one jam-jar and the other three cubes into the solution in the second jam-jar.

7   Cover each jam-jar with a lid, or cling-film, to prevent the solutions drying out. Then place both jam-jars in a warm place (the airing cupboard, or next to a radiator) and leave them there.

8   About two days later, empty the contents of one jam-jar into one of your clean containers and empty the contents of the second jam-jar into the other container. (Avoid handling the egg cubes or the washing-powder solutions.)

9   Examine each cube of egg white carefully. Pay particular attention to the size of the egg cubes from each jar. Write down your observations in a couple of sentences.

10   After you've completed your observations, dispose of the remaining egg white and the solutions of washing powder safely.

Not all 'student' experiments follow this 'recipe' format. You'll come across more open-ended experiments in which you have to decide for yourself what to do. However, for the moment it is important to practise doing exactly as you're told.

Results

When you wrote down what you observed about the cubes of egg white at the end of the experiment, you were *recording your observations*. The observations you recorded are now the *results* of the experiment.

Conclusions

You must now *interpret* your results. Do they support your hypothesis? Did you find a difference between the *sizes* of the egg-white cubes in the two jam-jars? If you did, were the cubes that had been in the biological powder *smaller*? This result would support your hypothesis: it is consistent with the claim that biological washing powders digest proteins. And because you had a control (the non-biological powder), you can discount the possibility that the egg white would have dissolved in a non-biological powder.

If you found that all the cubes in both jam-jars were the same size as at the start of the experiment, it suggests that neither form of washing powder has an effect on protein. If you found that all the cubes were smaller than at the start, it suggests that egg white is broken down whichever kind of washing powder is used.

I hope you *did* find that the cubes in the biological-powder solution were smaller. As the experiment has been done before, I can tell you that this is the most likely outcome. So, what if you didn't get this result? Even in the best laboratories and kitchens, disasters can happen. Here are some 'didn't-work' reactions from students doing this experiment for the first time.

- ◆ 'I was *disgusted* – nothing happened to any of my egg cubes.'
- ◆ 'I was *baffled* – the cubes in the non-biological washing powder were smaller than the others.'
- ◆ 'I was *heart-broken* – the liquids dried up and left a gungy mess.'

Now I'll pass on something straight out of my favourite book: *1001 Ways to Smile Through Life*. The only way to respond to failure is to learn from it. First, look back and check that you did everything 'as instructed'. Did you make the egg cubes small enough? (This might explain the 'disgusted' outcome: the enzyme needs to get at the egg white. If the portions are too chunky, there isn't enough egg white on the exposed surfaces to allow the enzyme to work.) 'Baffled' confused the two jam-jars (he hadn't used labels). 'Heart-broken' wanted a quick result and picked an oven as her 'warm place'. When an enzyme solution is cooked, as opposed to warmed, it no longer acts as effectively. (But if the solutions are not warm enough, the enzyme acts too slowly to exert any significant effect.)

Troubleshooting is always the first step when things go wrong. The second step is to do the experiment again. This time, you vary the procedure in some way – for example, use a different sample of biological washing powder, or choose a warmer or cooler place in which to store the solutions. See what happens if you use another type of control: this time, with the egg cubes kept in just water. Changing one step in the process is better than changing many things – it makes it easier to identify the problem (and is another example of restricting the number of 'variables').

If you found no difference in size between the cubes of egg, and troubleshooting hasn't identified an obvious problem, the result remains unexplained – which isn't the same as saying that it's wrong. This can be frustrating, but it isn't the same as failure. There's probably a logical reason, although it may be unknown to you. If both batches of egg cubes are smaller, it may be that your particular non-biological powder contains other ingredients that have an effect on egg white. What if the egg cubes in biological powder are no smaller? Some biological powders contain fat-splitting enzymes that don't act against proteins. Egg white contains little fat, so perhaps these new biological powders have little effect. (Most biological powders, however, contain fat-splitting and protein-splitting enzymes.)

All this means that experimental results may perplex you, even though you carried out the experiment correctly. You may be tempted to think of radical explanations for your results. For example, perhaps you've discovered a new form of egg white, one not made of protein (it's unlikely!). In general, when you don't get the 'expected' results, you suspect your execution of the experiment before you set out to challenge the scientific establishment.

Why 'experiment' when you already know the results you're supposed to get?

'Real' experiments are genuine leaps in the dark – the outcome is always uncertain. Most of the 'experiments' you'll do as a beginning student have a 'desired' outcome, but they are still worth doing.

◆ They develop the thinking skills that help to build up a 'scientific frame of mind'. (You spend time planning, observing, evaluating, drawing conclusions, considering alternative hypotheses, and so on.)

◆ 'Hands-on' experience develops practical skills, accuracy and attention to detail – all part of the 'craft' of the subject.

Scientific experimenting is a highly skilled activity. Everyone begins by learning to *replicate* experiments established by experts. When you can do this consistently, you are ready to convince other people with your own experiments.

Following an established procedure does not turn you into a robot. Intelligent observation leads to creative thinking. Did new questions come to you during the experiment you have just done, or when you looked at the results? Did you wonder …

◆ Why are some people allergic to biological washing powder?

◆ How is washing powder made, and from what raw materials?

◆ Who invented washing powder?

◆ If I'd left the jam-jars longer, would the egg cubes in the biological washing powder have disappeared altogether?

If these experiments lead you to new questions, the exercise has been a success. Another component of your mental 'tool kit' is in place: curiosity. And curiosity is just as important in studying MST subjects as a critical frame of mind or the ability to learn 'facts'. It can lead you to expand your knowledge by chasing up answers in books, newspapers or experiments of your own. Answers to all the questions listed above are known.

Key Points

◆ The observations you record are called the *results* of the experiment.

◆ The results have to be interpreted very carefully to see whether they support the hypothesis.

◆ When experiments 'go wrong', you should go over what you did, step by step, to see if you can spot the problem.

◆ If the results cannot be readily explained, you should repeat the experiment to see if the outcome is the same.

◆ Replicating results that are well-established plays a very important part in building experimenting skills.

◆ Good experiments should prompt fresh insights and raise new questions.

4.2 Experiment 2:
How do pendulums keep time?

Experiment 1 required you to make a general judgement, 'by eye', of the sizes of cubes of egg white. Experiment 2 develops your skill in making more precise, *quantitative* measurements.

Initial question

I've always wanted a grandfather clock and, as luck would have it, I was able to buy one at a recent sale. Although it was still working, I found it gained ten minutes a day. I knew the pendulum made the clock keep steady time. So, I guessed I should make the pendulum swing more slowly. But how? Make it longer? Make it heavier? Try to make it swing further from side to side? What would you suggest?

Background information

The distance a pendulum travels from side to side is known as the *amplitude* of its swing. The time a pendulum takes to swing from one side to the other *and back again* is known as its *period*. So, if I want the pendulum to swing more slowly, I want to increase its period.

Hypotheses

I came up with three hypotheses, each in the form of a prediction.

1   *A longer pendulum will have a longer period.*

2   *A heavier pendulum will have a longer period.*

3   *An increase in the amplitude of the swing will increase the period.*

Equipment

We can test these predictions quickly by means of another improvised experiment involving no special equipment. You'll need:

◆ three lengths of string: one about 1.2 metres long, one about 70 centimetres long and one about 50 centimetres long

◆ two small, heavy objects, one heavier than the other (two bunches of keys are ideal)

◆ a watch with a second-hand (better still, a stopwatch)

◆ a note-book in which to record your observations. (This will become your Practical Notebook, a continuing record of your practical work.)

Figure 8.1 will help you to set up your apparatus.

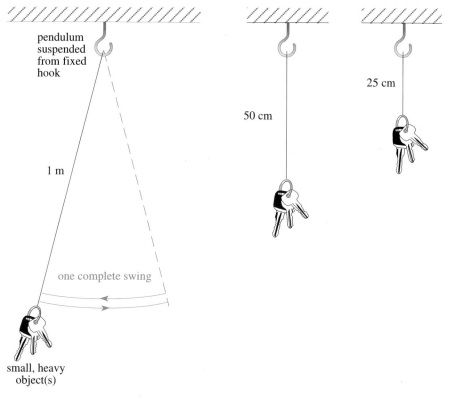

Figure 8.1

There are three points to note before you read the following method. First, there's no control; the design of the experiment allows us to discount the effects of all complicating variables (one at a time, as you'll see). Second, the full experiment involves a lot of separate steps, some of which must be repeated. You'll have to be very organized in your approach to gain a sense of the overall plan of the experiment. Remember to read through the entire method before you start. Third, if you've read Chapter 5 you'll be familiar with this experiment. In particular, you'll know something of how to present data in the form of a table. The results table here is a little more complex than the one in Chapter 5 because the full experiment involves five steps, A to E (see Table 8.2).

Method

1   Take the piece of string about 1.2 metres long and tie the *lighter* of your small, heavy objects securely to one end. (We call the weight at the end of a pendulum the *bob*.)

2   Tie the other end of the string to a fixed point, such as a hook or a door frame. Ensure that the total length of the pendulum (measured, for convenience, from the hook to the middle of the bob) is within a few millimetres of 1 metre. Make sure that the pendulum can swing freely.

3   Copy Table 8.2 into your Practical Notebook or stick in a photocopy.

4   Hold the watch so that you can see the pendulum and the second-hand at the same time.

5   Draw the pendulum about 10 centimetres to one side (that is, a displacement of 10 cm). When you are ready to start timing, let the pendulum go. Measure the time in seconds that the pendulum takes for 10 complete swings. Enter this figure under the 'First reading' heading in row A of your table of results.

6   Repeat step 5 exactly, and enter the new result under the 'Second reading' heading in row A. (The two results should be similar or identical.)

7   Add the first reading to the second reading and divide your answer by 2. Enter this new figure under the 'Average' heading in row A.

8   Divide the average by 10 and write this new figure under the 'Period' heading in row A. Give your answer to 1 decimal place (consult Section 6 of Maths Help if you are not sure what this means).

9   Untie the string and, using the same bob and the piece of string 70 centimetres long, make a new pendulum with a total length of 50 centimetres (plus or minus a few millimetres).

10 Repeat steps 4 to 8, but this time write your results and calculations in row B.

11 Untie the string and, using the same bob and the piece of string 50 centimetres long, make a new pendulum with a total length of 25 cm (plus or minus a few millimetres).

12 Repeat steps 4 to 8, but this time write your results and calculations in row C.

13 Make another 1 metre pendulum with the longest piece of string and the *heavier bob*.

14 Repeat steps 4 to 8, but this time write your results and calculations in row D.

15 Repeat steps 4 to 8 once more, but this time, at step 5, draw the pendulum *20 centimetres* to one side. Write your results and calculations in row E.

Results

Table 8.2 The results of experiments A to E

Row	Light/heavy bob	Length of pendulum (cm)	Displacement (cm)	Time for 10 swings (seconds)			Period (seconds)
				First reading	Second reading	Average	
A	light	100	10				
B	light	50	10				
C	light	25	10				
D	heavy	100	10				
E	heavy	100	20				

I have set out Table 8.2 to help you to record your results and calculations. You will usually have to work out the best way of recording and presenting results *for yourself*. Neatness and clarity are all-important. If tables are rough and ready, with lots of crossings-out, there is always a risk that values will be wrongly entered or misread (see Chapter 5).

> **Key Point**
>
> The results of experiments (your data) should be recorded neatly in a book kept for that purpose.

Conclusions

You are now ready to start interpreting your results. How well have the three hypotheses stood up to the test? Look at the hypotheses again (on page 218) and note down your own conclusions before reading on. (If it helps, compare your results with those on page 152.)

◆ You test Hypothesis 1 by comparing row A with rows B and C. Look at the figures for the period in the last column. Unless something very strange has happened, you should find that the period in row B is *less* than that in row A (in fact, it's approximately equal to the square root of the value in A). The period in row C is about half that in row A. In other words, the longer the pendulum, the greater the period. So, Hypothesis 1 is supported.

◆ You test Hypothesis 2 by comparing the 'period' figures for rows A and D. This time, you should find virtually no difference in period between the lighter and heavier bobs. So, Hypothesis 2 has not been supported.

◆ You test Hypothesis 3 by comparing the 'period' figures for rows D and E. Again, you should find virtually no difference in period between the smaller and larger amplitudes. So, Hypothesis 3 has not been supported.

Of 10 students I recently asked to try this experiment, four were surprised by the results. Common sense might suggest that a heavier bob should swing more slowly. But, as your experiment should have confirmed, neither weight nor amplitude affects the period of swing. The length is the crucial thing. This is one of those examples in which common-sense thinking doesn't lead to the correct, scientific answer (unexpected results of this sort are sometimes labelled *counter-intuitive*). We can see once again the importance of the 'doing' side of science. Things that seem 'obvious' sometimes prove not to be so straightforward.

Notes on the method

Before we leave this experiment, try to answer the following questions.

1   Why do you think I asked you to time ten full swings, rather than one?

2   Why did I ask you to repeat this measurement?

3   Why did you have to add the first and second readings and then divide by 2?

4   Why did you have to divide by 10 to get the period?

Here are my answers.

1   In timing a single swing, a lot depends on how accurately you can synchronize:

    (a)   letting go the bob with starting to time

    (b)   judging when a full swing is complete with noting the time.

    By timing ten swings, you spread any error at the beginning and end of the timing across all ten swings. So, you reduce the possible influence of this error by a factor of ten.

2/3 Repeating measurements and averaging them out also reduces the influence of errors in individual timings. In fact, if the experiment had involved a more 'messy' kind of measurement, it would have been worth repeating the measurements several more times, to cancel out the errors even more.

4   The first calculation for each row was simply to find the *average* of your two timings of ten swings. You then divided this 'average time for ten swings' by 10 to get the average time for one swing (the period).

You can see how important it is to take precautions to ensure that measurements are obtained and recorded as accurately as possible.

Now we know what I should do to my grandfather clock: I should lengthen the pendulum. And, lo and behold, it has a screw for doing just that.

Key Points

♦ Well-organized recording and presenting of data play an important part in scientific experimenting.

♦ A hypothesis that seems 'sensible' may not be supported by the results. This is why experimenting is so important to science.

4.3 Experiment 3:
Are young seedlings sensitive to light?

I'll leave you to work out the later stages of this experiment for yourself (it's an opportunity to apply what you have learned in this chapter). And, as I noted earlier, the experience gained from doing this experiment will be useful when you come to study Chapter 9.

Initial question

You've probably noticed that plants on a windowsill 'bend' towards the light. Why? How does it happen? Is it just a matter of 'leaning', or is it the way the plants grow? Is it the light itself that causes the bending, or something else? Does it always happen? These are all fascinating questions, but our hypothesis needs to start with the basics.

Hypothesis

I predict that seedlings exposed to light from just one direction will bend towards the light.

Equipment

You need:

◆ ruler and scissors

◆ three saucers

◆ some kitchen roll or blotting paper

◆ four small, empty, plastic pots – 5 oz yoghurt cartons or something similarly opaque.

◆ one clear glass jam-jar or drinking glass (about the size of a yoghurt carton)

◆ a packet of cress seeds.

·The pots should be as light-proof as possible. If you're in any doubt, wrap each pot in aluminium foil.

Method

1   Fold three sheets of kitchen roll and place one on each of the three saucers.

2   Moisten each folded paper pad with tap water, so that it is soaked but not immersed in water.

3   Sprinkle cress seeds on to the centre of each soaked pad. The patch of seeds should be small enough to fit under an inverted yoghurt pot. (About a quarter of a teaspoon of seeds per saucer will be sufficient.) The precise quantity of seeds is not critical, but try to put roughly the same amount on each pad. Don't overcrowd the seeds – there should be at least one seed's length between them.

4   Place the three saucers near a window and cover each patch of seeds with an inverted yoghurt pot. (This provides a dark, moist environment, which encourages the seeds to germinate.)

5   Take the fourth yoghurt pot and, using sharp scissors, cut a slit 3 to 5 mm wide from the top to the bottom of the carton (see Figure 8.2). Put the carton to one side for the time being.

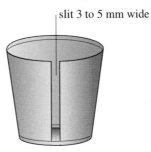

Figure 8.2

6   After about 24 hours, most of the seeds should have germinated, and the experiment proper can start. Remove one of the yoghurt pots and replace it with the pot with a slit in it. Arrange the slit so that it points towards the window. Replace one of the other yoghurt pots with the jam-jar or glass. Leave the third yoghurt pot undisturbed.

The experimental set-up should now look like Figure 8.3.

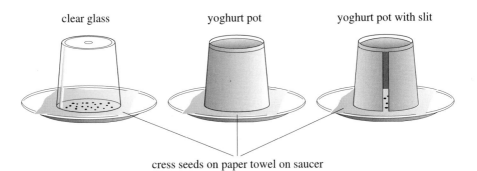

cress seeds on paper towel on saucer

Figure 8.3

Leave the cress to grow. Don't let the seedlings dry out (you may need to moisten the pads every day). You can tell how well the seedlings are doing by looking at those under the jam-jar. Resist the temptation to peep at the seedlings on the other two saucers, as this will let in light.

Make daily observations of a *qualitative* type. What do the seedlings under the clear jam-jar look like? Are they all healthy, with green leaves? Are all the seedlings roughly the same height? Write all your observations in your Practical Notebook.

You need to record the height of the seedlings under the clear jam-jar on a daily basis. How are you going to do this without disturbing them? The stems of the seedlings will be crowded together. Perhaps you could measure their height by holding a ruler next to the jam-jar, although an unsteady hand and difficulty in 'lining up' will result in a rather 'rough and ready' estimate. (How accurate do you think your seedling measurements will be? Within 2, 5 or 10 mm of the actual length?)

It will be impossible to take exact measurements of *all* the growing seedlings. It's better to measure a few seedlings to get an average. But how many is a few? You will have to wait for growth to begin to see how much variation there is between individual seedlings. If they vary greatly (say, at day 14, some are over 40 mm and some under 20 mm), then measuring a few will not give you a good measure of the 'average' height. But if the seedlings are roughly the same height, taking a small sample (perhaps about five) *is* reasonable. (This problem of *biological variation* occurs in many such experiments.)

If estimating the average seedling height is tricky, then estimating the 'extent of bending' is even more so. You'll need some way of measuring angles; if you're stuck, try to get hold of a protractor, which is a semicircle of clear plastic with angles marked around the edge. As with all experiments, the accuracy of your data will be influenced by how you set about making your measurements. You will be limited by the 'instruments' you have to hand and the time you can devote to the experiment. Don't take the quest for precision too far. Some experiments work fine by relying on 'decent-enough' estimates. Rough averages will be perfectly adequate in this case.

You'll need to judge for yourself when to stop the experiment and make your final observations. Two weeks should be enough unless seedling growth is very slow for some reason (for example, low temperatures).

Finally, a word about controls. There are two controls in this experiment: the seedlings that grow in the dark and the seedlings under glass that grow with light all around them.

One student who tried this experiment was critical of the second control. She pointed out that the seedlings under glass weren't evenly illuminated: the light came predominantly from one direction (the window). In her view, a genuine control of this type should be turned around to ensure even illumination. So, she rotated the saucer a quarter of a turn every day. How clever! Don't think that criticism of this type is in some way 'out of order' or risky. In the context of a scientific experiment, it's entirely constructive and should be welcomed. The problem needn't necessarily alter our thinking here, but it's a refinement that would be important if we were investigating the growth of seedlings in a more rigorous fashion.

Results

Your concern is the *growth* of the seedlings, so *you will need to record*:

◆ the average height of the 'jam-jar seedlings' throughout the experiment

◆ the average height of all three batches of seedlings at the end of the experiment

◆ the average extent of any bending in the seedlings, especially those seedlings under the yoghurt pot with the slit in it.

You also need to work out *how to display* your results. You want to compare the results from three conditions:

(a)   seedlings exposed to 'normal' light conditions (controls)

(b)   seedlings kept in the dark (controls)

(c)   seedlings exposed to light from one direction (experimental).

Try a rough sketch or two to see how you might arrange a table to show your results to best effect. Work out how many columns and rows you need and the title of each. (For example, one column might be labelled 'Average stem length (mm)', another might be 'Leaf colour' – combining quantitative and qualitative information in the same table.) Draw the table neatly and add your results. Could any of your results be expressed as a graph?

For the moment, I want to leave the cress seedlings, although I'm conscious that there are a good many points left for you to think about. You've probably found that the seedlings do indeed bend towards a light source from one direction (the control seedlings tending to grow straighter). So, this suggests that the original hypothesis (on page 223) has been supported. We've not addressed all the questions that first came to mind, just the particular point about seedlings bending towards the light. And doing the experiment has raised new questions: Were the control seedlings in the dark taller than the control seedlings in the light? Would the controls in the dark carry on growing if they were left there? Can you be sure that it's light and not warmth that the seedlings react to? Can the overall design of the experiment be improved (for example, by making the yoghurt pots more light-proof)? Again, as with any good experiment, one question may have been answered, but many more have been raised.

5 Conclusion

One aim of this chapter has been to develop your scientific 'thinking skills'. These skills include working out rules for observations, planning rigorous tests of hypotheses, interpreting results, drawing logical conclusions, being critical of the design and execution of experiments, and perhaps above all, thinking creatively about how to conduct practical investigations. These are powerful skills and they will be of use to you in areas far removed from science and technology.

Another equally important aim has been to develop the practical skills you need as a student of science and technology. Some of these skills are rather down-to-earth: following instructions, not knocking things over, labelling clearly, being tidy and well-organized. But I suspect that more experiments have been spoilt by sloppy organization and bad practice than by sloppy thinking. Yet doing experiments is never entirely mechanical, you have to keep using the thinking skills all the time: Why has that colour developed? What's happened to those seedlings? How can that be explained? Is this a sensible observation? At times like this, doing science is more about finding new questions to ask than finding clear answers. When things don't go according to plan – and they seldom do – asking yourself 'Why did this happen?' is especially important.

You've learnt the importance of being sceptical, of looking at ways in which experiments can be faulted. Being critical in science isn't perverse; sound experiments and good interpretations should be able to withstand criticism. But at other times, acceptance of the facts seems the order of the day. New students understandably find it difficult to marry up science's reputation for concrete facts with an encouragement to doubt everything. You'll have to learn from experience which attitude to adopt at any given time.

I started this chapter by stressing the importance of accurate *observing* – and I'll end it on the same note. Planned observations are one of the hallmarks of science and technology. You observe (normally by measurement) the effect of changing a particular variable. And as you observe, you ponder how your results can be *interpreted*. But you need to think in advance, at the design stage, about how to get as much useful information as possible regarding the hypotheses you want to test. More often than not, *controls* are required, and you'll have to judge what constitutes a sufficient *number* of measurements.

One thing on which scientists agree is the importance of practical work of the type introduced in Experiments 1 to 3. I hope you are now convinced that scientific thinking is as likely to happen in your kitchen as in the comfort of an armchair. The experimental basis of science is what sets it apart from other ways of knowing about the world. Experimenting is one of the engines that drive science forward. Experiments confirm the universality and constancy of scientific rules and relationships. Pendulums swing now as they did for Galileo, and present-day students of science from Bahrain to Birmingham can swap tables of results. Yet experiments also raise *new* questions, leading to *new* hypotheses to be tested against reality. In this way, a genuine understanding of the natural world is acquired via theories, models and laws. This is the 'exciting' science of breakthroughs and new hopes for the future. Your first steps along this path may seem small, but I hope they mark the start of an exciting and rewarding journey.

CHAPTER 9

Writing and assignments

1 Introduction

Earlier chapters have helped you with the two-step process essential to learning:

1 *taking in* information
2 *making sense* of it.

If both steps are achieved, the result is *understanding*.

When you understand something, it's intellectually satisfying. But if you are formally learning MST subjects, via lectures, texts or practical activities, others will require evidence of your hard-won understanding. You'll need to *communicate* what you know – perhaps by writing an essay, or producing a short answer to a question. In other words, you'll need to be able to write well on science subjects.

This chapter, therefore, outlines a number of practical suggestions to help you with the more technical type of writing you'll have to undertake as a beginning student. The advice I'll give has a direct bearing on the different types of writing you're likely to be set in assignments. With a few exceptions, the points I'll mention are relevant to good writing in general – the type of everyday writing you'll be familiar with. So, the chapter is concerned less with learning *new* skills than with improving skills that you very probably practise already, without ever having thought much about them.

A ctivity Break Think about the types of writing you have tried in the past weeks, for example:

◆ an instruction, such as a note to the milkman
◆ a letter to a friend or relative
◆ an entry into your diary
◆ a letter of complaint.

Briefly write down how you felt about a particular piece of writing – for example, how easy or hard you found it to do.

My own example is a monthly letter to my brother living in the USA. I remember having put the job off several times – mainly because writing a good letter takes me a long time. But when I got down to it, I had a clear picture of whom the letter was aimed at and I knew what my brother expected of me – a mix of current news, gossip, and future plans. But even with an audience that I knew so well, I needed to *think* as well as write. More than likely you did the same thing with the example you chose: namely, you had to think about the *purpose* of what you wrote and about your intended *audience*.

2 Different modes of science writing

You are probably already familiar from earlier chapters with a variety of types of MST writing. For example, mathematical 'writing' often communicates information by using *symbols* to express relationships.

This chapter is concerned with *words* and how they can be put together to get across knowledge and ideas. Less attention is paid to diagrams or to symbols and numbers, though these are all important forms of communication, as other chapters of the book make clear. First, it will be helpful to say something more about the different types of writing you're likely to come across in your early studies of the sciences; this should help you as you begin to write different types of text yourself.

2.1 The factual account of accepted knowledge

This is perhaps the most familiar type of writing in science and technology. It presents well-established information about a particular subject, explaining the underlying science at a level appropriate for the intended audience. The author is usually less concerned with presenting a particular point of view; he/she tries to report what is known and generally agreed. The following extract from the Collee article should be familiar (see paragraph 3 on page 397).

> *The term 'food poisoning' is a misnomer. A range of micro-organisms, including viruses, bacteria, fungi and protozoa, can cause such infections. The diseases that these organisms cause may arise as a result of two possible mechanisms. They may be true infections, in which the microbe gains access to the human body and multiplies within it; or they may occur when a microbe multiplies in the food, producing a **toxin**, which poisons the person who eats the food. So a better term is 'food-borne infections and intoxications'.*

The style here is fluent and the author proceeds logically from one point to another. The text is factual without being overly technical, but the reader needs enough basic knowledge of science to understand some of the terminology – terms such as fungi and protozoa. So, the author has in mind an audience with a particular level of knowledge and sees a particular *purpose* to the article.

2.2 Reporting what's been found out through observations and experiments

Libraries within universities and colleges house a wealth of technical publications in science and technology. Some of these are journals, which publish papers and letters that report the latest findings in scientific and technological research. These are so rich in specialist jargon and make so many assumptions about how much readers will already know that they are notoriously inaccessible to 'outsiders'. Clearly *audience* and *purpose* here are very different from what we saw in the Collee article.

Research papers are structured in particular ways. Almost certainly, there are sections called *Method, Results* and *Discussion*, and probably another called *Summary* (or *Abstract*). Headings of this type are evident wherever practical findings in the sciences are reported. For example, part of a student write-up of the cress seedling experiment described in Chapter 8 reads as follows. (Later in this chapter, you'll look at some of these samples of student writing rather more critically.)

Summary

It was found that with no light there is however growth, and with a directed light source the seedlings are 'forced' to grow at an angle compared to the seedlings grown under normal conditions and in the dark, there was no evidence of bending to the same extent.

Aim

The experiment was set up to either prove or disprove that light and the direction of light affects growth of plants.

Hypothesis

To see if house plants on a windowsill always seem to try to grow towards the light and if they are turned in an opposite direction they still manage to turn themselves around.

Method

Firstly the three pads of blotting paper were placed on each saucer and then watered with tap water so that they were saturated but not immersed in water. Next …

For the moment simply note that the text has a particular *structure*, as revealed by the headings. You might also say it has a particular tone of voice, in keeping with the aim of presenting a dispassionate account of 'what I did and found'. You'll know from Chapter 2 that the desire to reduce the personal element in some forms of science writing (especially in reports) is so strong that the passive voice is sometimes adopted – the three pads of blotting paper *were placed,* rather than *I placed* the blotting paper.

2.3 Arguing a point of view or a particular interpretation of results

It would be wrong to conclude from what's just been said that all science writing has to be devoid of the voice and opinions of the author. A good deal of lively and inspiring writing involves constructing an argument. However, persuasive and logical argument involves much more than simply saying what you believe – your assertions have to be supported by evidence. Let's consider an example.

Recently, I gave a student of mine the Collee article to read. Coincidentally, soon afterwards, she read a letter in a newspaper putting all the blame for the current high incidence of domestic food poisoning solely on modern techniques of food manufacturing. She believed that the problem was as much to do with sloppy kitchen hygiene as anything else, and felt sufficiently strongly about the issue to write a letter in reply, part of which is reproduced below.

To the Editor,

John Burleigh correctly insists on the highest standards of food manufacture but ignores the importance of good kitchen hygiene. Incorrect storage of food causes bacteria to multiply rapidly. Ingestion of toxins often then leads to food poisoning. For example, Staphylococcus aureus *is commonly found on skin blemishes in healthy humans, and can readily contaminate cooked meat and processed food via careless handling. If food storage is inadequate, the risks of acute poisoning (with vomiting and diarrhoea) are increased – the very old and very young are particularly vulnerable. In less than 12 hours a few bacteria can increase in number to many hundreds of millions. This alarming fact alone should remind all consumers that they share responsibility with food manufacturers for good hygiene.*

What my student's letter implies is that John Burleigh selected just those facts that suited his point of view – in other words, that his claim was partial, perhaps even biased. The counter view from my student assembled facts to make a different argument – perhaps another slanted point of view. So, it's not a case of one view being right or wrong – both authors probably agree on the facts – it's more about which facts to highlight. This is typical of many present-day disputes in science – for example, whether global warming is a reality, or nuclear power safe – and the fact that our knowledge is incomplete adds to the problem. But the key point for us is that scientific writing of this type aims to persuade by rational argument and is structured accordingly: that is, clear statements supported by *facts*.

So, what can we conclude from these few examples? They remind us of the many different forms of writing in science and technology – and writing tasks in mathematics are equally varied. So, when preparing a particular writing task, you'll need to keep the needs of a particular *audience* in mind. You should ask 'Who am I writing this *for?*' You'll also need to think about *purpose* – does this writing seek to inform, to report, or to persuade? Finally, you'll need to think about the *structure* of what you write. How can the sentences and paragraphs best be organized? These are all examples of the *thinking* aspects of writing that I mentioned right at the start of the chapter.

3 Some basic ground rules

At this point I want to identify some of the key skills involved in good writing in the sciences; I'm going to do so by outlining some basic 'dos and don'ts'. They are basic because other skills (such as organizing writing effectively) depend on them. What I say here relates mainly to the individual small ingredients of writing – the words, phrases and sentences. Think of them as the bricks and mortar that are the building blocks of writing. Later in the chapter I'll be concerned with the overall structure of writing – how sentences and paragraphs are put together to create different types of text – and at that point I'll develop the issues of audience, purpose and structure that I stressed a moment ago.

3.1 Five hints

To give my approach a clear structure – I'm practising what I preach – I'll outline five *hints* for good writing. These will include a number of useful tips and plenty of opportunity to practise, which should help you gradually build up your skills and confidence. If you are not used to writing, the approach I adopt here – moving quickly on from one potential problem area to the other – may not always suit you. You may need particular help with key aspects, such as grammar or punctuation; in which case some of the publications listed at the end of the book should be helpful.

Hint 1: Write in proper sentences

As a general rule, include a recognizable verb in each sentence. You'll know that the verb is the 'doing' word; there also needs to be something or someone ('the subject') that does the doing. Including both verb and subject is essential if what you write is to 'sound right'. What's more, verb and subject have to agree. To say, 'I placed the seeds on the windowsill' sounds right; *I* is the subject and *placed* is the verb. To say 'I places the seeds' sounds wrong because subject and verb don't match. The abbreviated 'Placed seeds on the windowsill' might be an acceptable way to record what you did in note form (see Chapter 2) but it isn't a proper sentence.

> ### *I'm a hopeless speller, and as for grammar!*
>
> Scientists have a reputation for dismissing the rules of grammar, but I don't think this is fair. Most tutors of science I know become irritated when they read text with bad grammar (or bad spelling). This is because the text becomes less easy to read and its good points are therefore less obvious. Occasional lapses of good grammar or spelling usually aren't too unsettling but if the faults are frequent or persistent, you'll need to act.
>
> Rules of grammar in the sciences are no different from those of good writing in general. To help you to identify where you're going wrong, make a list of your mistakes of spelling or grammar (ask your tutor to underline problems such as misspellings or grammatical hiccups). Look for a pattern – it's more than likely that the examples follow some kind of common thread.

Try to get into the habit of carefully reading through what you write to make sure it sounds 'right'. Reading aloud by yourself, or perhaps to a good friend, might help. Sometimes things sound wrong because the tenses of verbs are mixed. If you write in a particular tense, do so consistently; the sentence 'I placed the seedlings on the window sill and I examine them carefully each day' mixes the past and present tense.

Is it better to adopt the passive voice – 'the seeds were placed on the windowsill' – or the active form – 'I placed the seeds on the windowsill?' You'll remember from Chapter 2 that some authors favour the passive. Certainly it shifts attention away from the subject – *I* did such and such – to what is being done, be it placing, measuring or observing. But others argue that the passive voice is old fashioned and wastes words. As a student, you're likely to encounter tutors from both camps. My advice is to find out what your current tutor prefers and go along with it. Avoid the temptation to argue – what contact you do have with your tutor is better spent on matters of greater significance.

Hint 2: Make each sentence convey a single and particular point

You'll need to be flexible here; two points can be conveyed in a single sentence, but they need to be related in some way. The key part of the advice is not to write sentences that are too long and complex – they are no guarantee that what you are writing is 'good science'. Simple, short sentences are usually easier to understand.

Long sentences can all too easily become muddled. You might recall an earlier example …

It was found that with no light there is however growth and with a directed light source the seedlings are 'forced' to grow at an angle compared to the seedlings grown under normal conditions and in the dark, there was no evidence of bending to the same extent.

Too much is being said here in one sentence. Better to say:

In the absence of light the seedlings grew relatively straight. In contrast, seedlings illuminated from one side bent towards the light.

Of course, there's an important balance to strike here. A string of very short sentences can be bitty and monotonous:

The seedlings grew. Some seedlings were bending. The direction of bending was towards the light. Other seedlings did not bend.

Far better to write … *Some of the growing seedlings bent towards the light –* which is still brief. As a general rule, writing in sentences that are too short is the lesser sin; tutors quite often write critically on student texts that 'this sentence is too long', but they're unlikely to write 'this sentence is too short'.

Key Points

♦ Write in proper sentences, including a verb and subject that match.

♦ Aim for sentences that are short; ideally, each sentence should convey a single point.

Hint 3: Write sentences that are concise

Implicit in the need for short sentences is the need to say things in few words. In everyday writing and speech, using more words than we need is almost second nature, but in science writing you should avoid it.

For example, it's all too easy to use adjectives that convey a meaning that is already included in the noun they refer to; for example, 'the great majority of' (better to say more simply, 'the majority of'), or 'undesirable disadvantages' (better to say 'disadvantages'). The words 'great' and 'undesirable' in the context are redundant.

Look out for phrases that can be abbreviated to one word:

along the lines of	becomes	*like*
it being the case that	becomes	*because/since*
at some future point	becomes	*later*
due to the fact that	becomes	*because*
in the first instance	becomes	*first.*

Using too many words, or too many awkward, multisyllabled words, tends to clutter the text and reduce the impact of what you write.

Which of the following, in general, would you prefer to write:

♦ *enough* or *sufficient?*

♦ *shown* or *manifested?*

♦ *find out* or *ascertain?*

♦ *began* or *commenced?*

♦ *use* or *utilize?*

♦ *need* or *necessitate?*

I hope you feel more comfortable with the short words; they are easier to write, read and understand.

> **Key Point**
> ◆ Avoid 'redundancy', and use short words and phrases to convey your point.

For this sort of exercise, a dictionary helps a lot. Or, if you can, try using a thesaurus, either in book or computer software form. A thesaurus lists words that have the same meaning as others; that is, it lists synonyms. If I look up necessitate in mine, it lists: *need, demand, entail, involve, take, want* and *warrant*.

Sometimes words listed as synonyms have subtle differences of scientific meaning. For example, the terms *melt* and *dissolve* are common enough in everyday speech. If I look up one in my thesaurus, the other is listed, implying they are synonymous. But scientifically, this is not so; *melting* happens when a solid changes into a liquid on heating – think of ice melting. When a solid like sugar or salt *dissolves* in liquid, the particles of solid are taken up and disappear into the liquid, which remains clear – by which I don't mean that the liquid remains colourless but that it doesn't become cloudy.

In everyday life, confusing these two matters little. In a scientific account, using the wrong word would matter because those reading your account would presume (perhaps wrongly) that you don't appreciate the difference between these two processes.

Activity Break Suppose you read the following examples in write-ups of the cress seedling experiment. How would you rewrite them, to make them shorter, more accurate and free of redundancy?

1 Firstly the three pads of blotting paper were placed on each saucer and then watered with tap water so that they were saturated but not immersed in water.

2 After 24 hours one mug was then replaced by the clear glass tumbler, one mug was left unaltered and on the third saucer the plastic beaker was first covered with aluminium foil and then a 3 mm slit cut in from top to bottom and then it was placed over the cress seedlings ensuring that the slit was facing towards the window that was nearby.

3 A number of problems concerned with errors of measurement could have produced a variety of problematic results in this experiment.

4 Hypothesis: to see if house plants on a windowsill always seem to try to grow towards the light and if they are turned in an opposite direction they still manage to turn themselves around.

This is how one particular tutor changed them, adding a comment that the style needed to be more concise and 'direct'. (Your revisions are likely to be different in detail, but I think you'll agree that the following revisions are rather better than the originals.)

1   First, three pads of blotting paper were placed on each saucer and saturated with water.

2   After 24 hours one mug was replaced by a clear glass tumbler, another was left unaltered and the third was covered with aluminium foil that had a 3 mm slit cut along its length, with the slit facing the window.

3   The results were influenced by errors of measurements.

4   Hypothesis: that growing seedlings bend towards light from one direction. (Turn and bend are listed as synonyms in my thesaurus, but bending much more accurately describes what seedlings do.)

But short words may not *always* be best. Sometimes you may want to avoid repeating the same word. Looking around for alternative words has the advantage of increasing your vocabulary. Sometimes the longer word conveys your meaning better or has more impact. For example, from the last chapter you'll know that seedlings need both light and water to grow normally. You might write, therefore, that 'water alone is necessary but not enough for normal growth'. But the more commonly used phrase 'water is necessary but not *sufficient* for normal growth' is no different in meaning but strikes me as more forceful and, therefore, more memorable.

Another difficulty you'll face is knowing when to draw the line in cutting out extraneous words. Certain words may need to be present to make correct sense of what's there and to make the sentence 'flow'. Consider the phrase 'one source of error must be the accuracy to which the measurements were made'. It isn't clear which particular measurements are being talked of – mass, density, and so on. More significantly, the statement is meaningless without the words 'limited' (or 'degree of') before the word accuracy; accuracy alone cannot be a source of error. So, a better (and shorter) way of saying this is 'one source of error must be the limited accuracy of the measurements'.

Another item that you leave out at your peril is *units*. You know from Chapter 5 that nearly all scientific quantities consist of two components – one a number and the other a unit of measurement; both are of equal importance, so much so that omitting one produces a half-statement which is meaningless.

Hint 4: Write sentences that are precise

If conciseness encourages you to use few, short words, preciseness requires you to use the right words. This means avoiding ambiguity and saying what you mean.

A ctivity Break None of the following statements is incorrect, but what information is lacking? Consult the Collee article to make each more precise and informative.

1 Food poisoning happens when certain substances are produced.
2 Bacteria can multiply at rather a rapid rate.
3 Sometimes when bacteria attack food, the result is certain different types of food poisoning if the defence mechanisms of the body do not work well.
4 Bacteria produce spores within the gut.

There's the opportunity in the first statement to use the correct technical term – 'Food poisoning results from the action of *toxins*.'

In the second statement, 'rather a rapid rate' is very vague; the Collee article refers to 'a doubling of numbers every 20 minutes', which is much more informative.

In the third statement, more can be said in about the same number of words by placing events in the order in which they are most likely to occur – 'If the natural defence mechanisms (the gut and the immune systems) fail to kill bacteria that contaminate food, food poisoning can result.'

Finally, the fourth statement is a generalization; this is not true of all bacteria. And what stomach does this refer to? It's far better to indicate a particular type (that is, species) of bacteria that does so – 'Some bacteria produce spores within the human gut, for example, some types of *Clostridium perfringens*.'

What these brief examples illustrate is that using technical terms can make what you write more exact and informative, a point I'll come back to later in the chapter.

> **Key Point**
>
> Don't be afraid of scientific terms in your writing – they can help you convey particular and exact meanings.

For convenience, I've separated conciseness (Hint 3) and preciseness (Hint 4), but in practice they go hand in hand.

A ctivity Break Suppose that after reading the Collee article, you've written a piece on the same subject. Imagine you're now reading through your draft text. Rewrite each of the following to make them more concise and precise.

1 When large numbers of bacteria are taken in or ingested, this means that it is more likely that someone will become ill rather than if they had taken in just a few.

2   Food poisoning is the name given to what happens when bacteria and viruses get into a body and produce there a toxin within the food.

3   When food is stored at a temperature of below 5 °C or at a temperature which is greater than 50, bacteria can no longer survive and food poisoning can be avoided.

Example 1 is 32 words; you should be able to get it down to 20 or fewer. Some words are redundant; 'ingested' means the same as 'taken in'. The phrase 'just a few' rather hangs off the end – a few what? A better sentence is:

The chance of falling ill is greater the larger the numbers of bacteria ingested.

Example 2 can also be more direct; the phrase 'is the name given' is redundant. It's also not clear where the toxin is produced – in the body or in the food? Another problem is that it misrepresents what was in the original article, which stated that food poisoning can arise in one of two ways (either microbes gain access to the body, and subsequently produce toxins, or the toxins themselves are directly ingested in food). Example 2 highlights just one of them and muddles it with the other. Better, therefore, to say:

Food poisoning arises when bacteria and viruses produce toxins, either before or after ingestion.

This inaccuracy leads me to my final hint.

Hint 5: Report facts accurately

Example 3 is also both wordy and inaccurate, though the distortion is rather subtle. The upper temperature is 55 °C, not 50 (note too that the unit – °C – was left out). More significantly, the original author does not say that bacteria 'can no longer' survive below 5 °C or above 55 °C. He merely states that in between the limits bacteria 'multiply rapidly'. No food can keep indefinitely in the fridge. Better, therefore, to say:

Storing food below 5 °C or above 55 °C reduces the chance of food poisoning because bacterial multiplication is slowed down.

Good writing isn't easy

I hope all this good and earnest advice is not putting you off as a beginning student. Inevitably lots of dos and don'ts of this type are a little hard to swallow at first. But no-one expects a faultless performance from you – these are skills you strive for, rather than achieve in one bound. It's also true that a writing style remains a matter of individual taste. You should be reassured by the fact that even experienced authors wittingly or unwittingly sometimes 'break the rules'. If you need convincing, go through the text of this chapter. You may well find some evidence of redundancy, lack of clarity or maybe even suspect grammar. Doubtless, some sentences are constructed in ways that are not to everyone's taste. But although there's no single correct way of writing, good writing has to be 'worked at'. The less attention you pay to getting it right, the more critical and disheartening will be the comments of your tutor.

Another important writing skill is to make it clear by your choice of words whether what you say is conjecture – how things *might be* – or fact – how things *are*. For example, a student wrote in the conclusions to his experimental report that 'The seedling bent towards the light because the cells of the stem furthest away from the light grew faster than the cells adjacent to the light source.' This is a very intelligent suggestion (and, as it happens, quite close to the truth) but the tutor wrote next to it 'how do you know?' What was needed was a clear indication that this was a only a *possibility* that further work would have to investigate. So, don't be afraid to speculate if the occasion is right but choose your words carefully. This is the reason that phrases such as 'it is possible that', 'it may be' or 'this suggests' are so frequently used in scientific accounts.

Distinguishing between facts and possibilities and reporting information correctly are both important for good writing in the sciences. They help give *authority* to what is written. Indeed some forms of MST writing require authors to go one step further in the same cause and give *references* when they draw on information from other published sources. For example, other authors on food poisoning might quote (or, as it's sometimes called, 'cite') the publication by Collee at the end of their text. This would enable any reader to check that the author has reported Collee's views accurately and, if their appetite is whetted, to read more about them. I'll come back to the use of references later in the chapter (Section 5).

Why you must be your own text editor

I've already urged you to read through what you write – and I've given you the opportunity to practise this. Why is it important enough for me to repeat the point here? It goes beyond the need for good grammar; it's a way of checking the academic correctness of what you say. Not only should you ask yourself questions about what you've said, but you should also reflect on the way you've said it. Try to be gently self-critical – this will prompt you to 'edit' your own text. Does that point come across? Is that the right word? Can I say that more concisely? How is that different from what I've said before? Should I say this here or in an earlier paragraph? Asking questions of this type shows you're extending the *thinking* aspects of writing well beyond the phase of simply putting your first words on paper. Remember your overall aim – to improve the clarity, flow and impact of what you write. Getting rid of all the complicating and unnecessary bits and pieces that clutter your first efforts will identify more clearly the essential message you want to convey.

---

4 Using scientific vocabulary

As mentioned in Chapter 2, beginning students of MST subjects will be subject to a host of unfamiliar terms, some of them cumbersome and multisyllabled. Even the brave-hearted will sometimes feel overwhelmed by the demands of this new and complex vocabulary. How on earth will you be able to learn what amounts to a new language, to the point where you can use scientific terms in your writing? The answer is short but disguises a long and sometimes difficult process – *by practice and persistence*. This is how an arts-oriented student friend of mine put it, writing to me in a light-headed frame of mind, late at night, soon after starting an OU science course:

> *When I was sent the OU study texts, I straightaway thought, hang on, there's been a mistake here. I've been sent the science fiction version – it's in Klingon language, for followers of Star Trek. This wasn't the scientific plain-speaking that I expected. The terms came thick and fast – I was thick and they came fast. I was in a spin about planetary motion, knocked over by seismograms, all at sea with plate tectonics and changed forever by metamorphic rocks. This was not good for my confidence, especially because part of my first piece of written work asked for a brief account of how metamorphic and sedimentary rocks differ. So I'd be expected to use these alien words in my own writing. But once I started to write, struggling to express myself scientifically, I found that I'd learnt more than I thought from the written text, and slowly things began to make sense. Within a week or so of study, I was using many of the technical terms I'd been so scared of!*

What my friend found was that much of his apprehension of this strange new language diminished with familiarity and practice. He found that reading texts repeatedly helped, following the sort of advice given in Chapter 2. He looked to see in what particular contexts terms were used. He used a highlight pen to pick out all unfamiliar words; at least one dictionary was always at hand. But it was the need to include the correct technical terms in his writing that gave my friend the greatest spur. As he wrote:

> *I worked out that if I could use a scientific term in the right way in my own writing, this would tell me I was making progress. It's the difference between simply reading a word – just taking it in – and applying it correctly. Apprehensive I may have been but I wasn't going to let 'fear of failing' rule the day – I reasoned that it was better to have a go and learn from my mistakes, rather than duck the issue. (I know I sound so positive and determined looking back on events, but you know this was a real practical and intellectual struggle, with lots of ups and downs. This wasn't the only thing on my mind at the time.)*

Aim for a reasonable understanding of what a technical term means *before* you use it. This should widen and deepen your knowledge and help you gain confidence – but it won't happen straight away. Just like learning a foreign language, you'll need time and patience. Don't be over-ambitious; as a beginning student you should aim to become proficient in only the most basic terms – which ones these are should be made clear if the teaching materials are well-constructed.

4.1 Scientific usage against everyday terminology

There's another feature of scientific language that can cause beginners problems. This is less to do with long unfamiliar words but more to do with short, everyday ones – words such as 'force', 'energy', 'fusion', 'stress' and 'strain', 'inertia' and 'fitness'. These all have familiar everyday meanings but, rather than invent new words, the enterprising scientists of yesteryear borrowed them to apply to particular phenomena. They, therefore, redefined words for some new purpose. (Remember from Chapter 4 that mathematicians have the same problem with words such as 'power' and 'root'.) When you use such terms in technical writing, make sure it's in the proper scientific sense, not as you would use it in everyday writing. For example, you'll be familiar with the word 'force' in contexts such as 'you can't force me to follow all the advice you give me on good science writing'. A force means something quite different to a physicist – it can be precisely defined and measured. So the phrase 'this book is exerting a force on the table upon which it rests' is a world away from 'the advice in this book is given with a lot of force'.

A useful purchase

Getting into the habit of using a technical vocabulary may be a lot easier for you with a specialist dictionary to hand (and Chapter 2 noted how useful they can be). It's probably worth buying one. Almost certainly, it'll be invaluable throughout your student days, as a very useful complement to a standard dictionary/thesaurus. Of course, the terms you need will be defined in your teaching texts (and any accompanying glossaries) but it's often helpful to look up an alternative way of explaining a particular term. Don't buy a specialist dictionary until the course has begun – you'll then be in a better position to know what's required – and buy one only after you've browsed through a number of alternatives.

Importing everyday words into particular usages in science still goes on. Sometimes it makes writing more vivid and memorable but there are risks too. For example, Richard Dawkins, whose popular writing in science is a fine model of good practice, uses the phrase 'the *selfish* gene' to describe the behaviour of the chemical constituents that determine many of the features of living organisms. He's fully aware that selfishness is a moral property confined to humans, and that genes aren't really selfish. He's using the word as a metaphor – he thinks genes behave *as if* they were selfish – and he is hoping to make the idea more comprehensible (and memorable) by drawing an analogy with something familiar. But despite these good intentions, a literal interpretation of the word will mislead the reader. Therefore, this isn't a practice I recommend, especially for beginning students. Don't (as others have done) refer to your cress seedlings as 'ambitious' growers or suggest they're *'trying* to grow towards the light', or talk of bacteria as 'malevolent beasts'. Keeping what you write plain and simple will mean an occasional loss of drama but an increased likelihood of reader and writer thinking in a common language.

An apology

I'm presenting you with a bit of a quandary. I've suggested that it's *usually* better to use short words. I've urged you to use *ordinary* words to help you express yourself simply, but I've also said that *technical* terms are important in science writing. I've also said you should be watchful of how common words are applied to technical phenomena. But I can't present you with the golden rules of when long or technical words are better or a comprehensive list of what common words to watch out for. You'll have to work this out for yourself, and the learning involved will often be by trial and error. All new ventures – learning a new language or developing a new skill such as touch typing – require patience and practice. You'll find that the skill of using the right words for the right purpose develops with time and practice.

---

5 Putting it all together

Between now and the end of the chapter, I'll be less concerned with words and phrases but more with the overall planning and structure of what you write. To get you thinking on the right lines, I'll start with an analogy, although, mindful of what I said at the end of the previous section, I had better not push it too far.

Good writing has many parallels with creative cooking. Preparing a finished product doesn't involve grabbing ingredients at random from the kitchen shelves. From all the available ingredients, a selection has to be made, just as the relevant facts have to be selected for good writing. The creative skills of a good cook – for example, sifting, blending – produce something different out of the starting materials. All cooks benefit from following some basic guidelines of dos and don'ts and from following the rules in a sensible order. But no set of rules should be applied slavishly – the outcome is usually all the better for creative thinking. Both cooks and authors need to ask themselves what kind of meal is expected of them – something elaborate or something quick and off the cuff? And for what type of audience – are they preparing for the clients of the Rumblin' Tum Cafe or the Savoy?

Much of what I now want to say relates to the *thinking* aspects of writing I mentioned at the beginning of the chapter. I'll be concerned with the need to plan writing and I'll be coming back to the three important aspects of aim, purpose and structure that I introduced in Section 1. I'll also offer some practical tips to help write texts that are more logical and fluent and, therefore, easier to read.

5.1 Maintaining a flow

Let's start with a concrete example. A tutor set one of her more experienced students a writing exercise related to the seedling experiment. Part of it read as follows:

In fewer than 100 words, and using an appropriate diagram, write an account of the external structure of a 10-day-old cress seedling.

As you probably appreciate this was no easy task. The seedlings are small and require careful and detailed examination with a powerful hand lens. Nevertheless, the student felt quite pleased with his efforts – this is a complete version of what he submitted:

When the seedlings is removed from kitchen towel on which they have been growing, you can see using a lens small branched roots, which are pale in colour. There are also some small leaves, which are grouped together and are towards the uppermost part of the stem. The remnants of the seed itself is still visible, though the contents now seem empty. The seedling has the structure of a typical plant with leaves, roots and stem. The leaves are very small, as are the roots. The green colour is the result of a photosynthetic pigment called chlorophyll which is the place where the energy of light is converted into the plant's food, in addition to the nutrients getting into the material of the plant via the roots. The roots are branched and the stem is about 35 mm in length and grows up vertically from the kitchen roll.

This is 148 words long, so the clear advice given in the question was not followed. In other respects, the answer's not bad, but it could be improved.

*A**ctivity Break** Identify examples of incorrect grammar, redundancy and imprecision in the above writing exercise. Then re-write it, making your points in the same sequence as the original.

Here's one suggestion:

When seedlings are removed from the kitchen towel, the small, branched and pale roots are visible with a lens. The leaves are small and are located at the tips of the branched stem. The seedling has the structure of a typical plant with leaves, roots and stem. The empty seed is still visible at the base of the stem. The green colour is the result of the photosynthetic pigment chlorophyll which converts the energy of light into the plant's food, to supplement the nutrients absorbed via the branched roots. The vertical stem is about 35 mm in length.

This is 98 words. It's a lot better, but it could be improved even further.

*A**ctivity Break** Be critical of the *structure* of the shortened version of the student text. Could the logical flow of ideas be improved? Has the student chosen to write about the right things?

The account contains a lot of facts – the result of careful observation – but they aren't logically arranged. The first sentence talks about roots, but rather than say all that needs to be said about them here, another mention pops up unexpectedly towards the end. The next sentence suddenly introduces leaves and how they are arranged on the stem. The third sentence is more general than the others so it's more appropriate that it start the paragraph. This jumbled style makes the text less easy to read and increases the risk of confusion in the reader's mind. For example, is there an implication that the seed is green? Also, there's a greater risk of including irrelevant material. The question asks for information about structure, but much of the last part of the answer is concerned with what the leaves *do* rather than how they *look*. Do we need to be told about the removal of the seedling from the kitchen towel? Surely this is irrelevant to structure. Finally, no diagram was supplied, despite the instruction.

The student was disappointed with his mark for this exercise – just 6 out of 10. He felt that he'd put a considerable amount of work into writing it. He remembered planning to check that he'd provided all that was asked for and to read through his account (which was a first draft), but he never got round to it. That was a pity. The problems identified by the tutor were not so much the facts but how the writing flowed – how it was organized, or more accurately, how it was not organized. (Besides being over length, the other problem was the omission of the diagram, which meant that two marks were lost immediately.)

This was the suggested revision from the tutor:

The seedling has the structure of a typical plant with stem, leaves and roots (see Figure 9.1). The narrow vertical stem is about 35 mm in length, is branched and is pale in colour. The leaves are small, oval and located in groups at the tips of the stem. Each leaf is no more than about 8 mm in length. At the base of the stem is the remnant of the seed, now empty. The roots are pale and highly branched.

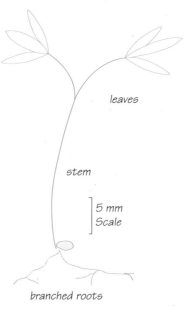

leaves

stem

5 mm
Scale

Figure 9.1 *A cress seedling*   branched roots

Note how the sentences have been reordered and a more concise style adopted. The first sentence sets the scene for all that follows. Stem, leaves and root are described in a logical order. Because there is less jumping around, the writing 'flows' much more naturally – you feel each sentence arises naturally from the one before. Move any one sentence and you risk upsetting the flow. A strong logical thread helps confine attention to just the relevant points – hence the deletion of the description of the function of chlorophyll.

Key Point

◆ To make writing flow you need a structure that allows a logical progression of related points.

Paragraphs and signposting

The seedling example should remind you of the importance of good *structure* in what you write. Because all the points here relate to the same topic (the external structure of the seedling) they form a single paragraph. If I added more information, perhaps on the reactions of the seedling to light from one direction, I'd need to begin a new paragraph.

Looks are important

There are few sights more unwelcome for a tutor than a undivided slab of text on the page, with no sensible paragraph structure. The assumption you make straight away (and more often than not you're proved right) is that a student has picked up the pen (or started to type) and just carried on, without the interruption of thought. Illegible handwriting adds to the impression. So you need to avoid giving what you write such a look – be as neat as you can, and don't make the layout of your answer on the page look too cramped, as if sheets of paper cost £1 each. Leave a decent amount of space on the page, with an obvious left-hand margin and clearly separate paragraphs. If headings are appropriate, make them stand out clearly.

Paragraphs provide an important means of structuring what you write. Two tips should help.

1   Paragraphs should group sentences that relate to the same subject. The start of a new paragraph should coincide with a change of emphasis.

2   You should reveal in your first sentence what a particular paragraph is going to be about. It provides a sense of direction and order to what you write.

For example, consider the following initial sentences from paragraphs in the Collee article:

Yet several factors may tip the balance in favour of the microbe being able to attack its new host. With some species ...

The term 'food poisoning' is a misnomer. A range of micro-organisms ...

Some bacteria cause disease by producing toxins not in food before it is eaten, but in the body of the host. The organism that causes cholera ...

In each case, the first sentence sets things up and the remainder of the paragraph develops the point. In each case, there's a clear thread of meaning flowing through.

Particular link words or phrases can act as 'glue', carrying over a clear line of argument or thought. Examples that I might use include:

Furthermore

On the other hand

But this doesn't take account of ...

Of the many factors that have an effect

This all boils down to ...

As a result

Consequently

What I'll discuss now is ...

Words or phrases of this type can link sentences, or paragraphs and so provide continuity. They often *signpost* the direction the author is planning to take.

The importance of link words

Don't think of link words as optional extras – if used well, they help communication between writer and reader. Sometimes you may be clear in your own mind what you're trying to get across – the key ideas and how they are logically linked – but you have to make this clear to your tutor. If you don't, the results are sometimes disheartening. Even the most patient tutor might offer comments along the lines of 'This paragraph rambles' or What point are you trying to make here?' or 'What's this got to do with the point on the previous page?' Link words help bring out into the open what's going on in the writer's mind.

5.2 Doing what you're being asked to do

Most likely, writing 'tasks' will be set for you, rather than self-imposed. Someone has defined, and made clear to you to a greater or lesser degree, a specification that you must follow. In their eyes, there is a particular *purpose* to the task, such as 'I want to find out how much this person knows about salmonella bacteria' or 'How careful and thoughtful has this student been in doing the cress seedling experiment?' Your job is to find out as much as possible about exactly what is expected – to identify the purpose of the assignment. Possibly, all you have to go on are the words written down in the question.

Very often there will be key phrases along the lines of 'write an account' or 'outline reasons for ...'. Very often small, modest words provide a disproportionately large clue.

---

*A*ctivity Break A to F below are instructions of the type that you are likely to encounter when you are set writing tasks. Read through them and note what you think each means. Then read though 1 to 6 and match the appropriate explanation to a particular instruction.

A criticize, B define, C illustrate, D describe, E explain, F discuss

1   Set down the precise meaning of a word or phrase, and/or examine different meanings of ...

2   Give a detailed or graphic account of ...

3   Make plain; give reasons for; interpret and account for ...

4   Identify the faults of ... (particular theories and opinions).

5   Give reasons for and against; examine by argument; sift and debate ...

6   Use figures or diagrams to explain or clarify; or make sense of using concrete examples of ...

Here's my version of the correct matches.

A and 4 – 'criticize' involves saying how convincing you find something.

B and 1 – the entry for 'define' in my dictionary includes the words 'explanation' and 'meaning'.

C and 6 – 'illustrate' also asks you to explain what something means, but by drawing on examples.

D and 2 – 'describe' implies a need to write about and say what you saw; in other words, to give an account.

E and 3 – if I was asked to 'explain' something, I'd need to go beyond description and look for reasons to account for what I saw.

F and 5 – 'discuss' implies looking at an issue from a number of angles; not just in a narrow sense of being critical, which is the sense behind A, but considering the pros and cons.

There are other words or phrases of instruction you'll come across, such as *state, list, calculate, evaluate* or *interpret*. Or perhaps you'll be asked to *précis* a piece of writing; in other words, to summarize its main points, in which case the skills you practised in Section 3 will be particularly useful. An old favourite is to *compare and contrast*. This means to set in opposition to each other, identifying similarities and differences. If just the word *contrast* was used, you'd concentrate on differences. Each time you come across words of this type you'll need to think about what is implied, given the particular context. Instructions will be embedded in phrases like:

- ◆ *describe briefly in your own words …*
- ◆ *write a definition of …*
- ◆ *explain what is meant by the term …*

These then are the *clues* to help you decide *purpose* – in the sense of what's expected of you. You'd be well advised to do exactly as you're told – no more and no less. If it's *compare and contrast*, for example, make this the core of what you write, not an incidental aside. When asked to *criticize*, the text has to contain criticisms.

There will also be key words for mathematical questions, such as *show*, *prove*, *find*, *calculate*, *write down*. The requirements for each may vary from course to course, but the precise meaning should be made clear within the teaching material.

Sometimes what you're asked to do won't be immediately obvious. For example, what if you're asked to *interpret* a particular observation? How is this different from *discussing* it? Does *criticize* mean the same as *evaluate*? Once again, there are no hard and fast answers – you'll have to use your judgement. This is all part of the important skill of interpreting questions – of working out what is being asked of you.

Picking out relevant facts

Once you've thought through what's required, you need to select appropriate material and start assembling it into a sensible order. Let's consider some examples based on the topic of food poisoning. First, suppose that, after reading the Collee article, you have to answer the following question:

Describe how food poisoning can be avoided.

The whole article contains information on much more than this single aspect – it talks of microbial growth; it identifies a variety of bacteria that can be spread by food or water; it gives information on some of the symptoms of food poisoning. All these particular topics relate to food poisoning, but they are not central to the particular aspect raised in the title. Don't feel that you've got to put them in, for completeness. You're unlikely to get marks for doing so. Even worse, their inclusion will mean you'll have neither the time nor the words to spend on the aspects central to the topic.

So, you need to pick out just the *relevant* aspects. Clearly, storing food properly is an important aspect, deserving at least a paragraph. Effective cooking of food is also important; the section entitled 'Canteen culture' contains information on the perils of keeping food warm. In the next section, there is information about salmonella and contaminated eggs.

Now that you've identified the areas you want to write about, there are two further steps. First, you have to put these particular points into your own words. Secondly, you have to construct an account that logically weaves together all the bits of information that you've decided are relevant.

The answer I've just sketched out here reflects the demands of that particular question. Different questions require very different responses, sometimes a good deal less elaborate. Suppose you'd been asked to:

State the name of a species of bacterium which is known to contaminate eggs and cause food poisoning.

All you would need do is provide the name. Any more than this would be a waste of your time and that of the person assessing your work. The answer, given in paragraph 21, is *Salmonella enteritidis phage type 4.*

Suppose you'd been asked to:

Describe briefly how eggs can become contaminated with bacteria of the type that you have named.

In this case, 'describing' requires you to give an account of events, so you need to hunt for the relevant parts in the Collee article. The ways in which eggs become contaminated are described in paragraph 22 under the heading 'Infected hens, Contaminated eggs'. First of all, the egg inside the shell may be contaminated directly as a consequence of the infection of the hen's reproductive organs – the ovaries and oviducts. Secondly, the outer shells of the eggs may carry the infection due to contamination by faeces. So, there's your answer, briefly stated.

Explain why hard-boiling eggs before they are eaten is likely to reduce the risk of food poisoning.

This involves a bit more thought. In order to provide an 'explanation', you are going to have to make links between the observation stated in the question, that hard-boiling reduces the risk, and the general discussion in the article about measures that could be taken to reduce risks. This link is not made explicitly in the article and so the question is testing whether you can use the information provided to help understand a new situation.

All these questions relate to only one aspect of the article – that of the contamination of eggs. Other questions would require you to draw in information from different parts of the article. For example, supposing the question was:

Discuss whether or not the use of antibacterial agents·in the processing of foods should be encouraged.

The answer isn't sitting ready made within the Collee article – you have to work at extracting the key information. Neither is there a right or wrong answer; you are going to have to argue the case for their use or non-use. So, evidence *for* would include a mention of the effectiveness of antibacterial agents in retarding the growth of bacteria (see paragraph 33). Evidence *against* would need to mention the development of resistance to antibiotics and the possibility of allergic reactions to antibiotics.

What the examples we've used illustrate is that responses to questions have to be tailor made. You have to identify the *purpose* of your answer and construct it accordingly. Remember to construct a response that is relevant to what you've been asked. Avoid the temptation to answer a quite different question – perhaps the one that you wish had been asked.

You may have only a very few clues as to what's expected; if you have the opportunity, ask for more. The more information you can get the better. If you have only the guidance contained in a written question, don't just read it – think about the content carefully. Ask yourself questions about the task you've been set.

Are there key words of special significance?

We've mentioned key words of instruction such as 'show', 'describe', 'evaluate' and 'contrast'. When you come across such words in questions, highlight them in some way, to remind you of their importance. Sometimes such words will already be in italics or bold type for emphasis. Try to use the same words in your answer; this will help you keep to the point and provides evidence to the tutor that what you write is relevant to the question. Suppose, for example, that having read the Collee article you are asked to write about 'the differences between botulism and salmonella poisoning'. Your answer could include phrases such as 'both bacteria', 'one difference of particular importance is ...' and 'by contrast'. If you're discussing whether or not something should be 'encouraged', phrases such as 'one potential problem' or 'one particular advantage' would convince the reader that you're on the right track. If you are asked to provide examples, then use the phrase 'for example'.

Does the question give you any guidance about how to answer?

You're rarely left completely high and dry with a writing task. Probably, the fewer words given in the instructions, the more difficult the task. If you were simply asked to 'write about food poisoning', this would be difficult because so much of the Collee article is relevant. It's almost an invitation to write all you know about the subject. As we've seen in earlier examples, it's far more likely that questions will require you to focus on particular aspects, rather than to 'write all you know about ...'. Sometimes you're given clear guidance about how to answer. Perhaps you're given a list of paragraph topics or told to refer to particular parts of your source texts. This is an enormous help to put you on the right track, so follow the suggestions in every respect.

Do I 'stick to the facts' or give my own opinions?

Make sure that your answer demonstrates your factual knowledge and understanding to best effect. If you are required to express a point of view, facts have to be quoted to support your opinion. Again, you need to look carefully at the wording of the writing task set you. You may be asked to 'justify the view that' or 'be critical of the statement that' or 'discuss the point of view that such and such is the most important feature'. As always, ask yourself: what is being asked of me? How can my answer be structured to address that particular purpose? If you decide to argue in support of a point of view, bring it clearly into the open. Opinions shouldn't be shelved until the last minute, sprung on the unsuspecting reader only in the conclusion. Remember, you'll be marked on the quality of your argument, not simply on the facts. An essay arguing that food poisoning is the greatest threat to public health might well be awarded the same high marks as one arguing that its importance as a health threat is exaggerated.

Would diagrams help?

Diagrams are nearly always useful in answering questions, and assignments often instruct you to use them. Use the context of the question to help you work out whether to copy out all or part of a diagram from the teaching text or to invent one of your own. In general, avoid slavishly 'copying out' diagrams. In most cases, it's better to modify the original diagram – for example, by simplifying it or by selecting the relevant portions. Chapter 3 has more to say about the skills involved in interpreting and producing diagrams.

Is there a word limit?

If you are given a word limit, maybe your reaction will be one of irritation – the task of counting words has to be added to the demands of writing them! And then maybe you'll have to cut out words you have spent time writing. Crazy? Perhaps, but maybe I can convince you that word limits are 'a good thing'.

First, they provide a very good indication of the depth of answer required. Writing 50 words on food poisoning needs a different approach from writing 500. It isn't constructive to say 'it can't be done in that number of words' – difficult, perhaps, but not impossible.

Secondly, a word limit is a very strong inducement for you to edit your own text, and particularly to be concise. You'd be a very unusual author if there were no words that could be cut from your first draft. Long answers are more likely to contain irrelevant material, so editing what you write will improve its quality.

Bear in mind that word limits are usually given for *guidance*. If a phrase such as 'answer in about 100 words' is used, then you've got some leeway – anything between about 80 and 120 is probably acceptable. But if it's made clear that 100 is the upper limit, you may well be penalized for exceeding it. At the very least, this is likely to trigger a warning from a tutor. Often marks are awarded for the overall quality of answers; overly long answers will probably be marked down. Sometimes, penalty marks will be specifically deducted for over-the-limit answers, though this should happen only if the question specifically draws this risk to your attention. In order to avoid nasty surprises, find out your tutor's policy on the issue.

Should I include full details of my mathematical calculations?

Broadly speaking, yes (see Chapter 4). Doing so will help you if your final answer is wrong. If you give your calculation in full, your tutor can see the problem and correct it. Normally, marks are available for each step in a lengthy calculation. You'll lose marks for the maths steps that are wrong, but gain some credit for the steps that are correct.

Can I just copy out material from my sources?

Suppose I'd been asked to 'compare and contrast botulism and salmonella poisoning', and that part of my answer read:

Both botulism and salmonella poisoning are caused by bacteria. Botulism is caused by Clostridium botulinum, *which grows only in the absence of oxygen and produces an extremely powerful and often lethal toxin. By contrast, some salmonella infections derive from the carcasses and egg shells of chickens and they are not usually fatal.*

The phrase 'grows only in the absence of oxygen' is lifted verbatim from Collee and 'the carcasses and egg shells' is almost an exact copy. But this modest usage is legitimate – it helps me get my facts right and pitch the answer at the right technical level. Besides, it's quite possible that Collee and I could have devised the odd identical phrase by coincidence. The remaining parts of my answer are expressed in my own words. However, had my answer consisted of nothing but 'lifted' phrases and a borrowed structure it would be severely marked down – and lifting is relatively easy for tutors to spot. You can understand why the practice is frowned upon. Lifting entire sections of text implies not just a lack of imagination but also a lack of understanding of the underlying science. Little wonder, therefore, that plagiarism (in other words, copying out from your sources) is seen as cheating in the academic world and is very strongly frowned upon. It isn't simply academic 'bad manners', plagiarism is theft and, in some cases, can infringe the laws of copyright.

You can avoid lifting phrases by making notes from your study texts (see Chapter 2) and refer to these as you write, rather than have the source texts open. If you feel there's a clear reason to quote text from your sources verbatim, use quotation marks and cite the reference, in a form something like ... *As Collee (1989) states, 'the term "food-poisoning" is a misnomer'* ... and give the full reference at the end of your answer, in the following style:

Collee, G. (1989) 'Inside Science: Food poisoning', *New Scientist,* 21 October, insert between pp. 56–7.

How to quote references

There are certain set rules to follow when quoting references, though they alter a little from one book to the next. Start developing good habits now, though you needn't worry about all the fine details until more advanced stages of MST study. First, give the author's surname, followed by a comma and then the forenames (or initials). Next, the year of publication (in brackets). Then give the title of the article (if applicable), followed by the book/journal title in italics. For academic journals, you need to give volume/part numbers too. For books, the place of publication is shown next followed by the publisher. Finally, give page references where possible. If the book has been edited, this is shown by using the abbreviation (ed.). Visit an academic library and look at lists of references to become familiar with the conventions

---

Should I make use of other sources besides the main texts?

This is something you should do if you can, particularly where your sources are geared to the needs of beginners in the sciences. Reading around the subject will give you new ideas and introduce you to a variety of writing styles. The schedules of full-time students usually allow a good deal of time for private study, so that the study of textbooks and journals can supplement what is learnt in lectures and tutorials. But for part-time students, of the OU for example, there are fewer opportunities for general reading, so it's assumed that their teaching texts will be the major source they call upon in their writing. As a general rule, with substantial pieces of writing, you should always acknowledge the sources you have used by writing them out at the end, following the standard convention.

At what level should I pitch my answer?

In other words, what level of knowledge should you assume in your audience? Your *audience* is, of course, usually your tutor. But students often assume that since (they fondly imagine) the tutor knows so much, only the complex ideas have to be discussed. Others go to the opposite extreme and spend so long on the elementary points that their answer never gets off the starting blocks. The best advice is to write at a level consistent with your current level of study. So, if you are studying a level 2 course or its equivalent, assume you are addressing someone with a full command of level 1 knowledge. That way you can avoid getting bogged down in what is too elementary and adopt a style and vocabulary that demonstrates an understanding of the current course material.

Should I use headings?

If you are writing up an experiment in a report, it's a good idea to use headings. Section 2 included an example of how headings indicate the purpose of different sections of the write-up of the cress seedling experiment. If you're writing a continuous piece of flowing text, headings are not normally required. (If you're set small writing tasks, each identified by number or letter – for example, Question 1(a), (b), and so on – you should always begin your answer by clearly indicating the question number it relates to. You don't need to write out the question.)

Key Points

♦ Hunt for key words in the question, and quote them in what you write.

♦ Target your writing exactly to what's asked of you.

♦ Support points of view with factual information.

♦ Remember that word limits are there to help you.

♦ Stick to the word limit; if you are warned, exceed it at your peril.

♦ Show mathematical calculations in full and include appropriate units.

♦ Use your sources for ideas and information but avoid full-scale copying.

♦ Read round the subject if you can, though opportunities may be limited.

♦ Write at a level that reflects the technical content and style of your major sources.

♦ Use headings only if the type of answer requires it; for example, an experimental write-up.

5.3 Planning what you write

With all these good intentions to hand, you're ready to 'launch forth'. But it's risky doing so without a plan. Before a journey of this type you'll need a sense of where you're going – a map.

The type of plan you sketch out beforehand is up to you. Try different sorts and see which suits you best. With a short bit of writing you'll probably jot down just a few key words. For example, a plan for the question on the difference between botulism and salmonella poisoning (see the bottom of page 251) might be no more than:

para. 1; both bacterial infections – where found

para. 2; different symptoms/effects

In general, plans are produced for your benefit rather than the reader's. Feel free to alter it, by crossing out, adding, and so on. (I'm always suspicious of plans written out in exemplary handwriting, with no sign of alteration. Chances are they've been written after the main writing, simply because a plan has been asked for.)

Plans can be diagrammatic. One approach is to sketch a series of boxes, each containing key phrases, linked together by arrows that show the logical flow of ideas – in the language of Chapter 3, this is a flow chart. Figure 9.2 is a very simple example relating to one of the questions mentioned earlier, the one that asked you to 'describe how food poisoning can be avoided'.

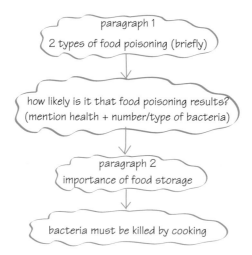

Figure 9.2 *Part of a preliminary plan*

This approach can be extended as your plan develops to produce a more complex and complete picture that reflects how your mind is drawing together different strands. This involves jotting down on paper all the ideas and terms that relate to the topic. This time the thinking doesn't have to follow a neat and linear progression of ideas. It doesn't matter if you don't get things right first time or if it looks a jumble. The whole point of the creative exercise is to let your mind range freely over the topic. Look for links between the items. Delete items that you feel on reflection are less important or irrelevant. Use colours, symbols, arrows or numbers to tidy up the map. Look for patterns and themes and how the ideas flow. Think how what you plan to write can be organized into a logical sequence of paragraphs.

What you might end up with is not very different from what Chapter 2 called a 'spray diagram', which is used in note-making to show the relationship between ideas in texts (see Figure 9.3). Here though, it's *your* ideas, and the links between them, that you'd be expressing diagrammatically.

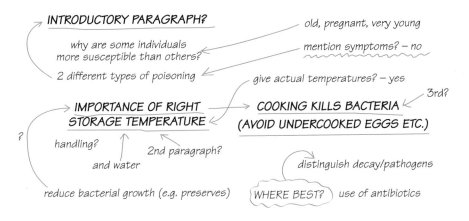

Figure 9.3 *Part of an informal spray diagram relating to 'how to avoid food poisoning'*

Whatever device you use, try to ensure that your final plan reflects the content of your individual paragraphs and the links between them.

Plans provide tangible evidence of thought and planning. Of course, don't spend an eternity on them, making them so comprehensive that you end up answering the question twice. Their purpose is threefold:

1   to clear/organize your thoughts

2   to focus on what is relevant

3   to help construct an answer that is logical and coherent in form.

Have a go at devising plans early in your studies, developing a style that suits you best. Planning what you write should soon become second nature; you'll find that it helps a great many aspects of study, including answering examination questions (see Chapter 10).

5.4 Writing essays

In the chapter so far I've emphasized different forms of writing – factual accounts, report writing and arguing points of view, and I implied that you'll have to tackle all these types in your early studies. Now I want to add another type where the good practice I've outlined is just as important – the essay.

In a standard dictionary, an essay is defined as 'a literary composition'. On this basis, most bits of writing could be termed essays. Therefore, much of what I have talked about up to now could be termed 'good essay writing'. But the term is usually used in a scientific context to refer to a continuous and substantial piece of writing (that is, 1000 words or more) that adopts a 'sandwich' model.

The word 'sandwich' is used because essays usually have three layers: an introduction; a 'filling' or main section; and a conclusion.

The introduction

An introduction is meant to set the scene. Often it's just a single paragraph, though it can be more. The aim is to get the reader tuned into the subject and to place the particular subject in a broad setting (or context). Another aim is to indicate to the reader what's to come, by announcing the approach you intend to follow. If it arouses interest in the topic, so much the better.

In the Collee article, the first paragraph grabs the reader's attention with some vivid symptoms, familiar to all of us. He then goes on to define what he means by food poisoning, revealing that there is more to the term than meets the eye. He starts paragraph 4 by announcing that this article 'will concentrate mainly on bacterial infections' and defines what he understands by the title of the article. Note that Collee doesn't take too long to get to the 'nitty-gritty', probably less than 5% of the entire article. So, with an introduction, follow four rules:

1   keep it brief
2   explain the approach you will be taking
3   sketch a broad context and then narrow down
4   present your interpretation of key terms.

Here's a concrete example to put into practice what I've said so far.

A ctivity Break Imagine you've been asked to write an essay on 'The pros and cons of using *The Sciences Good Study Guide*'. Write an introduction for this essay.

This is just one of a range of introductions I'd be pleased to read as a tutor. It follows all four of the golden rules.

Last June, once I knew I was to study technology after a gap of many years, I started to read The Sciences Good Study Guide. *I was attracted by what the cover of the book promised: 'indispensable study hints' for science study. So far, I have read six of the ten chapters – enough I think to make a preliminary judgement. In what follows, I'll describe examples of how I think the book has worked well for me, and then indicate the ways in which I think I still need extra help.*

The main section

Now for the substantial middle portion of the essay, where you develop your major points. Aim for a 'luxury' sandwich – this portion is substantial and gives both bulk and flavour to your account. Try to get views and information across in as straightforward and accessible a way as possible. Shortish, precise paragraphs help, with link words and signposting (see Section 5.1).

In an essay on this book, the middle section might be structured as follows:

paragraph 2; how Maths Help helped me

paragraph 3; how Chapter 2 prompted me to change my reading habits

paragraph 4; how much I got from Chapter 8

paragraph 5; how I learnt to find out where things are in the book

paragraph 6; what I needed more help with – grammar, assignments.

Finally, you need to round off the essay and reach a modest conclusion.

The conclusion

Conclusions should be brief; there is certainly no need to repeat what you've said before, but don't bring up a totally new point unless the groundwork has previously been well prepared. Comparing your introduction and your conclusion should reveal how the main body of the essay has moved the topic forward.

So, conclude by capturing the essence of what you're saying 'in a nutshell'. Imagine your predicament as follows. A Martian rushes into your room, desperate for particular information to take home. Two extraordinary and happy coincidences occur; the Martian understands English and the information required is on the very topic you're writing about! But alas, the alien has only the briefest of moments with you before having to rush back to the spaceship – enough for about 100 words or so. There is not a moment nor a word to lose. Your conclusion is what you communicate to the alien in your precious moments together.

In this case it might be along the lines of …

So, in many respects The Sciences Good Study Guide *has lived up to expectations. Both Maths Help and Chapter 2 were particularly useful, and Chapter 8 revealed to me for the first time the importance of the experimental approach. But, as I've described, working out 'what was where' in the book took some time. I also found that I wanted further opportunities to practise key skills. Finally, I found some chapters of the book more useful than others. So, I feel the book has helped me a lot, and I've managed to get around the minor problems I've identified. It remains to be seen how useful I'll find the book later in my technology course.*

Checking the draft

After you've written the first draft of an essay, it's a good idea to work through a checklist of questions to ensure that the essay has all the right features, in terms of both its overall structure and the fine detail. If you develop your own checklist, you can use it for all your essays, refining it as you gain experience. Where your questions identify problems, you'll need to think of solutions. There's an example checklist on page 258.

Questions	Solutions
Have I kept to the essay topic?	Cut out irrelevant material
Does the introduction clarify what I am dealing with?	Redraft to make clear what approach to take
Is the purpose of each paragraph in the essay clear?	Use preliminary sentences to cue in the paragraphs
Does my conclusion just repeat the points in the introduction?	Conclude by showing how the arguments have advanced
Is there a logical flow to the essay?	Rearrange paragraphs to ensure topics are set out logically
Have I included link words to make my intentions explicit?	Use link words (including signposting) to improve flow
Do my sentences ramble and repeat information?	Rewrite sentences so they are more concise and precise
Have I written enough/too much in the essay?	Add/delete material to achieve recommended length

Hints and Tips

Writing up experiments and projects

The usual good writing rules apply – for example, you'll need to write concisely and include only essential, relevant information. However, writing up an experiment or a small project makes extra demands.

◆ Writing to a particular structure is important – you'll need sections entitled 'summary', 'introduction', 'method', 'results', 'discussion', 'references'. Your write-up will need a title too.

◆ It's very unlikely you'll be expected to repeat information presented in the guidance notes for the experiment. It wouldn't make sense to copy out all the details of the methods, for example, just those points where you had to do something differently from the instructions.

◆ Use diagrams to show the apparatus you used, particularly if they refer to a procedure you devised yourself. Remember the 'good diagram' rules in Chapter 3. If you need extra guidance on how to draw experimental set-ups, look in your library at the drawings in textbooks on school science, and aim for the same high standards of clarity and accuracy.

◆ Present your own data neatly using tables, graphs and so on, in the 'Results' section. Don't at this stage try to interpret the results – that belongs in the discussion section. Provide headings and number each set of data – Figure 1, Table 1, and so on; and label the axes of all graphs carefully. Give clear headings to the rows and columns in tables. Use SI units throughout (see Chapter 5). Remember to explain how you made your measurements – for example, in the seedling experiment, how did you select the seedlings to measure? At random? Don't feel you have to present all the measurements you took (sometimes called the raw data).

It's often better to give average values, but say how many measurements were taken and indicate the spread of the data (as your studies progress, you'll probably be shown how to express measures such as the range and standard deviation of data).

◆ How confident can you be of the accuracy of your measurements? Use no more than the proper number of significant figures (see Maths Help on pages 349 to 352).

◆ Draw conclusions that are valid on the basis of the data presented. For example, are differences (in seedling height) significant if they are very small – such as an average of 26.3 mm in the dark controls and 25.9 mm in the light controls? You will learn more about tests of significance when you are further on in your studies. Remember to draw conclusions cautiously ... this evidence *suggests* that seedlings bend towards the light, rather than *proves*. When speculating, use phrases such as 'it may be' or 'one interpretation is that ...'

◆ In the 'Discussion' section, besides saying what you think the results mean, identify the questions that remain and suggest experiments that could help investigate them.

6 Managing assignments

'My study week was fine until the assignment deadline loomed.'

'The exercises in the text seem fine, but those in the assignments always seem so much harder.'

'As soon as I write for somebody else, my writing style goes to pieces.'

Assignments set you specific tasks, to be completed by particular deadlines. As these student comments make clear, they cause considerable anxiety. In my experience, they cause equal degrees of agitation to those who set and mark assignments. So why do we all bother?

Assignments are used for 'testing' purposes: to see what new knowledge understanding and skills you've acquired and how you can apply what you've learnt to new situations. However, it's too narrow and negative a view of assignments to see them *simply* in that light. After all, some people take tests entirely for the sake of it – piano playing or swimming, for example. They do it as a way of setting *targets* and notching up *achievements*. In addition, assignments and the feedback you may receive actually help you to think about what you're doing and how you might be able to do it better. So, being tested is not a wholly negative process. The experience is a key part of the learning process – good testing can help the process of understanding. It presents a challenge that puts you under pressure and provides an opportunity to gain constructive feedback, thereby producing very positive effects. So, feeling 'stretched' is an important part of doing an assignment – you'd gain very little understanding by answering a question that involved only copying out portions of text or changing the numbers in worked examples.

In fact, *pressure* has interesting effects when it comes to complicated mental activities. We are often able to think very efficiently under pressure. In our daily lives, our minds churn away doing the work that has to be done – thinking through the various issues that crop up, weighing things up, organizing our actions, and so on. But when we hit a deadline or crisis the whole mode of operation shifts. Our attention narrows down instantly to the matter in hand and we sift rapidly through the options. We find ways of thinking about difficult issues much more simply, and we draw conclusions that we would never be able to reach under normal circumstances. When we have time on our hands, there is always another day for thinking through the really difficult issues, but when it's 'now or never' we launch ourselves into this deeper thinking.

In the rest of this chapter, I'll outline some of the techniques that can help you improve your performance on assignments. I'll encourage you to think not just of the academic demands of assignments but also of what they require from you in terms of organization and a sense of determination – and how the stress we've just mentioned can be managed and used to good effect. The next chapter suggests how you can deal with examinations, which present their own study problems.

Key Points

♦ Assignments test not only what you have understood but also how well you can pull together the facts and ideas of a course and apply them in different contexts.

♦ The stress created by doing assignments is a positive force which you can harness to help you pull the course together and consolidate your grasp of it.

6.1 Types of questions asked in assignments

One of the problems you face in studying maths, science and technology is that there is a wide range of questions you may be asked to answer in assignments. These can range from multiple-choice questions that cover straightforward factual aspects of the course, to short-answer questions aimed at demonstrating knowledge and understanding in a specific area. Or perhaps a skill in a particular process is being tested, or your ability to handle deeper analytical questions, where you apply a variety of techniques in new contexts. Or maybe you're asked to write an essay or report of several thousand words that requires you to pull together the whole course, integrating different topics.

A single assignment is likely to contain a mixture of questions, aimed at different aspects of the course and testing different skills of writing or of calculation. But whatever the assessment strategy, you should be given a clear statement relating the assignment to the aims and objectives of the course and some guidance on what skills the assessment is trying to test. If you do not have such statements, you should ask for them, as they will help you plan your assignment strategy.

6.2 An assignment strategy – ten guiding points

I've already mentioned various broad types of question you might be asked – multiple-choice, short-answer – but within each category there is a huge range of approaches: It's impossible to go through each of them systematically; there are simply too many to predict. Presenting you with general guidelines, which you can adapt to particular circumstances, is likely to be far more useful. So, I'll set myself an assignment for your benefit:

Using your knowledge as a tutor and a setter of assignment questions, provide ten points of guidance to beginning students on submitting assignments in the sciences. Write each in the form of one or two concise paragraphs of advice with short headings; the account should be about 1500 words. Provide general guidance that would be useful for a wide variety of types of question.

Now I need to think how to tackle this assignment. First, I decide to *structure* my response exactly as suggested. Next, I can assume that my *audience* is already familiar with the basic aspects of writing mentioned earlier in the chapter. Finally, the overall *purpose* is to help and inform, passing on the benefit of my experience. I decide that my advice has to include not just the issues directly related to writing down answers to questions but the broader issues of organizing assignments – in other words how to plan and manage.

Here's my response.

Point 1: Decide what you hope to achieve by doing the assignment

Do you want to just pass or to do very well? This will depend on a whole host of factors. How interested are you in this part of the course? How much time do you have available to complete the questions? If you're particularly pressed for time you may be looking for a bare pass. It's unrealistic to expect that you'll always be able to give your best for all the course assignments. Sometimes, you'll have to put in less effort than you'd like, so don't be surprised if your marks reflect this. Most assessment strategies are sufficiently flexible to allow you the odd lapse. Broadly speaking, the amount you'll gain from an assignment – for example, in terms of consolidating your understanding of the course material – will be in proportion to how much time you can put into the exercise.

Point 2: Develop a timetable

You'll need to decide when to tackle the assignment. You'll probably be guided by a Study Calendar, which shows how assignments and their deadlines relate to your study texts – if one's not supplied, you should devise your own following the principles outlined in Chapter 1. Read through the entire assignment as soon as it's available. Work out what question you'll tackle and when you'll tackle it. That way, as you study relevant texts, you can think about how the content relates to particular questions. As you decide your approach, note how many marks are available for each part of each question and plan accordingly. Don't be tempted to spend a lot of time on questions that carry only a few marks.

Try to predict how long each question will take you – there should be some guidance on times in the questions. Set *realistic* targets, along the lines of ...

by Wednesday evening, I'll have finished the first draft of Question 3. This should help avoid a last-minute panic. It also helps if you slightly overestimate the amount of time you'll need; make an estimate and then add an extra third. An ideal plan would be to finish an assignment ahead of time, put it aside for a couple of days, and come back to it afresh. Of course, there will be times when the plan goes awry and so you'll be obliged to cut corners and improvise. If you don't start Question 3 until Wednesday midnight, you'll have to decide whether you rush through Question 3 there and then or adjust the plan to delay starting it until the following day. If you do get into a last-minute rush, don't be too cross with yourself – all students and authors are only too familiar with the experience. Predicaments of this sort are part and parcel of taking responsibility for your own learning.

Point 3: Scrutinize each question carefully and make initial notes

This is where you start deciding in detail how you'll do the questions. Decide what sources you are going to use. Does the question relate to a particular course element? Identify relevant material from the course text. Decide to what degree the course material will need to be adapted and placed in a particular context. Are there exercises that give you the opportunity to practise any relevant techniques? To get the ball rolling, you can start jotting some ideas down in pencil, no matter how rough and ready. Then go back to your text and begin to make notes. As you begin to plan your answer, remember the golden rules from Section 3.

Point 4: Decide how you're going to produce the assignment

I suggest you word process rather than hand write, working from the rough notes you've jotted down. If the technology isn't immediately available, think about acquiring it in future, though don't commit yourself until you know the technical specification that may be required for particular courses. Perhaps you can borrow or rent a machine to see how you get on. One of the advantages of word processing is that it's much easier to edit what you've written and much easier for the tutor to read. With a hand-written account, modifying your first draft in just minor ways can quickly lead to it looking a mess, so you tend to find reasons for leaving things as they are. However, there are risks with the free and easy frame of mind that word processing can create (Chapter 7, page 183, has more to say on this subject). Because you can chop and change, it's all too tempting to put anything down, telling yourself you'll look at it all again later on. All too easily, the text can become loose and unstructured. With longer pieces of text, the overall logic is lost because at any one time you can see no more than half a page on screen. Word processing therefore *increases* the need to edit what you write. Remember to use the features of your word-processing package (notably the outlining feature) that make planning and writing easier.

Point 5: Decide how your answers should be structured

We've mentioned the importance of *structure* a few times. How much text or detailed mathematical working is required and of what type? For textual answers, ask yourself if headings are required. How should the paragraphs be arranged? Are you producing a factual account or arguing a point of view? With longer bits of writing, this is the time to write a clear plan. My advice is to include this when submitting your full answer to your tutor – indeed sometimes you may be specifically instructed to do so. Ask yourself if it's appropriate to include graphs, tables, equations (either mathematical or chemical) and, if so, how many and where? For mathematical questions, think carefully about what you can assume and what you are asked to show. With all types of question, always ask yourself: what is the most effective means of communicating what I want to say?

Point 6: Write your draft in conditions conducive to concentration

Once you're able to concentrate, the thinking aspects of answering the questions become more achievable. Make sure the sources and accompanying notes are readily to hand. Remember to pause and think about what you're writing. Reward yourself by taking a break when you have reached particular targets; for example, when you get to the end of a question.

Point 7: Edit your draft, checking accuracy and style

For text, if you're working on screen, use your spelling checker. Count the number of words. Then read through carefully and alter the wording to make things more concise and precise. (I find it easier to check through a printed copy, rather than work on-screen. It provides a welcome break from the screen, and I find I can spot problems more effectively.) Pay attention both to the fine details of wording and to aspects such as logic and flow. To check calculations, try the same example with simpler numbers or try to get the same answer by a different method. In some cases, you can check your answer by 'plugging them in' to the given equation.

Point 8: Identify the strengths and weaknesses of what you've written

When you've finished your editing and produced a final version, make your own assessment of your assignment. This will help you develop the habit of being self-critical. Which bit worries you most, and why? What's worked well? Try to put yourself in the shoes of a tutor marking your assignment as one of many others. Keep a record of your private assessment; it'll be helpful when you receive your tutor's comments. If you've remained completely stuck on any of the questions – perhaps with a series of calculations or interpreting data – write down as much as you can to explain to your tutor where you hit the problem. This will help your tutor provide appropriate feedback – it might also gain you a few marks if your thoughts are in the right direction.

Point 9: Get the assignment to your tutor by the deadline

If you've a serious problem, such as illness, holding up your study, contact your tutor immediately. Otherwise, try to ensure that your assignment is delivered in good time. If you're posting it, check everything is included before you seal the envelope; check that you've answered all parts of the assignment. Get into the habit of numbering your pages – this makes it easier for both you and your tutor to check that everything's there. Once the assignment is out of your hands, reward yourself: relax and forget about study for a while.

Contact your tutor beforehand if you're in danger of missing the deadline. If face-to-face contact is impossible, make a phone call or email – the time spent writing a formal letter is better spent on the assignment. Don't be intimidated by the prospect of the phone conversation. Assume that your tutor will appreciate that you've bothered to call and explain the circumstances. Think through beforehand what you're going to say; be direct but friendly and don't be over-apologetic (that is, don't use the word 'sorry' more than once). If you have had academic problems with the assignment, say so, with reasons that have been thought out. Don't denigrate the efforts you've made so far, either in the phone call or in apologetic letters of the type that all too often are attached to assignments. Never say or think 'it's all rubbish'; almost certainly it isn't, and you're being unfair on yourself in view of the effort you've put in.

Point 10: Read the feedback comments when the assignment is returned

Understandably, the assignment grade will be the first thing you turn to. If the grade is disappointing, try to identify the reasons, which means looking in detail at the tutor's comments. Even if you think the overall grade is fair, these comments will be invaluable to you. They indicate how well you've interpreted each question, how well you've understood and adapted the course material; also they give an insight into the tutor's thinking. Highlight examples where you've gone wrong and think how you could improve your performance next time round. If you feel deeply perplexed and aggrieved by the grade or by the comments despite studying them for a decent time (30 minutes or so), you should contact your tutor and ask for an explanation.

That's the end of my assignment. When you're in a similar position, think positively and ask what you've learnt from the experience. Identify areas where you could improve and where more practice could help. *Reflecting* on assessment on this way is an important part of the learning process.

Reflection

At the end of my assignment I've the opportunity to reflect on what I've done. I'm conscious of shortcomings – does it sound too clever or smug? Have I left lots of important things out? But there's a lot of advice and it's unwise to say too much! Also, I've spent quite a bit of time reading it through and I've benefited from the comment of colleagues. There comes a time when fiddling about with text – thinking shall I change this or add that? – becomes counter-productive. It's near enough my best effort, so I'll leave it alone and hope that the feedback is generally favourable.

6.3 Multiple-choice questions

Multiple-choice questions don't involve writing of the type this chapter has discussed so far. They usually don't require thoughts and arguments on the same scale. They tend to involve a more straightforward response – answering short questions by selecting from an array of alternatives, one of which (sometimes more) is the right answer. But a good deal of what we've already said is relevant to multiple-choice questions, so it makes sense to cover them here. In particular, they require you to think carefully about the words in the question and to ask yourself – what is being asked of me?

Another similarity between multiple-choice questions and written assignments is that both require you to look closely at the fine detail of the course texts, testing your knowledge and understanding of particular facts or your mastery of particular techniques.

Multiple-choice questions cause a considerable degree of worry to students. Usually the anxieties relate to wording – what exactly is meant by a particular question? But in general, multiple-choice questions act very much to the student's advantage, which is reason enough to approach them in a constructive frame of mind. They are useful because:

◆ they help familiarize students with the details of the course text and give practice with the methods

◆ they help pace study of the course, because they have to be completed by particular deadlines

◆ most students usually score higher marks than for written assignments.

There are specific techniques for answering multiple-choice questions, just as for written answers. Here I'll give you a flavour of what's involved, using typical formats. In each example, the answer to the question can be found in the accompanying key. Your task is to find the right answer, and this isn't always straightforward. The two questions are designed to test your understanding of various concepts or presented data in the Collee article.

In the *first question*, only one of the statements listed in the key is factually correct. To find out which this is you'll have to evaluate each statement in turn. This is going to be time-consuming if you don't know the article well, or want to check your judgements carefully, as the statements are drawn from discussions in different parts of the article. When you have found what you think is the correct one, it's very important that you carry on and look at any of the statements that may be listed further down in the key, just in case you've made a mistake with your first choice.

---

*A*ctivity Break Select from the key the only statement about the causes or effects of food poisoning that is *correct*.

Key

A Food poisoning is caused by one particular species of bacterium.

B Food poisoning can only occur when a micro-organism multiplies in food before it is eaten.

C All bacteria which cause food poisoning can be killed by pasteurization.

D Domestic animals such as pigs and sheep are as susceptible to *Salmonella typhi* as are human beings.

E Someone who has ingested only a few bacteria causing food poisoning is as likely to develop an infection as someone who has ingested a lot.

F The effects of food poisoning by, for example, *Clostridium perfringens* are generally more severe among elderly people than among people in their middle years.

The only correct statement in the key is F. It is stated clearly in paragraph 18 that the effects of *C. perfringens* are not usually severe, except among the very old, the very young and pregnant women. The remaining statements are incorrect for the following reasons.

A: in paragraph 3, it's made clear that food-poisoning infections can be caused by a range of different organisms.

B: the same paragraph points out that, in some cases, poisoning occurs when a microbe (or micro-organism) multiplies *within* the human body.

C: in paragraphs 28 and 29, we are told that, *in general*, pasteurization kills pathogenic bacteria (provided they are wet); however, certain disease-causing bacteria produce spores that resist heat.

D: in paragraph 20, we are told that *S. typhi* causes disease only in humans.

E: in paragraph 7, Collee states that someone who has ingested a large dose of microbes is more likely to fall ill than someone who has taken in relatively few.

The *second question* (in the next Activity Break) is more tricky than it seems at first sight because it's testing three different things at once.

1 Do you understand how to work out the *rate* at which bacteria can multiply under ideal conditions?

2 Can you perform basic arithmetic (with or without your calculator)?

3 Do you understand how to convert very large numbers into scientific notation using powers of 10? (See Maths Help on pages 359 to 364.)

If you fall down on any one of these then you will not be able to find the right answer in the key.

Your approach to answering this question should be quite different from that used in the first question. You will have to work out for yourself how many bacteria you would expect to have developed, convert your answer into scientific notation and then check whether an answer close to your own appears in the key. If it doesn't, then you will have to check the various stages in your calculation, including the conversion into scientific notation, to see where you have made a mistake. Even if you do find an answer that matches yours first time, you should still check your working again, in case you have made an error and then found an answer which matches yours by coincidence. Note that the question says which answer is the nearest, so your answer doesn't have to match exactly.

Activity Break If a portion of food is contaminated by a single disease-producing bacterium, and the food is then stored at around 37 °C, approximately how many bacteria might you expect to have developed after six hours? Select the answer from the key that is nearest to your own.

Key

A 5.0×10^2	B 1.0×10^3	C 2.5×10^4
D 1.5×10^5	E 2.5×10^5	F 5.0×10^5

You should have selected item E. According to the information in paragraph 27, it takes only 20 minutes (or less) for a common disease-causing bacterium to divide. The diagram on page 401 shows that, at this rate, there will be 512 bacteria after three hours, as follows.

Time (minutes)	Number of bacteria
20	2
180	512

As there are nine more periods of 20 minutes between three and six hours, you have to go through the doubling process nine more times. You might calculate this as $512 \times 2^9 = 262\,144$; or you might feel more confident calculating each by doubling individually.

Time (minutes)	Number of bacteria
180	512
200	1024
220	2048
240	4096
260	8192
280	16 384
300	32 768
320	65 536
340	131 072
360	262 144

The number 262 144 is shown as $2.621\,44 \times 10^5$ in scientific notation which is closer to E (2.5×10^5) than any other number in the key. Notice that had you relied solely on pressing the calculator 2 key the appropriate number of times, you could easily have pressed one too few 2s (in which case you might have selected item D) or too many times (item F). This reveals two important things: first, that wrong answers within keys are not plucked out of the air – they often make sense if you've gone a little wrong; second, it's worth while checking your answers, perhaps by writing them out, as I've done above to reduce the chances of minor arithmetical slips.

We've considered here just two representative multiple-choice questions, but there are limitless variations on these basic formats. With all such questions, it's important that you read your sources in detail and think through the various alternatives carefully. Sometimes the thinking has to be protracted or inspired. You're likely to have to answer a large number of brief questions; when you first work through them, miss out any you're not sure about and go back to them later. Some questions will cause you genuine confusion, often because you can't find or think of the right answer or because you're not sure what the question is asking for.

Sometimes you might be tempted to work well into the small hours puzzling over a particular quandary. Working determinedly on a point that's buzzing around your brain is admirable, but don't let this practice become to much of a habit. When time is at a premium, you should ask yourself – Is this time well spent? Only a handful of marks is likely to be at stake for a particular question. Perhaps your precious time could have been better spent getting ahead by studying your texts, or perhaps you'd be better off taking a break. My advice in dire circumstances is to take an educated guess, or if that proves impossible, reach for a pin, and make a random guess – then move on to pastures new. Always have a go at all questions; sometimes random guesses are right!

Finally, if you have the opportunity of feedback on your answers to multiple-choice questions, all the better. Perhaps you'll only be given the right answers, but you gain even more from a reasoned explanation of what's right and wrong. Try to spend some time going through it. It may be difficult to get back into the details of the questions after what may be a long gap (this can be a problem with feedback on written assignments too) but it'll be worth the effort. It represents an additional learning element on top of what you've gained by tackling the questions first time round.

Key Points

◆ Answering multiple-choice questions forces you to read your sources very carefully.

◆ Selecting the correct alternative requires you to evaluate each in turn or to work out the correct answer yourself and compare it to those listed.

◆ Check your answer carefully – wrong options often correspond to common errors.

◆ Avoid spending disproportionate amounts of time on individual questions.

7 The importance of practice

I've mentioned before that writing skills need to be developed gradually through practice. To help you with the process, look back on the hints and advice given in this chapter. You'll need to keep reminding yourself of the important points; if you practise what I recommend, you'll develop more and more good writing habits over time. It also helps if you make an effort to read different styles of writing – from newspapers and science magazines, for example. Try different styles and approaches yourself. Getting it right is certain to be a process of trial and error for you. Try to become self-critical by reflecting on what you see as the virtues and shortcomings of what you write. Take advantage of the comments made by others, notably your tutor. Don't let criticism cause you to lose heart – you can learn from mistakes.

As you struggle to reach the high standards expected, you'll experience a mix of highs and lows. You'll never feel you've cracked all the problems – the skills that we've talked of develop gradually, and even the most experienced authors feel they have a lot to learn. So, the good writing journey I mentioned at the beginning of the chapter is protracted, perhaps never ending. Anticipating what remains of the journey ahead can be daunting; sometimes you need to look back and congratulate yourself on the progress you've already made.

Looking for genuine reasons to be confident is very important. Of course, once again it's a question of balance. Excessive confidence in beginning students is unappealing to others and can be counter-productive; fortunately it's very rare. Much more common is to find beginning students believing the worst of their efforts and running themselves down – usually for no good reason. This too is unhelpful and can reduce motivation. Try to look upon writing as something that can, at least in part, be *enjoyed* – something that increases your sense of well-being and provides a strong sense of achievement. Nothing I've said guarantees that the process will be easy, but writing well presents an intellectual challenge that is both satisfying and rewarding.

CHAPTER 10

Tackling examinations

1 Why do we have exams?

Do you look forward with eager anticipation to taking exams? Probably not; studying is a stressful occupation at the best of times. But tackling exams, during which you produce work within a limited time period and under strictly supervised conditions, is not most people's favourite pastime. Indeed, you may have a lot of sympathy for the group of students we met in Chapter 1.

Sushma drank the last few mouthfuls of her coffee and looked up at the clock. She looked down at her mock exam script once more. It still had a mark of only 43% on it. It had taken her three days to do the revision. OK, it was the three days just before the exam, and she had gone to the cinema one of the evenings, but even so ... The comments from her tutor on the script did not help either – they seemed very critical and made her feel angry. She thought she had answered the question, and as for those graphs ...

Just then, Mark and Kathy walked into the cafe, bought themselves some coffee and came across to her. Sushma could see they were talking animatedly and wondered why. Then she remembered. They had had their real exam for the Microbiology course this morning.

'How did you get on, then?,' she asked. 'Dreadful,' replied Mark. But Kathy quickly added, 'The way you were talking earlier, it sounded as if you were sure you had passed.' 'Well, yes, I do think I did enough to pass,' continued Mark, 'but I didn't do enough revision and I really made a mess of the food-borne diseases question. I find examinations a real nightmare. I get so uptight about them. I would much rather do an assignment, when I have time to think and plan and consider carefully what to do.'

'I am exactly like you,' said Sushma. 'Just look at this mock exam script of mine for the Food Hygiene course, and the comments made by Dr Jones.'

Kathy picked up the script and looked through it. 'I don't know what you are worrying about,' Kathy eventually said. 'You're lucky to have had a dry run, and these are all useful comments on how you could do better. You should see what Dr Smith does, or does not do, should I say. He barely talks about the exam and never gives us a test or advice of any kind.'

'But why do we need to be put through this torture all the time?' Mark exclaimed.

So, why do you have to do exams, if they cause so much stress and disruption in your life? Why do institutions keep setting them? Come to that, why do you, as an adult student, presumably of your own free will, put yourself through courses with exams? What's wrong with just studying for its own sake?

Of course, you might say that you simply take exams out of necessity, because that's the way qualifications are usually acquired. And certainly exams are used for 'testing' purposes, just as we saw for other assignments in Chapter 9, to check whether people have learned enough to be regarded as knowledgeable on particular subjects, skilled in certain techniques or capable of applying what they have learned to new situations. However, exams do create different stresses and pressures from those associated with other assignments.

In a way, exams are devices for focusing your attention; they enable you to find the will power and energy to pull together the facts and ideas of the course into the best shape you can manage. Studying is challenging work at the best of times, so one is always inclined simply to get on with the next task and not stand back and ask: 'How does this all fit together?' Assignments usually operate at a more localized level, drawing just one section of the course into a more coherent shape in your mind. Exams have a larger job to do as they help pull the whole course together. This additional pressure is one reason why they have a greater impact on you. You may feel that with science and technology subjects there are countless facts to be learned and repeated in an exam, or that maths requires you to learn and apply many new ideas. But there is real benefit to be gained from having to take an overview, linking material from one part of the course to that in another. It may not seem like it when you're revising, but exam answers often reveal features of this type.

Another reason why exams create this pressure is that they bring an element of *performance* into the task. With most assignments you can do them *when* you choose and for *as long* as you choose, right up to the point when you have to submit them to your *own* tutor. In an exam, however, you have to perform at a specified time and place, to the satisfaction of an audience you may not know. You have to 'think on your feet' and get it right first time. This puts you under much greater pressure. But, as long as you handle it properly, you can turn this pressure to your advantage.

There are many people, such as actors, sports stars and teachers, who regularly have to perform for others. They too experience the pressures of preparing for big occasions, feeling tense and sometimes even sick. In most cases, they go on to give outstanding performances. But if the effects of stress get out of hand, they can, and sometimes do, 'go to pieces'. What you are out to achieve in your approach to exams is not total freedom from stress, but techniques for successfully *managing* and *using* stress, just as many people do in other walks of life. The aim of this chapter is to outline many of the techniques you can use to improve your performance.

Key Points

◆ Exams are devices for testing not only what you have learnt but also how well you can pull together the facts and ideas of the course and apply them.

◆ The stress created by exams is a positive force which you can harness to help you pull the course together and consolidate your grasp on it.

◆ Your aim is to find ways to 'manage' the stress and put it to good use.

2 What types of question will you meet?

One of the problems you may face in studying MST subjects is the wide range of questions you may be asked to answer in exams, just as we have seen for assignments in Chapter 9. Science and technology questions can come in any of the following forms:

◆ multiple-choice questions, covering factual or basic computational aspects of the course

◆ short-answer questions, in which knowledge and understanding in a specified area are sought

◆ questions calling for an essay or report of several hundred words, in which you can pull together large sections of the course, integrating knowledge, understanding, skills, and so on.

Maths questions usually require you to demonstrate a particular skill or understanding, by asking you either to find a solution or to show that a given result is true. In a computing exam you will usually find both types of question, some requiring you to demonstrate skills, others calling more directly on your knowledge of facts.

Any single course, and any single exam, may contain a mixture of these 'tests' aimed at covering different aspects of the course. Whatever the overall assessment strategy, though, you should be provided with a clear statement on the aims and objectives of the course and what the various assessments (assignments and exams) are actually trying to test. If you don't have such a statement, you should ask for it, as it will give you an overview of the course from which to plan your own strategy for tackling the exam. Without it you may find that you are under unnecessary pressure, or that you are spending too much time on the less significant items and too little time on the more important ones.

2.1 Multiple-choice questions

Multiple-choice questions are used in two main ways in exams. First, they may be used to test your knowledge and understanding of particular aspects of the subject concerned – for example, the combination of factors that favour the rapid growth of specified food-poisoning bacteria. Second, they allow you to demonstrate your computational skills, that is, your ability to use mathematical skills and subject knowledge to solve a problem set in a particular context – for example, estimating the number of bacteria present in a food sample left for so many hours at such and such a temperature. (See Chapter 9 for specific examples and more advice on handling such questions.) In each case, there will be several suggested answers to the question from which you have to select the correct one(s). Arbitrary guessing of the answers will score only as well as the frequency of correct answers.

2.2 Short-answer questions

In science and technology, short-answer questions are designed to test your knowledge and understanding of key ideas, concepts or facts at a basic level. Normally, you will have to state what you know about a given topic, providing specific examples to illustrate your understanding. You may need to include a diagram or simple calculation using numbers and symbols, but much of the answer will be in words. (It is particularly important to interpret the phrases used in the question correctly, as discussed in Chapter 9.) You may have to comment on material given in tables or graphs but will probably not be expected to manipulate the information further. You would be expected to spend no more than 30 minutes, and usually much less, on such questions. Although writing the answer in note form is to be avoided, the answer is less likely to need a clear structure, with section headings and so on, than is the case with an essay or report. In maths and computing, short-answer questions are very precise and usually require you to carry out a calculation (which should include workings) to show that a given result is true, or to demonstrate your understanding of the course work by, for example, predicting the output from a given segment of computer program. Normally, such questions are meant to take between five and 15 minutes.

2.3 Analytical and problem-solving questions

In many cases the heart of the question involves the extensive application of numbers and symbols to solve problems. In this case the manipulation of the information given – whether it be a mathematical equation, a chemical equation, a table of results or some raw data from an experiment as shown in Chapter 8 – is the key skill being tested. It shows that you understand what the information means and that you are able to apply it to answer a specific question or problem. The question may be short and test basic understanding, or long and test deeper understanding. In particular, many maths exams may have a selection of 30-minute, long-answer questions requiring you to work on a problem in more depth – often drawing on skills from more than one part of the course.

2.4 Essays and reports

Essays and reports are substantial answers to questions which usually need a minimum of 30 minutes, and possibly as much as 90 minutes, depending on their importance as part of the exam as a whole. Such questions are designed to test your deeper knowledge and should be presented in a coherent and logical manner, with an appropriate emphasis on the structure of what you write. You should make full use of diagrams, symbols and numbers where necessary. Sometimes, the actual question is given beforehand to allow time for preparation. So, the advice on structuring and writing answers contained in Chapters 3, 4 and 9 is particularly important.

2.5 Projects and investigations

In some cases, the examinable component of a course may be a report on a specified project or investigation. These exams are aimed at testing the full range of your skills and knowledge and, because they are usually done outside exam conditions, are more like a normal assignment. However, they require a substantially greater amount of work than a normal assignment and will often need to be done in a very constrained time period. There is also much less chance of you receiving the kind of detailed feedback you normally receive with conventional assignments.

2.6 Practical exams

In MST subjects involving a large amount of practical work there is often a need to test your practical skills and abilities. This might involve, for example:

◆ looking at, making drawings of and commenting on the samples provided, for example, electron microscope photographs or colonies of different bacteria on Petri dishes

◆ undertaking a simple and quick experiment – for example, the pendulum experiment in Chapter 8 – and reporting on the results

◆ constructing some working equipment from the material and components provided.

This does not mean simply following a recipe; it usually requires you to design and think about experiments for yourself. Although more time is taken up doing and thinking about things during practical exams, the advice about writing down your results and comments is the same as for the conventional type of exam.

3 Some myths about exams

Let's rejoin our group of students a few minutes after we last met them.

'OK, I can see we need exams, but I don't know what I'll do if I fail! Become a layabout I suppose,' said Mark.

'I don't know what you are worrying about,' retorted Sushma. 'I've seen you slaving away all hours in the Library with your notes. I've hardly done a thing and I don't understand much of what I read anyway. I see little point in taking the exam in the first place.'

'My problem is I have such a poor memory and what I do know takes me ages to write down,' Kathy chipped in.

'That's nothing,' Mark replied, 'I ...'

We'll leave them there, but do you have similar views to these or have you taken part in similar conversations? Do you agree with what they say? Many unhelpful myths have grown up around exams. We see them only from the viewpoint of the person having to tackle them and not from the viewpoint of those setting them. This is made worse by the collective distortions of generations of students who elaborate the stories as they get passed on by word of mouth. It will be helpful to begin our discussion by disposing of some of these myths.

3.1 You have wasted your time if you fail

One of the benefits of the extra nervous energy needed for an exam is that it can bring about a better result than was expected. However, focusing all your energies on the exam can also make you believe that failure or performing badly would be the worst thing that could happen to you. Of course, it's unpleasant to do less well than you hoped after committing so much time and effort. But don't get it out of proportion. Exams are not a life and death matter. Most people don't do too badly and if you have tried your best, why worry? Taking the course will undoubtedly change your views and understanding whether you pass the exam or not. Life will go on. In many cases you can have a second attempt at the exam, by which point you may be more ready because you have got further round your personal study spiral (as set out in Chapter 1). Even if you fail a second time, it doesn't mean you can't go on to great success studying other subjects. In fact, many eminent scholars have failed exams at some time in their life. So, aim to do your best, but be prepared to recognize that failure can be no more than a faltering step in your educational journey.

3.2 The exam could expose you as a fool and a fraud, showing up gaps in your education

It's common to think that you don't know enough, that there are great areas of the course that you don't understand and that the examiners will pick your answers apart, exposing your ignorance. But exams aren't like that. First, no exam can cover the whole of a course and the pressures of exams mean it's not possible to put everything into an answer in the way you might for an assignment. Second, examiners are looking to award you marks for what you have *done*, not take away marks for things you have *left out*. And last, examiners are delighted to have students pass and they usually go out of their way to seek out what is good in the answers they read, recognizing that they've been written under exam conditions without the benefit of preparation and reflection.

3.3 You should have studied everything before attempting the exam

Most students have to cover some parts of the course in much less depth than other parts. Within reason, it's not usually much use at the revision stage to worry about what you've been unable to do. It's far better to consolidate what you *have* done rather than attempt to study new material. To put things in perspective, just think about the practical constraints that apply to exams. How much can you write in a three-hour exam? It's unlikely to be more than a few pages per question, depending on how many questions there are. Equally significantly, the script marker, rather than marking you on every last detail, will be more concerned to see whether the general approach of your answer is right, whether you have made a reasonable number of key points and included some appropriate examples and whether your answer is logically structured and set out. You can make a mistake in the detail but still get good marks if the approach is right.

3.4 If you have not understood what you have read it isn't worth taking the exam

All courses should be challenging and stretch your abilities. It's quite normal therefore to feel uncertain about your grasp of some areas of course content as you approach the exam. You can be sure that other students will feel the same. A major feature of learning, as set out in Chapter 1, is that there will be certain concepts and ideas that do not make sense at first and take time to understand. Often you will have developed more of an understanding than you realize. In fact, as suggested earlier, the exam may be just what you need to spur you on to sort out some of these central issues. The aim is to use your preparation for the exam to pull things together, to make the best sense of what you have studied. But in the end it's not necessary to get everything right to do well in an exam.

3.5 The questions are not easily understandable

Your first look at a past exam paper, or even the real paper when sitting the exam, may give you cause for concern. The questions may use terms you don't fully recognize or be phrased in ways that at first seem obscure. However, most exam questions are designed to point you towards a specific topic or part of the course without answering the question *for* you (which may be in contrast to assignments where you may be given advice on how to tackle them). You have already seen in Chapter 9 how the phrasing used (for example, describe, illustrate, compare and contrast) indicates the style of answer required, while the actual terms used (for example, types of food poisoning, the sources of contamination) point to the specific aspect that needs to be covered from a much wider topic. You need to remember at all times that the exam is a test of your understanding of the course you have been studying, not of your general knowledge. So somewhere within what you have been studying lies the technique or knowledge to answer each question on the paper.

3.6 You need to prepare for the exam until you drop

The folklore of exams is full of stories of amazing last-minute efforts involving working late at night. While it's true that we are capable of extraordinary feats when the pressure is on, it is *not* good practice to leave things to the last moment, nor is it helpful or productive to make yourself tired, or upset your friends and relatives, through overwork. The answer is to do your broad planning well in advance so that by the final stages of the course you have clear-cut strategies already worked out for tackling the revision, for allocating time in the exam, for choosing which type of questions to answer in which order, for structuring your answers, and so on. All this is discussed in more detail in Section 5.

3.7 Exams are for people with good memories

Everybody has a good memory. It's a matter of how you use it. However, that is not the key point. Most of the exams adults take are *not* intended as pure memory tests. The main purpose of a course is to develop your ideas and skills. And the purpose of the exam is to provide you with the chance to show how well you have grasped the facts and ideas in the course. It's true that many science and technology subjects require you to know a lot of facts but, as far as is possible, these should generally be used to exemplify the key ideas. Few exams or questions test only factual knowledge and, if they do, this should be clearly signposted in the exam papers anyway. Many maths courses have handbooks, containing all the results and formulas that you will need, that you can take into the exam. These allow you to demonstrate your mathematical skills rather than your memory skills in the exam. Similarly, in many science and technology exams you will be supplied with data and/or formula sheets to help with problem solving in a particular situation.

So don't worry about your memory. Concentrate on organizing your notes and/or practising examples during your revision (see Section 5). Let your memory take care of itself. It's the ideas that are vital.

3.8 Exams are just for speed merchants

Can you think quickly enough and write quickly enough to pass an exam? Probably! As far as the *thinking* is concerned, you need to make sure you have done most of that before the exam itself. So the extent to which sheer speed of thinking matters is very limited. What *will* matter is how well you have organized your ideas and how well you have planned your exam strategy. If you're working to a good plan you can be extremely efficient in your use of time in the exam.

Maths students in particular tend to worry about speed – they feel their assignments take a long time and they will never be able to perform mathematically at speed and to order. But assignments usually involve new ideas and techniques, which take time to absorb. In an exam you will be working on straightforward, familiar types of problems that you can practise before the exam. And as you practise doing similar examples you will find your speed building up.

As far as your speed of handwriting is concerned, this may have an effect if it seriously restricts the amount you can get down. Normally, the fact that you're geared up to peak performance will help you to write more quickly than usual. But, remember, it's quality rather than quantity that's most important. Some students write short pithy answers which are very effective while others write pages without saying much. It's worth practising writing for half an hour at a time to help develop a more fluent and concise style.

3.9 Calculations are either right or wrong

Many people dread the mathematical component of exams because they believe they have to get the answer right in order to get any marks at all. You may have struggled to produce 'perfect' answers in assignments and believe it's impossible to do the same under exam conditions. But examiners are not expecting perfect answers to calculations any more than they are expecting perfect essays. They will give you credit for getting the method right and for correct calculations following on from an error. They will also award marks if you show that you have checked your work and you note that you suspect something is wrong even if you cannot correct your error.

Key Points

◆ Failing an exam is not the end of the world, so keep your anxieties in proportion.

◆ Everyone *wants* you to pass, including the script markers and examiners.

◆ Don't worry about what you *haven't* done during the course. Work out how to make the best use of what you *have* done.

◆ No one understands or remembers everything. There are bound to be areas where you feel under-prepared and confused.

◆ Don't panic when you read the exam questions. Almost every question is linked quite directly with something you have covered on the course. You just have to work out the link.

◆ You will probably have to do a lot of preparatory work before the exam. But you need to do it in a *planned* way, using your time efficiently and conserving your energies. You don't want to turn your life into a complete misery just because of an exam.

◆ Exams tend to be about a mixture of what you can remember, what you understand and how you can apply that knowledge and understanding using skills you have acquired.

◆ Speed in doing an exam is to do with having a very clear plan as to how you intend to use your time and getting as much practice as possible.

◆ Your answers do not have to be perfect.

4 What examiners like to see in exam scripts

Having disposed of some of the myths, let's look in more detail at the reality. One way of getting a sharp focus on what is wanted in exams is to consider what the examiners are likely to say in their reports after marking exams. These reports will not only say how poorly some students did in answering the questions but will also highlight some of the good points.

Activity Break　With assignments, comments from your tutor indicate what things you did well. With exams, feedback is less likely. But imagine you are an examiner. Using your experience of what things are wanted in assignments (Chapter 9), what qualities would you look for in exam answers? Make a list of your major points and compare them with the headings in this section.

4.1 Answering the question set

When it comes to answering exam questions, it's not necessarily *what* you know that counts, but *how* you convey the knowledge that you have. Let's look at some of the key pointers to answering questions well.

◆ *Recognizing key words or phrases* – many of the phrases used in questions, for example, compare and contrast, describe, illustrate and so on, were covered in Chapter 9. The important thing is to read the question carefully. That way you can, for instance, avoid writing a long and comprehensive piece on all the major characteristics of various food-borne diseases if the question asked you to compare and contrast the chemical and physical methods of controlling food-borne diseases.

◆ *Recognizing key terms and concepts from the course in the question* – not treating a question on, say, viral diseases as though it were about bacterial diseases. If there is a key term or concept in the question you don't know, avoid the question. You will get very few marks if you guess and get it wrong. You have to think carefully about what each of the words in the question means.

◆ *Answering the question in the appropriate format* – if the question asks for a report, then an essay-style approach will lose marks allocated for format, and if a mathematical question wants solutions to be given to two significant figures then don't do something different. Similarly, if the question asks for a diagram, not including one will be throwing away available marks and will · mean you'll have to do even better on the rest of the answer to score well. So be clear about what type of answer is required.

◆ *Including all your thinking or steps in undertaking a task* – many questions will require or include mathematical calculations or problem-solving tasks. If a question asks you to find the temperature at which to kill 50% of the bacteria present in a food sample using the data and equations provided, then simply giving a figure, even if correct, will not gain many marks. More marks will be allocated for showing how you worked out the answer and your reasons for using that approach even if a numerical slip meant your final answer was wrong. So always include all the steps in your thinking.

◆ *Checking any mathematical expressions in the question* – making sure that the problem you are trying to solve is the one the examiners set. Often examiners take great care to devise questions that in some sense work out nicely. If, in copying an expression from the paper, you leave out a minus sign or change a letter, for example, you may be setting yourself a much harder problem to solve.

These are, of course, familiar points. We have come across many of them in Chapter 9. So there's nothing particularly new for you to think about here; you should simply note that, although exam answers are judged on roughly the same lines as assignments in terms of content and approach, allowances are made for the inevitably much shorter and less polished answers produced under the constraints of an exam.

4.2 Clearly drawing upon material from the course

Examiners complain that it's sometimes hard to tell whether some students have actually studied the course. In other words, these students completely forget one of the basic principles of an end-of-course exam; namely that it's an opportunity to demonstrate that you have worked on and thought about the content of the course. One example of this would be to include anecdotal reports on the number and causes of food poisoning incidents you have heard about or experienced instead of quoting any data or references given in the course materials.

You can't expect to impress the examiner by including your own opinions only and not mentioning what respected authors have said on the subject, whether they be specific course texts or other sources you have read. Equally, you can't base your answers on your own experiences or those of other people you happen to know. You have to bring in some more generally recognized evidence, as appropriate.

Similarly, you should use the methods taught in the course rather than those taken from somewhere else. This is particularly important for mathematical questions if you are asked to prove something – you should only call on the results and theorems given in the course.

4.3 Discussing course material critically

You should use course material in a discriminating manner. The exam marker is less interested in whether you can memorize a diagram or a piece of text and repeat it than in whether you can select material from all you have come across in the course and use it to answer a specific question. Simply including a diagram of, say, the transmission routes of bacteria from one person to another does not get full marks if the text neither discusses transmission routes nor refers to the diagram in any way. If you have a handbook in the exam, by all means quote results from it, but don't waste time copying out chunks of it (the examiner will have a copy too).

4.4 Using your time well

Suppose your exam paper asks you to answer four questions in three hours, each of which is worth 25% of the total marks. A very common failing is to produce a very long first answer, followed by a slightly shorter second, an even shorter third and a fourth that is just a paragraph and some scrappy notes or is even missed out entirely. This may also happen with multi-part questions.

Even if you score very well on the best answer or part of an answer, your overall score may be less than if you had submitted moderate answers for all the questions. Suppose you managed to get 90% for your first answer, but followed it with 45%, 30%, and 15% of the available marks because you spent too long on the first answer. Your overall exam score would be 45%. On the other hand, if you allocated your time better and got, say, 75% of the marks for the first question, and then set about the easier task of improving the scores on the other questions rather than polishing the first question, you might end up with, say, 60%, 55%, and 50% on the remaining three. This would give you an overall exam score of 60% which, as you can see, is a much better result.

The point is that it's much easier to gain a solid base of marks from a reasonable effort than to try and squeeze out the last few marks for a very good, but lengthier answer. Of course, you will always aim to build extra marks on that solid base in the time available, but not at the expense of the easy marks to be gained on other questions. The important thing is to allocate your time in *proportion* to the marks available on a question. So, if a paper has one compulsory question worth 50% and several short-answer, optional questions carrying the same marks each, of which you have done six, then you should spend 50% of your time on the compulsory question and 8% of your time on each of the other questions. I shall return to this issue in Section 5.

4.5 Good presentation

Examiners often remark on how good answers:

- are well-structured (that is, with a beginning, a middle and an end) or in the format required by a particular question
- are clearly divided into paragraphs or sections
- are written in well-constructed sentences (whether mathematical or English) rather than note form
- have the calculations or thinking presented in full
- include symbols or units on numbers or calculations
- include properly labelled diagrams with titles and explanations when asked for
- are in legible, well-spaced handwriting.

All of these requirements are familiar enough from assignments and other writing as discussed in Chapters 3, 4 and 9. It's harder to pay attention to presentation under exam pressures, but sloppy presentation often indicates sloppy thinking and makes it harder for the script marker. Of course the style has to fit the need, so in short answers the writing style is less important than the facts, but in essays the way the facts are strung together in well-constructed arguments is more important. Whatever the style of answer, the exam marker's job is harder than your tutor's as he or she has to work through a large number of scripts. No matter how well-disposed the examiner may be, it's hard to do justice to a statement or sentence which is poorly written. Unlike your tutor, the script marker does not know you and cannot draw on previous knowledge of your approach to guess what you might be trying to say, so it's all the more important to provide coherent and legible answers.

Key Points

◆ Answer the question set. Ensure you understand it fully before beginning to write.

◆ Apply and use relevant course concepts and facts in your answer.

◆ Plan and use your time effectively.

◆ Pay attention to presentation and style.

5 Revising for exams

5.1 What is the point of revision?

The most important purpose of revision is to pull together all the work you have done in studying the course. Revision is not primarily a massive *memorizing* task, as people sometimes think. It's a much more *constructive* activity than memorizing. It serves the function of rounding off the course. While you are studying you are constantly changing and developing how you organize and understand the facts and ideas you cover. Revision is the process of tidying up the mess and getting your knowledge and ideas into a usable shape. Without a period of revision the course would just drift away from you.

The consequence of this is that revision has to be made into an *active* process – not just a mechanical 'scanning through pages hoping something will stick'. It needs to be planned in a *purposeful* way and designed around *activities* which are meaningful, engaging and thought-provoking, not repetitive, tedious and mind numbing. Revision is but another learning step in the course which you have chosen to study, so you should make sure you get some pleasure and value out of it. Don't do it just for the sake of the examiners.

5.2 When should you start your revision for the exam?

There is no 'correct' answer to this question. It's something you have to work out for yourself. Some students leave it to the last fortnight, while others make a start two months before the exam. Yet others see revision as part and parcel of the whole course. The right time to revise for you depends on:

◆ your personal commitments in addition to studying and the time you can spare for the revision process

◆ your personal style of studying – whether you are more capable of short intensive bursts of effort, or longer sustained periods

◆ what you are trying to get out of the course.

It would be a shame if you began too early and spoiled the latter parts of the course by being obsessed with revision. On the other hand, it's a grave mistake to avoid all thinking about the exam until the very last moment and then just hope for the best. It's a good idea early on to jot down a first attempt at a plan of the last weeks of the course, sketching out how you might try to fit in some blocks of revision time alongside the normal course work. It doesn't matter if you have to scrap the plan and draw up a new one (or have to keep scrapping plans and drawing up new ones as suggested for normal course work back in Chapter 1). The effort of making a tentative start on a revision plan will set in process the necessary shift in orientation as you move towards the final stages of the course.

In drawing up a plan, you need to retain a balance between the exam and the rest of your life. You need to see how many hours, in total, you can reasonably hope to devote to revision. Allow a proportion of your time for studying the last part of the course. Set aside some time for practising exam questions and for the final stages of polishing up your act. Then divide the remaining time into equal parts for each of the areas of the course you have decided to revise. It's tempting to allow more time for sections of the course where you feel particularly strong and to try to squeeze the weak areas in at the end. However, it's all too easy to end up with too little time for the topics which need the most sorting out, or conversely to leave no time for brushing up the very topics you had hoped to do best in.

5.3 Getting hold of old exam papers

This is an excellent idea. In order to focus your mind on the task at hand, there is no substitute for looking at past exam papers. (Can you get hold of past exam papers? If this is the first year of your course, clearly you can't. However, in such circumstances you may be supplied with a specimen paper instead. If this is not the first year, make a point of finding out how to get hold of old papers. Ask your tutor, or experienced fellow students, or write to the examining body.) Exams vary in length and in the number of questions you have to answer. By looking at past papers or a specimen paper you will be able to see exactly:

◆ how the questions are set out on the page

◆ how many questions there are

◆ whether there are separate sections from which to choose questions

◆ what kinds of questions are set

◆ how the questions 'map' on to the content of the course

◆ what sort of language they employ.

By the time you sit down to take the real exam you need to be very familiar with what the paper is going to look like and to have a pretty good idea as to what questions you are looking for in it. You can't be guaranteed to get the specific questions you want, but you should be able to form a reasonable idea of the *general* areas the questions are likely to cover. Both for your general revision strategy and for detailed planning for the exam itself, you need to make yourself very familiar with the way the exam paper is likely to look.

With time at a premium, it's important to be realistic and think clearly about how you are going to use it. To assist with this you can draw up a plan of how, ideally, you would hope to use the time in the exam based on the specimen paper or past exam papers. Figure 10.1 shows one possible version – a paper asking for four answers of equal length. Of course, you'll have to adapt this approach to your own circumstances and the structure of the paper you are to sit, and you may prefer different allocations of time (for example, leaving some time for checking through at the end).

Time

10:00   Turn over the paper and glance through it, marking the questions you think you might attempt. (5 mins)

10:05   Start planning your first answer. Underline key words in the question. Jot down relevant course material. Return to the question and work out a plan. (10 mins)

10:15   Start writing out your first answer. (35 mins)

10:50   Finish the first answer and plan out the other three. (25 mins, that is, 3 × 8.3 mins)

11:15   Write out the second answer. (35 mins)

11:50   Write out the third answer. (35 mins)

12:25   Write out the fourth answer. (35 mins)

13:00   Finish

Figure 10.1 *Sample time plan for a three-hour exam involving four answers of equal length*

This is, of course, a very idealized plan. You wouldn't be able to stick to it exactly. In fact, you would certainly have to modify it as you went along in the exam. But it's not important whether this is the 'best' possible plan. What *is* important is that *you* draw up your *own* plan, so that you have a clear idea of how you intend to use the time.

5.4 Sorting out your course material

One of the central features of revising is getting yourself organized. Unless you have a superbly efficient filing system, you will have accumulated mounds of assorted bits of paper, notes, handouts, photocopies of articles, and annotated teaching texts. Setting aside an evening to do nothing other than sort everything out is more than just 'housekeeping'. The act of putting all the material into new tidier mounds reminds you of what material you have and pushes you into thinking about the overall shape of the course and how things can be grouped together. When you can look around you and see *what* you have got and *where*, you will be in a much better position to get a clear run at a spell of revision.

5.5 Should you re-read all the course materials?

This is hopelessly idealistic. It would take far too long, but more importantly it would be dreadfully tedious. You need to take a much more selective and more active approach as you return to your earlier weeks of study. You need to make a careful judgement, based on your study of the type and choice of questions available from past papers and on any advice you can get from your tutor, about *how* selective you can afford to be. Then decide exactly which parts of the course materials you are going to focus your efforts on. It's not 'cheating' to do this. The most successful students are often those with the confidence to select precisely how much of the course they need to revise in order to achieve their own goals, for example, just to pass, to get the highest mark possible, and so on. They then give their full attention to revising the chosen areas very thoroughly. Alternatively, success can flow from concentrating on redoing activities and exercises from the course rather than reading the text as it will show up gaps and give you more practice at answering questions.

5.6 Should you try to just memorize your course notes?

No, it would probably be a waste of time and effort. If you set out to do routine, boring things like dutifully scanning over old notes without thinking until you can recite them, your mind might switch off in protest. You need to be able to *think* in the exam, not simply *recite* back your notes. So you need ideas and facts in your head, not strings of words. Do something much more constructive as you read your course notes, such as picking out key points or trying to work out what questions you might be asked. Most likely, any straight 'memorizing' of the course material that is needed should come in the last few days and be based on 'summary' notes.

5.7 Is it worth writing new notes at this late stage in the course?

Yes, it's an excellent idea to actually *create* something as you work! This gives a much more constructive feel to the task of revision and will engage your mind more effectively for long spells of work. Some students like to dictate notes into a tape recorder. Another very good way of working is as follows:

1 Make *very condensed notes* from the various course booklets, notes, and so on, that you have gathered together for revision on a particular *topic*.

2 Next, extract the main points from these condensed notes to produce a single *summary sheet* of headings with key points, names, and so on for that *topic*.

3   Finally, having done this for the topics within a given section of the course, take the main headings from all the topic summary sheets and produce a single *master summary sheet* which outlines the main subject matter for that whole *section* of the course. The use of highlighting pens can help with all these stages.

The effort to 'boil' the course down in this way, so as to extract its concentrated essence, is extremely valuable because it converts the broad themes and the detailed discussions of the course into a form which is much more manageable for the purposes of answering questions in exams. As you know, you don't have time to write at tremendous length in exams, so what you don't want is to have to wade through mounds of detail in your mind in order to sift out an answer. This condensed version of the main points of the course is much closer to what you will have time to think through and write about.

What's more, when you come to answering a question on a particular section of the course in the exam, you can think back and remind yourself of the 'master summary sheet' in order to identify what main topics lie within the section. You can then work out which of the topics are relevant to the question and remind yourself of the 'topic summary sheets' concerned. You can scan mentally through the main items on any given topic summary sheet and select whichever are relevant. This will lead you back to the condensed notes which 'lie behind' those items on the topic summary sheet. In other words, having, in your revision, constructed pathways *down* from the basic source materials through condensed notes and topic summary sheets to a master summary sheet, you can then, in the exam, quickly trace your way back *up* those pathways to locate exactly the material that is relevant to the question. (It also helps if you have practised tracing up before the exam to identify any blank spots.) Perhaps the practice is rarely quite as neat as that, but at least this 'note-condensing' approach gives you the basis for a systematic overview and retrieval system.

5.8 Identify the central questions at the heart of each section of the course

This is a very powerful strategy. Try to identify one or two central questions in each section of the course that you are revising, and try to write notes that answer those questions. In other words, what is this part of the course all about? What is the point of it? Sometimes an author or tutor will have identified the key questions for you. At other times you will have to tease them out and pose them for yourself. Often assignments are key pointers to the essential areas.

Similarly, the author or tutor will sometimes have made a point of drawing conclusions on the main issues for you, while at other times you will have to summarize and draw conclusions for yourself. The process of seeking out key questions and answers to them will get your mind working in the way it needs to during the exam. It will alert you to the kinds of questions that could be asked on the course content you have been studying. It will also help you to think in terms of the broad sweeps needed for putting together answers based on the course material.

5.9 Should you try answering past exam questions?

Probably the single most useful revision activity of all is to attempt old exam questions or the ones given in the specimen paper. You don't need to write out a full answer every time, though the occasional practice at that would probably be useful. A quicker exercise that you can do much more frequently (and which you should try to do over and over during the final stages of revision) is to rehearse the vital first few minutes of working on a question; in other words, the minutes when you examine the question carefully and sketch out rough notes for an answer. Give yourself, say, ten minutes to produce an outline answer to a question you haven't looked at before, then look back at the course material (or the specimen answer to a question from the specimen paper) to see what you have left out. If this works well then you could build up to producing full-length answers to help with speed and confidence. And, where you can take a handbook into the exam, practise using it as you work through past papers.

As you tackle each question, go through the routine of answering the following points.

◆ What is the question getting at, what are the key words and phrases?
◆ Which section of the course does the question relate most directly to and which topic(s) within that section?
◆ What themes, examples, evidence, ideas can you draw on from the course?
◆ What would be a good order in which to take the points (that is, a sketched outline of the content)?

The reason this is worth doing many times is that it helps you develop the intellectual agility to do what examiners so clearly want you to do, which is to answer questions precisely and to draw on relevant parts of the course. In doing so it helps you organize your knowledge in the right sort of way for the job in hand. You get used to going very quickly through the processes of:

◆ *sifting* through what you know of the course material
◆ *selecting* the most relevant items for the question
◆ *arranging* them in a suitable order for a coherent answer.

You don't need practice at writing out full answers quite so urgently because, once you have an outline, the writing itself is pretty much the same as writing an assignment, except that you have less time. In other words, you have already practised that skill during the course. What you have not had practice at is 'thinking on your feet' and fixing very quickly on a line to take. Our normal modes of thinking about assignments are too reflective and lumbering for an exam. You need to practise a much more nimble style to get yourself into the right frame of mind.

One of the greatest benefits of this exercise of regularly sketching out quick outlines for answers is that you soon begin to discover that the ground you covered early in the course, which had seemed no more than vague shapes in a haze, soon comes back into sharp focus, and you find that you have learned much more than you had realized.

5.10 Try to think up exam questions for yourself

If you run out of questions from sample papers, you can always make up some more of your own or, better still, exchange made-up questions with another student. Apart from stretching your mind, it makes you step over to the examiners' side of the fence, which helps you develop insight into the way they think. It also helps you to take a broad view of the course, looking for the big issues and the underlying themes.

5.11 Should you set yourself a full-scale 'mock exam'?

If you haven't taken exams for a long time, your course does not have a mock exam anyway or you are a regular computer user and don't write very often, it's obviously useful to get some practice at working on exam questions 'against the clock'. On the other hand, you might find it hard to make the time, or find the stamina, for a full-length practice. It depends on your own abilities and inclinations as to how useful it is to spend time this way. It might be just as useful and more practical to set yourself the task of writing a single timed answer every now and then. After all, you will have the benefit of a lot more nervous energy to help you perform on the exam day, so you may underestimate your powers in an informal try-out. A further word of warning – don't be discouraged if the answers you produce look unimpressive compared with your assignments. Due allowance is made for the fact that answers produced under exam conditions are always less polished than assignments.

5.12 Have you time to attend tutorials during the revision period?

Make time! It's easy to develop a distorted perspective on exams during revision. You begin to think your problems are much worse than they really are, or you bias your revision too sharply in one particular direction. The best way to keep a sense of proportion is to talk to other people about what you are doing. This is probably the time when attending tutorials is most useful. This does not mean that if you are obliged to study on your own your chances are necessarily poor. It's just that if you can get to classes you will make your revision a lot easier and more pleasant. It's a mistake to think that time spent at a tutorial is simply time lost from revising on your own. Group revision can be extremely efficient. It throws up all sorts of insights into problems and misperceptions which might otherwise remain hidden. It helps to sort out your ideas and offers many valuable clues and tips. And if you can't get to a tutorial, talk to your tutor by phone, or email if that is available.

5.13 Should you team up with other students for your revision?

In a similar way, it can be very valuable, particularly if you are new to exams, to meet or talk on the phone fairly regularly with other students, to compare your revision strategies and your progress, to set each other questions, to comment on and criticize each other's outline answers, and to provide mutual support in general. Since exams have a tendency to draw out our anxieties and to foster myths, it's extremely useful to be able to make contact with other people's ideas of reality as it helps to keep your own perceptions and plans within reasonable bounds.

5.14 Should you get yourself a new calculator for the exam?

In general, no. You will be far more effective with the calculator you are used to. However, if your make of calculator is not allowed in the exam, do practise with what is allowed. It's a good idea to put new batteries in your calculator a week before the exam, to reduce the risk of them running out during the exam.

Hints and Tips

Here are some strategies you can use when revising for an exam.

◆ Study *past exam papers* and specimen papers thoroughly.

◆ Carefully *select* the parts of the course you intend to revise.

◆ Make a *timetable* for revising each of the parts of the course you have chosen to revise.

◆ *Condense* the content and key points of your chosen sections into very brief summarizing notes.

◆ Practise doing the *activities and exercises* in the course materials

◆ Think up *questions* you might be asked.

◆ Practise jotting down *outlines* for answers to questions.

◆ Practise *writing* out one or two answers in full against the clock.

◆ Practise *using* what resources you will have in the exam, for example, calculator, handbook.

◆ *Keep in touch* with other students and with your tutor to broaden your ideas and maintain contact with reality.

6 Getting yourself 'geared up' in the last day or two

Is it a good idea to relax and get plenty of sleep and outdoor exercise in the day or two immediately before the exam? Perhaps you ought to get away for a couple of days. But is this a realistic option? For many, particularly part-time students, it won't be, but for others it can be worth while. It all depends on your situation and your own preferred revision strategy. That last day or so is when you can gradually build yourself up to a peak of preparation. You can forget your plans for re-reading that course material, for instance, or for looking at that theory you never really understood, and instead concentrate all your energies on making the best job you can of marshalling what you do know. So, 'relaxed' is the last thing you want to be when you enter the exam. Calm and unruffled (if you can manage it), possibly, but you should be keyed up like a tennis star at a tournament, or a stage performer on the first night, ready to give your big performance of the year.

6.1 Get your thinking in before the exam

How will you do justice to everything you have learned in months of study, when you only have three hours in the exam? How long do you spend on an assignment? Six hours – ten hours – a week? How on earth can you condense all those writing processes into three hours? Clearly you can't. This means that you need to have done a lot of your *thinking* prior to the exam itself, just as I described in Section 5. In other words, you have to get yourself into a very particular frame of mind for the exam – a highly organized, efficient and pragmatic one. One in which, having stopped worrying and wondering, you have focused on making the best of the immediate tasks in hand.

6.2 Changes to your mental powers

The last couple of days, then, are about going over your summary note sheets and generally winding yourself up for action. Because the pressures build up in these final days, your mental powers will change. You will probably be less good at deep thinking tasks, such as sorting out the underlying meaning of a difficult chapter of a set book. But you will be better at working at routine things like checking over your notes, practising answering questions and reminding yourself of your strategy for the exam. So don't extend the core aspects of revision into the last few days – you'll only depress yourself and get into a panic. Use these days as your 'polishing up' period for the big performance. As with the actor at the dress rehearsal, it's too late to learn new lines or decide on a different interpretation.

6.3 Anxiety

It is possible that, as the exam draws closer, you will begin to find the tension gets on top of you. There are several varieties and levels of anxiety which can develop at exam time. As already mentioned, you may experience a general uneasiness about the task ahead that builds up gradually over a long period. What you need to do is to make sure you use this tension productively. Set yourself practical revision and relaxation tasks in preparation for the exam to keep yourself busy. Remind yourself from time to time that this is *your* exam; you are doing it because *you* have chosen to, and use the tension it creates to help you with your learning and other activities.

Your anxiety may, however, develop into a pall of gloom which spoils the last part of the course. You may find that all your thoughts become centred on the exam. In this case, you will find it useful to keep talking to other students and to your tutor. You need to share your thoughts about the exam and about your plans for tackling it. Talking to others will release tension and help you to keep things in a realistic perspective.

For a few students, though, this is not enough. Their anxiety in the period immediately before the exam builds up to a point where sleep is difficult and their health begins to suffer, or where work or family and friends begin to be affected. They may even become unwell for other reasons. If you find this happening to you, then go to your doctor for advice and inform the proper authorities at your college or university of your health problems. Some people find breathing exercises or meditation helpful, or find some other way of focusing intensively on reducing the physical manifestations of tension. If you feel bad, don't suffer in isolation. Look for help.

6.4 Checking the arrangements

Because of the need to get 'geared up' in the last day or two before an exam, you may become rather inattentive to the practicalities of life. People have been known to make quite odd mistakes, like turning up for the exam on the wrong day or at the wrong place. So it's a good idea to get all the details of the exam sorted out well in advance. You don't want to be worrying about anything trivial on the day. Mark the time very clearly on your calendar. You might even consider making a practice journey to the exam centre and finding the room, so that you don't have any last-minute panics about which bus to catch, where you left the address of the exam centre or where the entrance to the building is.

Similarly, you should check what equipment you need and also what you are allowed to take in. The list will depend on the actual exam, but is likely to include pens and pencils, a ruler, a rubber, a calculator and a watch. You might also want to take a drink and sweets with you. A very important detail to check is whether you need to take a handbook with you or if a formula or data sheet is provided.

6.5 On the day

On the day itself, try to approach the exam calmly. Go about the normal business of getting up and starting the day in an unhurried way. Take a short stroll perhaps, or do a few exercises, to get yourself tuned up and functioning properly. Get to the appointed place for the exam in good time and keep walking around if you have to wait to get into the exam room. Don't let the other candidates disturb you. Remain aloof if you need to. When you are in the exam room, find your desk and calmly settle yourself in your seat. Set out whatever you have with you on the desk and check once again that you have everything you need. The exam room always seems a strange place – full of people you don't know, all fully absorbed with their own thoughts – but don't let the strangeness distract you. Just keep your mind 'ticking over in neutral', ready to slip into gear when the lights change.

7 Working out your tactical plan for the exam

We now need to consider in detail what you are going to attempt to achieve in the exam itself. You don't want to let yourself drift towards it like a leaf caught in a whirlpool, circling round passively for ages until you are sucked down the hole in a rush. You can't afford to leave everything to chance. You need to work out exactly what has to be done in the exam and exactly how you think you will tackle it. If you do, you will improve your performance enormously.

7.1 The nature of the task ahead of you

Before you begin the exam you have to be ready to work at peak efficiency. You have three hours to make the best show you can of all the work you have done during the course and during the final revision stages. You can't afford to waste time dithering, moping, or staring at the ceiling. You must have a clear plan of attack on the task in front of you. You may not be able to stick to it, and in the end that may not matter. What is important is that you are clear at all times about what you intend to do next. And you need to have decided exactly how you are going to use your *time* in the exam. Then, in the exam:

◆ pick your questions
◆ after a few minutes, settle on a particular way of using what you know to answer them
◆ stick to your chosen questions, avoiding the temptation to change mid-answer.

Some exams allow you to take in course books or even notes, though this is a very doubtful privilege. It's scarcely consistent with the style of high-speed work you are doing in an exam to be thumbing through books and notes and reading them. You might imagine it would be reassuring to have your books with you. However it's just as likely that, if you're the nervous type, you would spend far too much time desperately trying to find things to be sure you have them right! Nevertheless, in some MST subjects it may be reassuring to know that if you need a particular formula or result you can look it up in the handbook or data sheet provided. It all depends on the nature of the exam.

7.2 Reading the exam paper

The signal that the exam has started is when the invigilator tells you that you can turn the exam paper over. The general appearance of the paper should not be a surprise to you if you have done your work on the specimen paper or past papers. However, you may find it difficult to take in the words at first because you are so keyed up. So, although it might seem sensible to read carefully through the whole paper first, you may not be able to do that effectively. It may be better to do something more active to get you moving.

Certainly, it's no bad idea to scan quickly through the questions, putting ticks against possible ones and crosses against ones you definitely won't attempt. This will give you a first impression of what is on offer. But don't ponder over every question in detail. Search out the questions you have prepared yourself for. It's a desperate gamble to allow yourself to be deflected from a prepared subject on to an unprepared one just because of the wording of the questions. Your chosen topic may look more difficult to you simply *because* you know so much about the topic. Other questions may look easier *because* you aren't clued up enough to realize their full implications. Don't attempt to 'flannel' your way through an unrevised area. You are much more likely to produce a solid answer on one of your prepared topics, even if you feel unhappy with the question. The exception to this is if you have run out of options. Remember that if you do not answer the number of questions asked for you are penalizing yourself even more as it reduces the total number of marks you can gain.

7.3 How soon to start writing

It may be a good idea to find a question you *know* you are going to attempt and pitch straight into it. If you are inclined to 'freeze up' under pressure, or if your mind tends to 'go blank', then starting to write can be a good way to get yourself past those opening moments and into action. There is no reason to worry about starting your first question before reading the rest of the paper if you are sure it's on one of your chosen topics. Many people prefer to scan through the whole paper first but, if it suits you better to jump straight into the swim of things, do it. However, you *will* need to think a bit about the wording of the question and to jot down some notes before starting to write the answer proper. Generally, if you cross out any notes or jottings these will be ignored by the marker. So don't cross them out if you want them considered. In any case it's worth asking beforehand what the policy is on such jottings for your particular exam.

7.4 The order in which to take the questions

You are allowed to tackle the questions in any order you like, so you may as well follow your own best interests. Some people recommend starting on your very best question, so as to build up your confidence. Others say take your best question second, when you are nicely warmed up and are not so likely to be tempted to run wildly over your time allowance for it. In any case, it's a good idea to take your best questions earlier rather than later to make sure you have enough time to score well with them, to give you confidence and to allow you to relax into your stride.

7.5 Examining a question

As with assignments, it's an excellent idea to underline the key words, figures or equations in the questions you intend to do. It makes you take a positive approach from the outset. It also focuses your attention on developing an answer to the precise question set, rather than producing a string of vaguely relevant information. The words, figures or equations you underline are the ones you will have to think about carefully in deciding what material you can use and how to organize it. These key words should also be used in your answer to help demonstrate that what is written is relevant to what is asked. If you rush into the question and make mistakes about the issues it addresses, you will lose marks.

7.6 Drawing together material to put into your answer

As soon as you have underlined the key aspects of the question, the next thing is to jot down very quickly those sections of the course and topics you think are intended to be used in answering it. Don't worry at first about *how* to use them. Just write down words, diagrams or equations to reassure yourself that you have enough material to work on. You need whatever concepts, theories, and examples you can conjure up. (This is where you think back to the summary sheets you produced from your condensed notes.) When you have a brief preliminary list (which may contain only five to ten words or a single diagram), you can begin to sort out what to use and what to leave out. The point to hold in mind is that exam questions are *always* asking for material from the course, so you need to write down a few headings and ideas from the course *before* you start taxing your mind with working out your plan of attack on the question. Once you are grappling with the challenge of constructing an effective answer to the question, your mind will be fully occupied. You will then be in danger of suddenly discovering that an important aspect of the answer has completely slipped from your mind. A single word is usually enough to trigger your memory and enable you to retrieve the point. Work fast and uncritically to get your list of potential material and don't hesitate to make a mess of your exam booklet. You can cross out all your jottings later.

7.7 Strike a balance between what you know and what the question asks for

As you answer a question, you have to steer a course between two equally dangerous traps. One is that you will become so confused and uncertain about the nature of the question that you will lose confidence in the fact that the answer to it lies in the course material. The danger here is that you will stop believing that if you search properly you will find the material you need amongst all that you have stored in your head; that you will feel drawn instead to blustering your way through, trying to answer 'off the top of your head'. The opposite danger is that your mind will become so fixed on all the material you have recently stored in it that you will not be able to resist the urge to spill your knowledge out all over the pages of the exam booklet, regardless of the specific question you are answering. Both these are very easy traps to fall into. The approach to tackling the questions set out here is deliberately designed to try to play these two temptations off against each other.

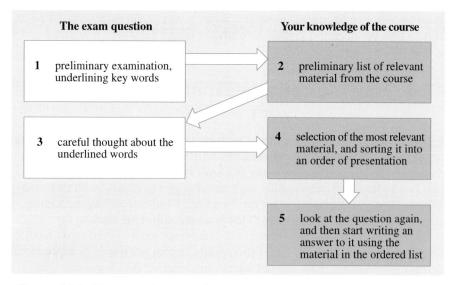

Figure 10.2 *Five steps in preparing an answer to an exam question*

What I propose is that you move back and forth between the question and the knowledge stored in your mind. In this way you can make sure that each has due influence on the other. In other words, you choose the question and do a quick 'first take' on what it's about. Then you leave the question and go to your knowledge of the course to jot down some possible content. Then you return to the question to get it more sharply focused in your mind. Then you go back to the preliminary list of course material to knock it into the shape you need. And finally, with a quick look back at the question, you start answering it in a way which brings the two together (see Figure 10.2).

7.8 Taking time to plan your answer

These preparations for your answers sound very well – but will you have time to spare for such refinements? It takes a lot of nerve to spend precious time in the exam preparing your answers. But bearing in mind the comments of examiners on 'good' answers, it's time very well spent. Of course, you will have to carry out your preparatory activities at high speed. So how long should you spend? In the end this is something you will have to judge for yourself, depending on the length of the required answer, but between five and ten minutes is a reasonable target. If you don't sketch out a plan, you will run the risk of 'going blank' in the middle of an answer, finishing off one point and reaching for the next point only to find it's gone. You will need to work with your tutor and fellow-students to form an idea of what you should be aiming for when sketching out a plan.

7.9 Sticking to the point

In your enthusiasm to show your knowledge of the course, don't forget the importance of keeping to the question. It irritates exam markers, who are searching for points which relate directly to the question, to have to wade through paragraphs of unsorted and uncensored material. You will never *gain* marks if you give the impression that you are uncritically throwing course material before the examiners' eyes in the hope that you will fool them into thinking you know what you are talking about. Exam markers have to follow specific marking schemes that detail what aspects are required in the answer and how many marks to reward those aspects with. Of course, you must make sure to draw in plenty of material from the course, but you must always do it with a clear purpose to avoid 'padding out' your answers with irrelevant material that will gain no marks. Everything you write should have a clear relevance to the question. Anything else is just wasting your time.

7.10 When to plan your later questions

When you have your first question under your belt, it's a good idea to 'rough out' plans for all of your other answers before writing out your second answer. The reason for this is that you need time on your side when planning.

It's very hard to think straight in the final stages of the exam as you become aware of the approaching deadline. All too often a last answer represents the desperate casting about of a mind which has long passed the stage of thinking in a coherent way about such broad issues as the relationship of a question to the course content. *You will probably be able to write at your fastest during the last hour of the exam* provided you know what you intend to say. So do any thinking that requires calmer analysis in the second quarter of the exam, when you have passed through the initial tension and have settled into a steady working mode.

If you find that you are falling behind schedule as you answer a question, draw the answer to a close as quickly as you can. Don't leave the question half finished in the hope that you will have time to come back to it. Most likely you will not since you are running late. But, more importantly, by then you will have lost the train of thought. Make the best of a bad job and write out whatever you can manage while the question is still fresh in your mind. Re-read the question to see if there are any more points you can make quickly. Remember that marks are given for the key points and the way they are presented. So notes will still score on the first criterion if not the second.

7.11 What to do if your time runs out

If, in spite of all your plans, you do end up with too little time for your last question, it will help to write out some notes showing how your answer would have developed if you had had time. If you present an answer *entirely* in note form, you are unlikely to scrape a pass. However, if you have *part* of an answer already written out, then some clearly written notes indicating where you intended to go might convince the marker that you are worthy of a reasonable mark. But it would scarcely be fair on the other candidates to allow you the benefit of the extra time you spent on the earlier questions and a generous benefit of the doubt on an uncompleted question. The marker will probably give you some *credit* for good notes, but basically you need to write out an answer in full to be safely in the running for a reasonable mark. So make sure you *don't* run out of time!

7.12 Presentation

Most people's writing is less than their best in an exam. But do try to do the best you can to make your work neat and legible. If the marker can't read your writing, he or she will not be able to give you credit. The responsibility for clear writing lies with you. Start each question on a new page and number the questions clearly. Draw a line across the page between your jottings and the answer itself. If your command of written English is poor, it's too late to worry; you can't do much to change your basic style of expression at short notice. And if you have problems with your handwriting, printing the letters rather than joining them up might be a better, albeit slower, option. You could also try making your writing well-spaced, leaving bigger gaps between words and writing on every other line. You can only work to improve these aspects gradually over your years of study. Just try to remember your reader a little as you write and avoid being so overwhelmed by the need for speed that your writing descends to a desperate scrawl.

Hints and Tips

Here are some practical tips for the exam itself.

- Scan through the paper finding the questions you have prepared for.

- Start writing soon, if it helps to 'unfreeze' you.

- Take your best question first (or second).

- As you tackle a question:

  - examine the wording carefully and use underlining or a highlight pen for key words

  - very quickly list some relevant points from the course

  - move back and forth between the question and your list as you sketch an outline plan for your answer

  - take the time to plan your answer before you start writing

  - ensure everything you write is relevant to the specific question asked.

- Consider planning later questions in advance.

- Draw up a time plan for the exam.

- Don't run wildly over your deadlines.

- Do your best to write legibly.

- Attempt the number of questions required, however limited the answer.

- If time allows, read your answers to check you have done all that is asked for.

8 Will you do as well as you ought to in the exam?

Of *course* you ought to pass the exam (assuming you have been getting on all right with the course itself). Really you should do about as well in the exam as you have been doing with the course itself (although the average score on examinations tends to be lower than for assignments and allowances are made for this when setting your grades). In principle, the exam is just another way of confirming what your work during the course has already shown. But, although this is more or less how things turn out for many people, it isn't so in all cases. After all, there are at least four possibilities.

1   Some people do *better* in exams than in their course work. Exams actually bring out the best in them. Perhaps you are one of these people (or could become one with the right approach to exams).

2   Many people do just about *as well* in the exam as in their course work. This is obviously fine and as it should be.

3   Some people tend to perform *less well* than their course work suggests they should (scoring say 10 to 20% lower).They pass, but at a lower level than they had reasonably hoped. *If you are one of these people, then this chapter is especially for you.* Read it regularly every year as you start the revision period and remind yourself of all the very practical things you can do to get a better performance out of yourself.

4   A very few people have a tendency to come crashing down *way below* their potential in exams. If you are in this category, then I hope this chapter has been helpful, but I would strongly recommend that you also try to *talk* to someone about exams and get direct support and advice. There is no point in struggling on your own if you persistently ruin your good work when it comes to exams.

Whichever of these categories you think you fall into, you have nothing to lose by thinking positively. Of *course* you deserve to pass. You will leave things out in the exam, but so will everyone else. Your exam answers won't look as impressive as your assignments, but the same is true for all the others. Your answers are only going to be compared with other rushed efforts. So don't let the exam intimidate you. *Be realistic!* You are *likely* to pass. Yes, it *is* a chore. Yes, you *will* have to focus a lot of attention and energy on it. But you *will* also learn a lot in the process. And if you follow all the suggestions in this chapter, you *can* make yourself into a more efficient exam *performer*, achieving feats way beyond your normal, everyday powers. Who knows, perhaps the exam might turn out to be the highlight of your course after all.

Maths Help

Introduction

This section will help you to understand some of the mathematics you will be using in your studies. It is for reference – for you to dip into when you need help with things you have forgotten or never properly understood. I hope that you will find this section useful as you work through the other parts of the book and in your studying in general.

I assume that you already have some everyday mathematical skills. In particular, I hope that you can do the sorts of things described in the following activity.

*M*aths Activity

1   Can you write whole numbers (up to a million) in words? For example, (finances permitting!) could you write a cheque for £2304?

2   Can you tot up a short shopping bill and work out the change?

3   Do you understand the symbols $+$, $-$, $\times$, $\div$ and $=$?

For example, can you work out the following problems without using a calculator?

(a) $642 + 397$

(b) $231 - 164$

(c) 70×8

(d) $63 \div 9$

4   Can you use a calculator to work out the answers to the problems in Question 3?

5   Can you measure lengths (in mm and cm) with a ruler?

6   Can you use a simple timetable or chart, such as a bus timetable or a distance chart?

Answers

1   The amount in words is 'two thousand, three hundred and four pounds'.

3   (a) 1039

(b) 67

(c) 560

(d) 7

If you found any of the above activities difficult, perhaps you'll find that Maths Help is not right for you as yet – you may need extra help. Maybe the course you are currently studying or soon to begin will cover some of the essential 'first steps', for example, help with using calculators. If you continue to have problems during your course, help is always at hand – from your tutor for example. If maths continues to be a 'black spot', your local College of Further Education may offer help with numeracy as part of its adult education programme.

For more advice you could contact The Basic Skills Agency, Commonwealth House, 1–19 New Oxford Street, London, WC1A 1NU. Telephone: 0171 405 4017

Maths Help attempts to cover the most common difficulties which trip up beginning students in mathematics, science and technology. It assumes that you already have a few basic skills – for example, that you can add, subtract, multiply and divide whole numbers up to three digits long (using pen and paper *and* using a calculator).

The later sections of Maths Help assume that you understand the topics covered in earlier sections. Often, you will find that you do – but should you come across anything you can't manage, try looking to the earlier sections for help. Use the contents list at the front of the book and the index at the back of the book to find your way around.

So that you benefit fully from this Maths Help section, I suggest that you now skim through it quickly to get an overview of the contents.

Contents

1 Calculations

This section will help you to write down calculations in a concise form using mathematical notation. It will also describe how to work out the answers quickly and accurately.

A lot of everyday problems can be solved by doing a little arithmetic. Have a look at the examples below.

Problem	Calculation	Solution
1 25 men and 34 women enrol on a course. How many students are there altogether?	25 + 34	59 students in all
2 I buy a calculator which costs £28 and pay with a £50 note. How much change will I get?	50 − 28	£22
3 Rolls of wallpaper cost £8 each. How much will 7 rolls cost?	7 × 8	£56 altogether
4 A holiday for 4 people costs £1500. If they share the cost equally, how much will each person pay?	1500 ÷ 4	£375 each

Each of these calculations involved just one step. So, once you've decided on the technique to use, they are fairly straightforward. (If you found these problems difficult, I suggest that you get some help with your numeracy skills – see page 301.) In scientific work, however, calculations are often more complicated and can involve two or more steps.

So, what happens if there are more steps in the calculation?

For example, how would you work out $25 − 22 + 36 − 15 + 4$?

Try it!

Here, you can start at the left and work through to the right, step by step.

$25 − 22 = 3$ $3 + 36 = 39$ $39 − 15 = 24$ and $24 + 4 = 28$

So, $25 − 22 + 36 − 15 + 4 = 28$

Now, have a look at $2 + 3 × 4$. What do you think the answer should be?

Can you think of another way of working it out which gives a different answer?

If you work from left to right, you will get $2 + 3 = 5$ and $5 × 4 = 20$

But, you could do the multiplication first and then the addition:

$3 × 4 = 12$ and $2 + 12 = 14$

So, which answer is right? 20 or 14?

Clearly, everyone has to agree on how to work out a mixed calculation like this one. The rule that is used is:

> In a mixed calculation, you do all the × and ÷ before the + and −, unless told otherwise.
>
> If the calculation involves only × and ÷, or only + and −, then you work from left to right.

So, for $2 + 3 \times 4$, you work out the × first, even though it is written last. The answer is then 14.

Try working out the same calculation on your calculator. If you have a scientific calculator* you should get 14 as the answer.

Look how the rule applies in the following examples.

1   Work out $8 - 4 \div 2$
    ÷ first: $4 \div 2 = 2$
    So, $8 \;-\; 4 \div 2 \;=\; 8 - 2$
    − last: $8 \;-\; 2 \quad\;=\; 6$

2   Work out $6 + 4 \times 3 - 2$
    × first: $4 \times 3 = 12$
    So, $6 \quad+\quad 4 \times 3 \quad-\quad 2 \;=\; 6 + 12 - 2$
    +, − last: $6 \quad+\quad 12 \quad-\quad 2 \;=\; 18 - 2 \;=\; 16$

3   Work out $23 + 7 \times 12 - 18 \div 3$
    ×, ÷ first: $7 \times 12 = 84$
                    $18 \div 3 = 6$
    So, $23 \quad+\quad 7 \times 12 \quad-\quad 18 \div 3 \;=\; 23 + 84 - 6$
    +, − last: $23 \quad+\quad 84 \quad-\quad 6 \;=\; 101$

4   Work out $3 + 16 \div 4 \times 5$
    ÷, × first: $16 \div 4 \times 5 = 4 \times 5 = 20$
    So, $3 \quad+\quad 16 \div 4 \times 5 \;=\; 3 + 20$
    + last: $3 \quad+\quad 20 \;=\; 23$

Maths Activity

1   Work out, without using a calculator:

   (a) $5 + 6 \times 2$

   (b) $4 \div 2 + 17 - 3 \times 4$

   (c) $22 \times 3 \div 11 + 4 - 2 \times 5$

   (d) $18 - 7 \times 2 + 6 \div 2$

---

* One with $\boxed{\sin}$, $\boxed{\cos}$ and $\boxed{\tan}$ keys – see Chapter 5 (page 135) for more information about different types of calculator.

Answers

1 (a) $5 + 6 \times 2 = 5 + 12 = 17$
        $\times$ first $+$ last

   (b) $4 \div 2 + 17 - 3 \times 4 = 2 + 17 - 12 = 19 - 12 = 7$
      $\div$ and $\times$ first $+$ and $-$ last

   (c) $22 \times 3 \div 11 + 4 - 2 \times 5 = 6 + 4 - 10 = 0$
      $\times$ and $\div$ first $+$ and $-$ last

   (d) $18 - 7 \times 2 + 6 \div 2 = 18 - 14 + 3 = 7$
      $\times$ and $\div$ first $-$ and $+$ last

Now, try the same calculations on your calculator. Does your calculator work out the $\times$ and $\div$ before the $+$ and $-$ as well? (If it does, it is a scientific calculator.)

Unless told otherwise ...

Sometimes you need to do the addition or subtraction in a calculation before the multiplication or division. Suppose you have two boxes of cakes to share between three people. The first box has five cakes in it and the second has seven cakes in it. How many cakes will each person get?

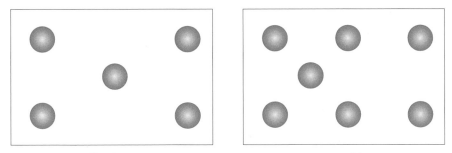

first box   second box

Here, you have to add 5 to 7, and then divide the answer by 3. That's not the order the rule uses, so we need another way of setting out this calculation. To make sure a particular bit of a calculation is worked out first it is written in brackets, like this:

$(5 + 7) \div 3$

This calculation is said as 'bracket, five plus seven, close bracket, divided by three' or 'five plus seven, all divided by three'.

The brackets mean:

(do me first, instead of what the rule says!)

So, you work out $(5 + 7) \div 3$ like this:

$(5 + 7) \div 3 = 12 \div 3 = 4$
brackets first   then $\div$

Maths Activity

2   Work out:

   (a) $6 \times (4 + 3)$

   (b) $12 \div (7 - 3)$

   (c) $(17 - 2) \div (4 + 1)$

3   In the following calculations, some of the brackets are unnecessary. Identify these unnecessary brackets and work out the answers to the calculations.

   (a) $24 - (3 \times 2)$

   (b) $3 + (14 \div 2) - 2 \times (2 + 1)$

   (c) $6 \div (3 \times 2)$

Answers

2   (a) $6 \times (4 + 3) = 6 \times 7 = 42$

   brackets first   then $\times$

   Note: $6 \times (4 + 3)$ is usually written as $6 (4 + 3)$, that is, without the multiplication sign outside the bracket.

   (b) $12 \div (7 - 3) = 12 \div 4 = 3$

   brackets first   then $\div$

   (c) $(17 - 2) \div (4 + 1) = 15 \div 5 = 3$

   brackets first   then $\div$

3   (a) You don't need any brackets here because $\times$ is worked out before $-$ anyway.
   $24 - 3 \times 2 = 24 - 6 = 18$

   (b) You don't need the brackets around the $(14 \div 2)$.
   $3 + 14 \div 2 - 2 \times (2 + 1) = 3 + 14 \div 2 - 2 \times 3 = 3 + 7 - 6 = 4$

   brackets first   then $\div$ and $\times$ $+$ and $-$ last
   As the extra brackets are not necessary they are usually left out.

   (c) The brackets are needed here: $6 \div (3 \times 2) = 6 \div 6 = 1$
   If the brackets are omitted, working from left to right gives:
   $6 \div 3 \times 2 = 2 \times 2 = 4$

Some powerful notation ...

In mathematics, expressions like $4 \times 4 \times 4 \times 4 \times 4$ are written more concisely as 4^5. This is said as 'four to the power five'. The number at the bottom (the 4) is called the *base*. The top number (the 5) is called the *power* or *index* (the plural of index is *indices*). It tells you how many of the base number to multiply together.

So, 3^2 means 3×3, which is 9

3^2 is usually read as 'three squared', because 3^2 is the area of a square whose sides are 3 units long. It can also be called 3 to the power of 2.

Similarly, 5^3 means $5 \times 5 \times 5 = 125$. 5^3 is read as 'five cubed', because it is the volume of a cube whose sides are 5 units long.

There are no special words for powers greater than 3; we just say, 'four to the power five', 'four to the power six', and so on.

*M*aths Activity

4   Write the following using power notation.

   (a) $3 \times 3 \times 3 \times 3 \times 3 \times 3$

   (b) $2 \times 2 \times 2$

   (c) $25 \times 25 \times 25 \times 25$

5   What is the value of:

   (a) 5^2

   (b) 4^3

   (c) 3^5

Answers

4   (a) 3^6

   (b) 2^3

   (c) 25^4

5   (a) $5^2 = 5 \times 5 = 25$

   (b) $4^3 = 4 \times 4 \times 4 = 64$

   (c) $3^5 = 3 \times 3 \times 3 \times 3 \times 3 = 243$

Writing expressions like $3 \times 3 \times 3 \times 3$ as 3^4 is quick and neat, so you will often meet this notation in calculations. You should work out the powers first (that is, even before $\times$ and $\div$) unless brackets tell you to do otherwise.

For example:

$3^2 + 4^2$	$=$	$3 \times 3 + 4 \times 4$	$=$	$9 + 16$	$=$ 25
powers first		then $\times$		+ last	
6×2^3	$=$	$6 \times (2 \times 2 \times 2)$	$=$	6×8	$=$ 48
powers first				then $\times$	
$(2 + 3)^2$	$=$	5^2	$=$	5×5	$=$ 25
brackets first		then power			

$3^2 + 4^2$ is read as 'three squared plus four squared'.

6×2^3 is read as 'six times two cubed'.

$(2 + 3)^2$ is read as 'two plus three all squared'.

*M*aths Activity

6   Work out:

(a) $2^2 \times 3^3$

(b) $3 \times 5 + 4^2$

(c) $(4 - 3)^5$

Answers

6   (a) $2^2 \times 3^3 = (2 \times 2) \times (3 \times 3 \times 3) = 4 \times 27 = 108$

powers first   then ×

(b) $3 \times 5 + 4^2 = 3 \times 5 + 16 = 15 + 16 = 31$

power first then ×   + last

(c) $(4 - 3)^5 = 1^5 = 1 \times 1 \times 1 \times 1 \times 1 = 1$

bracket first, then power

(Note that 1 to any power always has the value 1.)

We have seen that there are quite a lot of rules to remember when tackling a calculation.

To help you to remember the order, you can use the mnemonic:

B I D M A S

The letters stand for **B**rackets, **I**ndices, **D**ivision, **M**ultiplication, **A**ddition and **S**ubtraction.

In other words, work out the brackets first, then the indices or powers, then any multiplications or divisions and, finally, any additions or subtractions. Remember to work from left to right if any part of your calculation involves only multiplications and divisions or only additions and subtractions.

If you have a calculation which involves nested brackets, work out the innermost sets first. For example:

$2\{(13 + 2) - (4 + 5)\} = 2\{15 - 9\} = 2\{6\} = 2 \times 6 = 12$

↑   ↑ ↑   ↑

these brackets first

Note that using different sorts of brackets – for example, ( ), [ ] and { } – makes the calculation clearer than using the same type of bracket.

2 Negative numbers

This section explains what negative numbers are and describes how they are used in a few everyday situations. Negative numbers are common in science and mathematics, so it is important that you feel confident about using them and about working out calculations containing negative numbers.

Suppose that your bank account contains £50 and you decide to withdraw £60. Your next statement will show that your account is overdrawn by £10. The bank records this information using *negative numbers*. These numbers are written in the same way as ordinary numbers but they have a negative sign, or minus sign (–), in front of the number. So, the bank will record your new balance as –£10 ('minus ten pounds'). Note that the '–' sign does not mean 'subtract'; it just shows that you will have to pay £10 to clear your account.

Negative numbers arise in any situation in which you need to talk about numbers which are less than some agreed starting point (labelled zero). For example, on the Celsius temperature scale, the starting point is taken as the temperature at which water freezes. If the temperature drops 5 degrees below this freezing point, it is recorded as –5°C. The minus sign shows that the temperature will have to rise by 5 degrees to reach zero. If you look at an outdoor thermometer, you can see that the negative values are marked on the scale like this:

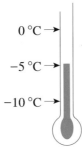

You can picture any negative number by drawing a number line.

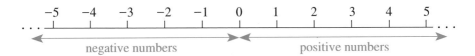

So, the thermometer is like a vertical number line!

You say the number –3 as 'minus three' or 'negative three'. Sometimes, 'minus three' is written ⁻3, with a raised minus sign, to distinguish it from 'subtract 3'. In the rest of this section, 'minus three' will be written (–3), in brackets. As you move along the number line from left to right, the numbers get bigger.

So, (–2) is greater than (–3) and less than (–1).

On this number line, just the whole number values have been marked. You can, however, mark any numbers (including fractions and decimals) on a number line if you wish.

On the number line opposite:

A is the value 25

B is (−15)

C is (−22)

and D is (−28)

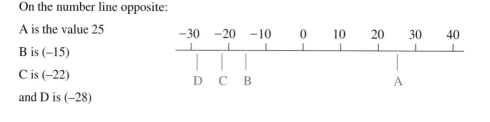

Draw a number line and mark on it the values:

A at 260   B at (−90)   C at (−170)   and   D at (−230)

Which is the greatest value out of A, B, C and D?

Which is the least value out of A, B, C and D?

Your number line should look like this:

The greatest value is A at 260, because it is the point furthest to the right. The least value is D at (−230), because it is the point furthest to the left.

Addition and subtraction

You can use the number line to work out how to add and subtract numbers.

Start with an easy problem first: 5 + 2

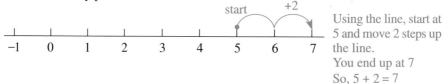

Using the line, start at 5 and move 2 steps up the line.
You end up at 7
So, 5 + 2 = 7

You can use the same method for (−6) + 4 (read as 'minus six plus four').

Start at (−6)
Move 4 steps up the line
to the right. You end up at (−2)
So, (− 6) + 4 = (− 2)

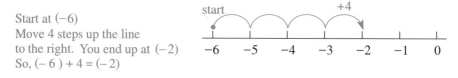

Now, try a subtraction: 5 − 2

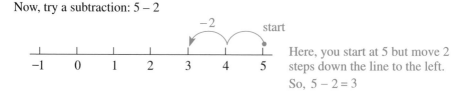

Here, you start at 5 but move 2 steps down the line to the left.
So, 5 − 2 = 3

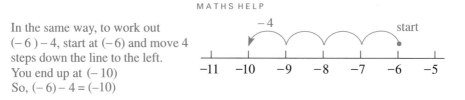

In the same way, to work out
$(-6) - 4$, start at (-6) and move 4
steps down the line to the left.
You end up at (-10)
So, $(-6) - 4 = (-10)$

(This calculation is read as 'minus six subtract four' or 'negative six take away four'.)
You can use these techniques to add or subtract any *positive* number.

How to add or subtract a positive number

for example, $(-2) + 1$ or $(-2) - 1$

1   Draw a number line and mark
    the first number on it:

2   To add a positive number, move right:

    To subtract a positive number,
    move left:

3   Your final position is the answer.

    So, $(-2) + 1 = (-1)$ and $(-2) - 1 = (-3)$

---

*M*aths Activity

1   Work out:

   (a) $(-2) + 4$ (c) $(-4) + 4$ (e) $(-2) - 3$

   (b) $(-3) + 2$ (d) $3 - 4$ (f) $(-3) - 5$

Answers

1   Draw a number line to help you to work out the answers.

   (a) 2   start at (-2), move 4 to the right

   (b) (-1) start at (-3), move 2 to the right

   (c) 0   start at (-4), move 4 to the right

   (d) (-1) start at 3, move 4 to the left

   (e) (-5) start at (-2), move 3 to the left

   (f) (-8) start at (-3), move 5 to the left

The rules above apply only if you add or subtract a *positive* number.

What happens if you want to add or subtract a *negative* number?

To help you to see what the rules for negative numbers might be, we shall look at a couple of examples.

Example 1

Imagine you are selling some of your things and you make a profit of £2 on one article and a loss of £3 on another. What is your overall profit?

You can represent profits using positive numbers and losses using negative numbers. So, the profit is +2 for the first article and (–3) for the second one.

To find the overall profit, you have to add up the individual profits: 2 + (–3)

(Remember, the negative number is written inside a bracket, as (–3), to avoid confusion with '–' meaning subtract.)

We can see that the overall profit is actually a loss of £1. So, 2 + (–3) must equal (–1). We know that 2 – 3 = (–1). So, 2 + (–3) must be the same as 2 – 3

In other words, it looks as if adding a negative number is the same as subtracting the equivalent positive number.

Example 2

The bottom of a pothole is 40 metres below sea level. The entrance to the pothole is 10 metres above sea level. What distance will a potholer climb if she goes from the bottom of the pothole to the entrance?

30 — ← viewpoint	You can work out the height the potholer climbs by subtracting the starting height from the finishing height. For example, if the potholer had previously climbed from the entrance to a viewpoint 30 metres above sea level, she would have climbed 20 metres, since:
20 —	
10 — ← entrance	$30 - 10 = 20$
0 — ← sea level	In the same way, the distance climbed from the bottom of the pothole to the entrance is:
	$10 - (-40) = 50$
–10 —	If you think about it in practical terms, the potholer has to climb 40 metres to reach sea level, and then another 10 metres to reach the entrance:
–20 —	50 metres in all.
	This means that $10 - (-40)$ is the same as $10 + 40$
–30 —	So, subtracting a negative number is the same as adding the equivalent positive number.
bottom of the pothole	
–40 — ←	

These rules work for any negative number. Explaining why involves some advanced mathematics, so I shall just summarize the rules here.

> Adding a *negative* number is the same as making it a positive number and then subtracting it.
>
> So, $4 + (-5) = 4 - 5$
>
> Subtracting a *negative* number is the same as making it a positive number and then adding it.
>
> So, $4 - (-5) = 4 + 5$

These rules change the problems back into the kind of problems you were solving before: that is, adding and subtracting positive numbers. The box below shows you what to do.

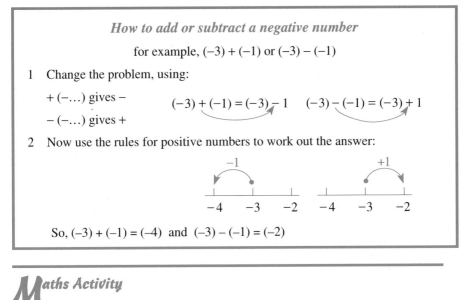

> ### *How to add or subtract a negative number*
>
> for example, $(-3) + (-1)$ or $(-3) - (-1)$
>
> 1   Change the problem, using:
>
> $+ (-...)$ gives $-$ $(-3) + (-1) = (-3) - 1$ $(-3) - (-1) = (-3) + 1$
>
> $- (-...)$ gives $+$
>
> 2   Now use the rules for positive numbers to work out the answer:
>
> So, $(-3) + (-1) = (-4)$ and $(-3) - (-1) = (-2)$

*M*aths Activity

2   Work out:

   (a) $3 + (-2)$ (c) $(-2) - (-6)$ (e) $(-2) + (-7)$

   (b) $3 - (-2)$ (d) $4 + (-7)$ (f) $(-4) - (-4)$

Answers

2   (a) $3 + (-2) = 3 - 2 = 1$ (c) $(-2) - (-6) = (-2) + 6 = 4$ (e) $(-2) + (-7) = (-2) - 7 = (-9)$

   (b) $3 - (-2) = 3 + 2 = 5$ (d) $4 + (-7) = 4 - 7 = (-3)$ (f) $(-4) - (-4) = (-4) + 4 = 0$

Multiplication and division

In one way, multiplication is just a shorthand way of writing an addition problem. For example, 3×4 means '3 lots of 4' or $4 + 4 + 4$

In the same way, $3 \times (-2)$ means '3 lots of (-2)' or $(-2) + (-2) + (-2) = (-6)$

So, $3 \times (-2) = (-6)$

The order in which you multiply two numbers together does not matter. Think of 4×3 and 3×4. Both give an answer of 12 So, $(-2) \times 3 = (-6)$ as well.

These examples illustrate the general rule.

If you *multiply* two numbers which have *different* signs, the answer is *negative*.

$(-) \times (+) = (-)$	and	$(+) \times (-) = (-)$
minus times plus gives minus		plus times minus gives minus

Work out $4 \times (-3)$ $3 \times (-3)$ $2 \times (-3)$ $1 \times (-3)$ $0 \times (-3)$

Check your results in the table below.

Calculation	$4 \times (-3)$	$3 \times (-3)$	$2 \times (-3)$	$1 \times (-3)$	$0 \times (-3)$
Answer	(-12)	(-9)	(-6)	(-3)	0

Looking at the table again, you can see that, as you read from left to right, the numbers multiplying (-3) are going down by 1 each time, and the answers are going up by 3. Following the same pattern, you can extend the table like this:

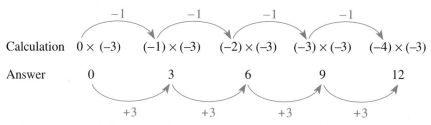

So, it appears that $(-1) \times (-3) = 3$, $(-2) \times (-3) = 6$ and $(-3) \times (-3) = 9$, and all the answers are positive numbers. Although this result can be shown to be true for any two negative numbers, I shall just state the general rule here.

If you *multiply* two numbers which have *the same* sign, the answer is *positive*.

$(+) \times (+) = (+)$	and	$(-) \times (-) = (+)$
you know this already!		minus times minus gives plus

Combining these rules:

$(-4) \times (-5) = 20$ $4 \times (-5) = (-20)$

↑   ↑   ↑   ↑   ↑   ↑

same signs give plus   different signs give minus

$4 \times 5 = 20$

↑   ↑   ↑

same signs give plus

$(-4) \times 5 = (-20)$

↑   ↑   ↑

different signs give minus

*M*aths Activity

3   Work out:

(a) $(-4) \times (-2)$

(b) $4 \times (-2)$

(c) $(-1) \times (-6)$

(d) $(-3) \times 6$

(e) $8 \times (-4)$

(f) $(-2) \times (-5)$

(g) $(-2) \times (-4) \times 3$

(h) $(-5) \times 6 \times (-2) \times (-3)$

Answers

3   (a) $(-4) \times (-2) = 8$

(b) $4 \times (-2) = (-8)$

(c) $(-1) \times (-6) = 6$

(d) $(-3) \times 6 = (-18)$

(e) $8 \times (-4) = (-32)$

(f) $(-2) \times (-5) = 10$

(g) $(-2) \times (-4) \times 3 = 8 \times 3 = 24$

(h) $(-5) \times 6 \times (-2) \times (-3) = (-30) \times 6 = (-180)$

We can think of division as 'undoing' multiplication.

So, to work out $24 \div 6$, you could say 'What do I have to multiply 6 by to get 24?' The answer is 4, so $24 \div 6 = 4$

Similarly, to work out $(-24) \div (-6)$, you could say 'What do I have to multiply (-6) by to get (-24)?' Since $(-6) \times 4 = (-24)$, the answer is 4 again: $(-24) \div (-6) = 4$

The general rule is:

> If you *divide* two numbers with the *same* sign, the answer is *positive*.
>
> $(+) \div (+) = (+)$ and $(-) \div (-) = (+)$
>
> plus divided by plus gives plus   minus divided by minus gives plus

How would you work out $(-24) \div 6$ and $24 \div (-6)$?

Can you suggest a rule for dividing numbers which have different signs?

You should find that $(-24) \div 6 = (-4)$, because $6 \times (-4) = (-24)$, and $24 \div (-6) = (-4)$, because $(-6) \times 4 = (-24)$

The rule is:

> If you *divide* two numbers with *different* signs, the answer is *negative*.
>
> $(+) \div (-) = (-)$ and $(-) \div (+) = (-)$
>
> plus divided by minus gives minus   minus divided by plus gives minus

*M*aths Activity

4   Work out:

   (a) $16 \div (-4)$ (c) $(-36) \div (-6)$ (e) $18 \div (-6)$

   (b) $(-25) \div 5$ (d) $(-36) \div 9$ (f) $(-12) \div (-3)$

Answers

4   (a) $16 \div (-4) = (-4)$ (c) $(-36) \div (-6) = 6$ (e) $18 \div (-6) = (-3)$

   (b) $(-25) \div 5 = (-5)$ (d) $(-36) \div 9 = (-4)$ (f) $(-12) \div (-3) = 4$

Sometimes, you have to work out the value of complicated expressions which use several of these rules together. You can use the BIDMAS mnemonic on page 308 to sort out the order of the calculation. Try working through the following calculations step by step.

Work out $3 \times (-4) + (-2)$
$\times$ first $3 \times (-4) + (-2)$ $= (-12) + (-2)$
then + $= (-12) - 2$
                                                     $= (-14)$

Work out $(-6) \times [2 - (-3)]$
[ ] bracket first $(-6) \times [2 - (-3)]$ $= (-6) \times [2 + 3]$
                                                     $= (-6) \times 5$
then $\times$ $= (-30)$

Work out $[4 - (-2)]^2$
[ ] bracket first $[4 - (-2)]^2$ $= [4 + 2]^2$
                                                     $= 6^2$
then power $= 6 \times 6$
                                                     $= 36$

Work out $[2 + (-3)] \times [(-3) - (-2)]$
[ ] bracket first $[2 + (-3)]$ $= [2 - 3]$ $= (-1)$
and $[(-3) - (-2)]$ $= [(-3) + 2]$ $= (-1)$

then $\times$ $[2 + (-3)] \times [(-3) - (-2)]$ $= (-1) \times (-1)$
                                                          $= 1$

3 Fractions

This section will help you to understand what fractions are and describe how to handle calculations that involve fractions.

Fractions are used to describe a part of something. For example, suppose you have a bar of chocolate containing eight equally sized pieces. Each piece is one eighth of the whole bar. If you eat three pieces, you will have eaten 'three eighths' of the bar.

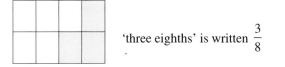

'three eighths' is written $\dfrac{3}{8}$

Note that the bottom number in the fraction (the *denominator*) tells you how many pieces there are altogether. The top number (the *numerator*) tells you how many

pieces you've eaten. If you eat all eight pieces, you will have eaten eight eighths ($\dfrac{8}{8}$)

or the whole bar. In other words, $\dfrac{8}{8} = 1$

Look at the bars of chocolate below. The bars are all the same size, but the pieces are of different sizes. You have decided to eat the shaded portions.

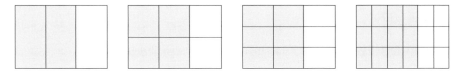

Write down the fraction of each bar you will eat.

You should find that the portions are:

$\dfrac{2}{3}$ (two thirds); $\dfrac{4}{6}$ (four sixths); $\dfrac{6}{9}$ (six ninths) and $\dfrac{12}{18}$ (twelve eighteenths).

Looking at the bars again, you can see that you will have eaten exactly the same portion of each bar.

This means that $\dfrac{2}{3}, \dfrac{4}{6}, \dfrac{6}{9}$ and $\dfrac{12}{18}$ all represent the same value, even though there are

different numbers in the fractions themselves. In other words, $\dfrac{2}{3} = \dfrac{4}{6} = \dfrac{6}{9} = \dfrac{12}{18}$

We could carry on dividing the bar of chocolate into smaller and smaller pieces, and

generating more fractions with the same value as $\dfrac{2}{3}$. But there is an easier way. If you

look at the fractions again, it is clear that we can get from one to another by multiplying the numerator and denominator by the same number:

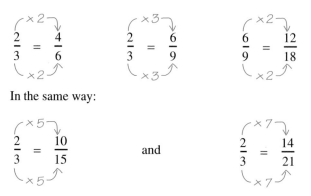

In the same way:

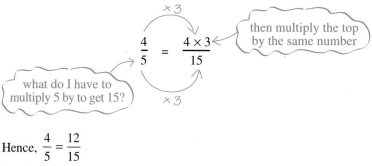

and

This method works for any fraction. So, to find how many fifteenths are equivalent to four fifths:

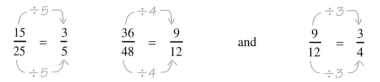

$$\frac{4}{5} = \frac{4 \times 3}{15}$$

then multiply the top by the same number

what do I have to multiply 5 by to get 15?

Hence, $\frac{4}{5} = \frac{12}{15}$

Fractions which have the same value are called *equivalent fractions.*

> If you multiply both top and bottom of a fraction by the *same* number (not zero), you do not change its size. The new fraction is *equivalent* to the old one.

We can also generate equivalent fractions by *dividing* the top and bottom by the same number:

$$\frac{15}{25} = \frac{3}{5} \qquad \frac{36}{48} = \frac{9}{12} \qquad \text{and} \qquad \frac{9}{12} = \frac{3}{4}$$

This is called 'cancelling down' the fraction. It is common practice to cancel fractions down *as far as possible* and leave them in their 'lowest terms'. Sometimes, you will see fractions cancelled down like this:

$$\frac{\overset{3}{\cancel{21}}}{\underset{5}{\cancel{35}}} = \frac{3}{5}$$

> To *cancel down* a fraction, divide both top and bottom by the *same* number.

Maths Activity

1 Fill in the blanks.

(a) $\dfrac{1}{2} = \dfrac{?}{4}$

(c) $\dfrac{1}{3} = \dfrac{3}{?}$

(b) $\dfrac{3}{5} = \dfrac{?}{10}$

(d) $\dfrac{2}{7} = \dfrac{?}{35}$

2 Cancel these fractions down to their lowest terms.

(a) $\dfrac{3}{12}$

(d) $\dfrac{20}{90}$

(b) $\dfrac{18}{21}$

(e) $\dfrac{36}{64}$

(c) $\dfrac{21}{63}$

Answers

1 (a) $\dfrac{2}{4}$ ($\times$ top and bottom by 2)

(c) $\dfrac{3}{9}$ ($\times$ top and bottom by 3)

(b) $\dfrac{6}{10}$ ($\times$ top and bottom by 2)

(d) $\dfrac{10}{35}$ ($\times$ top and bottom by 5)

2 (a) $\dfrac{1}{4}$ ($\div$ top and bottom by 3)

(d) $\dfrac{2}{9}$ ($\div$ top and bottom by 10)

(b) $\dfrac{6}{7}$ ($\div$ top and bottom by 3)

(e) $\dfrac{9}{16}$ ($\div$ top and bottom by 4)

(c) $\dfrac{1}{3}$ ($\div$ top and bottom by 21)

You can use these ideas to write one thing as a fraction of another. Suppose that out of a group of 2000 people, 1400 own a car. What fraction of the group is this?

Here, the 'whole' is the group of 2000, and the 'part' we are interested in is the 1400 people with a car. So, the fraction with a car is

$$\frac{\text{Number of people with car}}{\text{Total number of people}} = \frac{1400}{2000} = \frac{14}{20} = \frac{7}{10}$$

Similarly, the fraction of the group without a car is

$$\frac{\text{Number of people without car}}{\text{Total number of people}} = \frac{600}{2000} = \frac{3}{10}$$

Note that adding these two fractions $\frac{7}{10}$ and $\frac{3}{10} = 1$

In general:

> $$\text{Fraction of group with property} = \frac{\text{Number with property}}{\text{Total number in group}}$$

 **aths Activity**

3 In a book of 500 pages, 40 pages have mistakes. What fraction of the pages of the book contains mistakes?

4 In a group of car drivers, 80 use unleaded petrol and 50 do not. How many people are there in the group? What fraction of the group does not use unleaded petrol?

5 In a group of 60 students, 44 have not used a scientific calculator before. What fraction of the group have used this type of calculator before?

Answers

3 Fraction is $\frac{40}{500} = \frac{2}{25}$

4 $80 + 50 = 130$ people in the group

Fraction is $\frac{\text{Number who do not use unleaded}}{\text{Total number}} = \frac{50}{130} = \frac{5}{13}$

5 $60 - 44 = 16$ people who have used a scientific calculator

Fraction $= \frac{\text{Number who have used a scientific calculator}}{\text{Total number}} = \frac{16}{60} = \frac{4}{15}$

Fractions in which the top number is smaller than the bottom number are called

proper fractions. They describe part of one whole: for example, $\frac{2}{3}$ of an apple, or $\frac{3}{4}$ of a group of people.

If the top number is bigger than the bottom number, the fraction is called an *improper fraction* or a *top-heavy fraction*. Its value is more than one whole: for example, $\frac{7}{6}$, $\frac{9}{2}$ or $\frac{21}{4}$ (said as 'seven sixths', 'nine halves' and 'twenty-one over four').

Improper fractions can be changed into *mixed numbers*. These are numbers with a whole number part and a proper fraction part – for example, $3\frac{1}{4}$ or $2\frac{7}{9}$ (said as 'three and a quarter' and 'two and seven ninths').

To change an improper fraction into a mixed number, first think about what the fraction means. For example, $\frac{7}{3}$ means 'seven thirds'. This can be pictured as:

So, $\frac{7}{3}$ is the same as $2\frac{1}{3}$

If you divide 7 by 3, you get '2 with 1 left over'. In other words, you can group the seven thirds into two groups of three thirds with one third left over. Each group of three thirds makes a whole one, so seven thirds are the same as two wholes and one third or $2\frac{1}{3}$

> To change an improper fraction into a mixed number, *divide the top number by the bottom number.*

You can change mixed numbers back into improper fractions too. To change $3\frac{1}{2}$ into an improper fraction is the same as asking yourself:

'How many halves are there in $3\frac{1}{2}$?'

For each whole there will be two halves, so 3 wholes make $3 \times 2 = 6$ halves. Then there is the other $\frac{1}{2}$, which came with the 3 wholes. So, altogether there are $1 + 3 \times 2 = 7$ halves.

In other words: $3\frac{1}{2} = \dfrac{1 + 3 \times 2}{2} = \dfrac{7}{2}$

In the same way, $4\frac{5}{8} = \dfrac{5 + 4 \times 8}{8} = \dfrac{37}{8}$

Maths Help

How to change a mixed number into an improper fraction

1   Decide what sort of parts you are dealing with:

$$3\frac{4}{5} = \frac{}{5}$$

dealing with fifths

2   Work out how many of these parts you've got:

4 already

$$3\frac{4}{5} = \frac{4 + 3 \times 5}{5}$$

3 whole ones is 3 lots of 5 parts

3   Work out the calculation on top:

$$3\frac{4}{5} = \frac{19}{5}$$

Maths Activity

6   Change these improper fractions into mixed numbers.

(a) $\dfrac{17}{3}$ (c) $\dfrac{64}{5}$

(b) $\dfrac{27}{8}$ (d) $\dfrac{32}{8}$

7   Change these mixed numbers into improper fractions.

(a) $4\frac{3}{7}$ (c) $8\frac{6}{11}$

(b) $2\frac{5}{9}$ (d) $3\frac{13}{15}$

Answers

6   (a) $17 \div 3 = 5$ with 2 left over.   So, $\frac{17}{3} = 5\frac{2}{3}$

     (b) $27 \div 8 = 3$ with 3 left over.   So, $\frac{27}{8} = 3\frac{3}{8}$

(c) $64 \div 5 = 12$ with 4 left over. So, $\dfrac{64}{5} = 12\dfrac{4}{5}$

(d) $32 \div 8 = 4$. So, $\dfrac{32}{8} = 4$

7 (a) $4\dfrac{3}{7} = \dfrac{3 + 4 \times 7}{7} = \dfrac{31}{7}$ (c) $8\dfrac{6}{11} = \dfrac{6 + 8 \times 11}{11} = \dfrac{94}{11}$

(b) $2\dfrac{5}{9} = \dfrac{5 + 2 \times 9}{9} = \dfrac{23}{9}$ (d) $3\dfrac{13}{15} = \dfrac{13 + 3 \times 15}{15} = \dfrac{58}{15}$

Adding and subtracting fractions

There are two types of problems you might meet:

(a) those dealing with fractions of the same kind – for example, $\dfrac{4}{7} + \dfrac{6}{7}$ (both fractions involve sevenths)

(b) those dealing with fractions of different kinds – for example, $3\dfrac{1}{6} - 1\dfrac{7}{18}$ (the fractions involve sixths and eighteenths).

If the fractions are of the same kind, you can add or subtract them directly: $\dfrac{4}{7} + \dfrac{6}{7}$ means 'four sevenths and six sevenths', so the answer is ten sevenths. You can write down the solution like this:

$$\dfrac{4}{7} + \dfrac{6}{7} = \dfrac{4 + 6}{7} = \dfrac{10}{7} = 1\dfrac{3}{7}$$

In the same way:

$$2\dfrac{2}{5} - 1\dfrac{4}{5} = \dfrac{12}{5} - \dfrac{9}{5} = \dfrac{12 - 9}{5} = \dfrac{3}{5}$$

If the fractions are of different kinds, replace them with equivalent fractions.

For example, $\dfrac{2}{3}$ is equivalent to $\dfrac{4}{6}$ and $\dfrac{1}{2}$ is equivalent to $\dfrac{3}{6}$

So, $\dfrac{2}{3} + \dfrac{1}{2} = \dfrac{4}{6} + \dfrac{3}{6} = \dfrac{4 + 3}{6} = \dfrac{7}{6} = 1\dfrac{1}{6}$

Here, 6 is the smallest number which can be divided exactly by both 2 and 3.

The box below describes how to add or subtract mixed numbers.

> ### *How to add or subtract fractions*
>
> 1 Add (or subtract) the whole number parts: $\quad 1\frac{5}{12} + 2\frac{5}{6} = 3 + \frac{5}{12} + \frac{5}{6}$
>
> 2 Change the fractions into equivalent fractions
> with the same bottom number (denominator): $\qquad = 3 + \frac{5}{12} + \frac{10}{12}$
>
> 3 Add (or subtract) the fraction parts: $\qquad = 3 + \frac{15}{12}$
>
> 4 Simplify the answer: $\qquad = 3 + 1\frac{3}{12}$
>
> $\qquad = 3 + 1\frac{1}{4}$
>
> $\qquad = 4\frac{1}{4}$

This method works for subtracting fractions too:

Subtract whole numbers: $\qquad 3\frac{1}{6} - 1\frac{7}{18} \quad = 2 + \frac{1}{6} - \frac{7}{18}$

Change to equivalent fractions: $\qquad = 2 + \frac{3}{18} - \frac{7}{18} \quad = 2 - \frac{4}{18}$

Simplify answer: $\qquad = 1\frac{14}{18} \quad = 1\frac{7}{9}$

Maths Activity

8 Work out:

(a) $\dfrac{4}{21} + \dfrac{5}{21}$
(b) $1\frac{3}{8} + 2\frac{1}{3}$
(c) $1\frac{2}{3} + 3\frac{3}{4}$

9 Work out:

(a) $\dfrac{9}{13} - \dfrac{4}{13}$
(b) $1\frac{4}{15} - \frac{4}{5}$
(c) $4\frac{1}{5} - 2\frac{3}{4}$

Answers

8 (a) $\dfrac{4}{21} + \dfrac{5}{21} = \dfrac{9}{21} = \dfrac{3}{7}$

(b) $1\frac{3}{8} + 2\frac{1}{3} = 3 + \frac{3}{8} + \frac{1}{3} = 3 + \frac{9}{24} + \frac{8}{24} = 3 + \frac{17}{24} = 3\frac{17}{24}$

(c) $1\frac{2}{3} + 3\frac{3}{4} = 4 + \frac{2}{3} + \frac{3}{4} = 4 + \frac{8}{12} + \frac{9}{12} = 4 + \frac{17}{12} = 4 + 1\frac{5}{12} = 5\frac{5}{12}$

9   (a) $\dfrac{9}{13} - \dfrac{4}{13} = \dfrac{5}{13}$

(b) $1\dfrac{4}{15} - \dfrac{4}{5} = 1 + \dfrac{4}{15} - \dfrac{12}{15} = 1 - \dfrac{8}{15} = \dfrac{7}{15}$

(c) $4\dfrac{1}{5} - 2\dfrac{3}{4} = 2 + \dfrac{1}{5} - \dfrac{3}{4} = 2 + \dfrac{4}{20} - \dfrac{15}{20} = 2 - \dfrac{11}{20} = 1\dfrac{9}{20}$

Multiplying and dividing fractions

$\dfrac{5}{6}$ of the rectangle opposite is shaded.

If you split the shaded part into thirds, the fraction coloured is 'two thirds of five sixths'.

□ shaded

$\dfrac{2}{3}$ of $\dfrac{5}{6}$

□ coloured

'Of' means multiply. (Think what '3 lots *of* 2' means.)
So, mathematically

the calculation is $\dfrac{2}{3} \times \dfrac{5}{6}$

Looking at the rectangle again, you can see that it has been split into 18 equal pieces and

that 10 of them are coloured. So, the fraction coloured is $\dfrac{10}{18}$, or cancelling down: $\dfrac{5}{9}$

So, $\dfrac{2}{3} \times \dfrac{5}{6}$ must be equal to $\dfrac{10}{18} = \dfrac{5}{9}$

You can get the same result as follows:

$\dfrac{2}{3} \times \dfrac{5}{6}$ can be rewritten as $\dfrac{2 \times 5}{3 \times 6} = \dfrac{2 \times 5}{3 \times (2 \times 3)} = \dfrac{2 \times 5}{3 \times 2 \times 3}$

We can 'cancel down' this expression if we divide top and bottom by 2:

$$= \dfrac{\overset{1}{\cancel{2}} \times 5}{3 \times \underset{1}{\cancel{2}} \times 3} = \dfrac{1 \times 5}{3 \times 1 \times 3} = \dfrac{5}{9}$$

If you want to multiply fractions, including improper fractions, then follow the steps shown below.

How to multiply fractions

for example, $1\frac{3}{8} \times 2\frac{4}{11}$

1 *Always* change mixed numbers into improper fractions first: $\dfrac{11}{8} \times \dfrac{26}{11}$

2 Multiply top numbers together, multiply bottom numbers together: $\dfrac{11 \times 26}{8 \times 11}$

3 Cancel down: $= \dfrac{\overset{1}{\cancel{11}} \times \overset{13}{\cancel{26}}}{\underset{4}{\cancel{8}} \times \underset{1}{\cancel{11}}}$

4 Multiply out: $= \dfrac{13}{4}$

5 Change the fraction back into a mixed number if you can: $= 3\frac{1}{4}$

Suppose that $\dfrac{4}{5}$ of a group of people are right-handed. If there are 150 people in the group, how many are right-handed? We need to work out $\dfrac{4}{5}$ of 150

150 can be written $\dfrac{150}{1}$, since $\dfrac{150}{1}$ means '150 whole ones'.

So, the calculation is: $\dfrac{4}{5} \times 150 = \dfrac{4}{5} \times \dfrac{150}{1} = \dfrac{4 \times 150}{5} = \dfrac{4 \times \overset{30}{\cancel{150}}}{\underset{1}{\cancel{5}}} = \dfrac{120}{1} = 120$

multiply   cancel down

Hence, 120 people are right-handed.

---

*M*aths Activity

10 Work out:

(a) $\dfrac{2}{3} \times \dfrac{9}{14}$ (b) $\dfrac{15}{16} \times \dfrac{24}{35}$ (c) $3\frac{2}{3} \times 1\frac{4}{11}$ (d) $2\frac{2}{5} \times 3\frac{2}{3}$

11 $\frac{2}{3}$ of a group of 60 people have blood group O. How many people have this blood group?

12 Seven tenths of a journey of 540 kilometres is on motorways. What fraction of the journey is on ordinary roads? How many kilometres will be driven on ordinary roads?

Answers

10 (a) $\frac{2}{3} \times \frac{9}{14} = \frac{2 \times 9}{3 \times 14} = \frac{\overset{1}{2} \times \overset{3}{9}}{\underset{1}{3} \times \underset{7}{14}} = \frac{3}{7}$

(b) $\frac{15}{16} \times \frac{24}{35} = \frac{15 \times 24}{16 \times 35} = \frac{\overset{3}{15} \times \overset{3}{24}}{\underset{2}{16} \times \underset{7}{35}} = \frac{3 \times 3}{2 \times 7} = \frac{9}{14}$

(c) $3\frac{2}{3} \times 1\frac{4}{11} = \frac{11}{3} \times \frac{15}{11} = \frac{11 \times 15}{3 \times 11} = \frac{\overset{1}{11} \times \overset{5}{15}}{\underset{1}{3} \times \underset{1}{11}} = \frac{5}{1} = 5$

(d) $2\frac{2}{5} \times 3\frac{2}{3} = \frac{12}{5} \times \frac{11}{3} = \frac{\overset{4}{12} \times 11}{5 \times \underset{1}{3}} = \frac{4 \times 11}{5 \times 1} = \frac{44}{5} = 8\frac{4}{5}$

11 $\frac{2}{3}$ of 60 $= \frac{2}{3} \times 60 = \frac{2 \times 60}{3} = \frac{2 \times \overset{20}{60}}{\underset{1}{3}} = \frac{40}{1} = 40$

So, 40 people have blood group O.

12 The fraction on motorways is $\frac{7}{10}$. So $\frac{3}{10}$ (that is, $1 - \frac{7}{10}$) is on ordinary roads.

The distance driven on ordinary roads is $\frac{3}{10}$ of 540 kilometres.

Now, $\frac{3}{10}$ of 540 $= \frac{3}{10} \times 540 = \frac{3 \times 540}{10} = \frac{3 \times \overset{54}{540}}{\underset{1}{10}} = 162$

Hence, 162 kilometres will be driven on ordinary roads.

You can change division problems back into multiplication problems by following the steps shown below.

How to divide fractions

for example, $2\frac{4}{9} \div 1\frac{1}{3}$

1 *Always* change mixed numbers into improper fractions first: $= \frac{22}{9} \div \frac{4}{3}$

2 Turn the fraction after the $\div$ sign upside down and change the $\div$ to $\times$: $= \frac{22}{9} \times \frac{3}{4}$

3 Cancel down and multiply out: $= \frac{\overset{11}{\cancel{22}}}{\underset{3}{\cancel{9}}} \times \frac{\overset{1}{\cancel{3}}}{\underset{2}{\cancel{4}}} = \frac{11}{6}$

4 Simplify if you can: $= 1\frac{5}{6}$

Why does the rule 'Turn the fraction upside down and multiply' work?

Suppose you have $2\frac{1}{2}$ pizzas cut into quarters. How many quarters are there? The calculation is $2\frac{1}{2} \div \frac{1}{4}$

But, we know that each pizza has four quarters in it. So, $2\frac{1}{2}$ pizzas will have $2\frac{1}{2} \times 4$ or $2\frac{1}{2} \times \frac{4}{1}$ quarters. In other words:

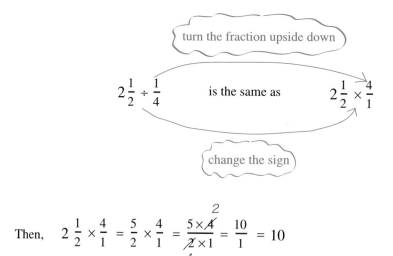

Then, $2\frac{1}{2} \times \frac{4}{1} = \frac{5}{2} \times \frac{4}{1} = \frac{5 \times \overset{2}{\cancel{4}}}{\underset{1}{\cancel{2}} \times 1} = \frac{10}{1} = 10$

Hence, there are ten pieces of pizza.

Maths Activity

13 Work out: (a) $\dfrac{2}{3} \div \dfrac{1}{6}$ (b) $2\dfrac{2}{5} \div \dfrac{24}{55}$ (c) $1\dfrac{4}{5} \div 1\dfrac{1}{2}$

Answers

13   (a) $\dfrac{2}{3} \div \dfrac{1}{6} = \dfrac{2}{3} \times \dfrac{6}{1} = \dfrac{2 \times \cancel{6}^{2}}{\cancel{3}_{1} \times 1} = \dfrac{4}{1} = 4$

(b) $2\dfrac{2}{5} \div \dfrac{24}{55} = \dfrac{12}{5} \times \dfrac{55}{24} = \dfrac{\cancel{12}^{1} \times \cancel{55}^{11}}{\cancel{5}_{1} \times \cancel{24}_{2}} = \dfrac{11}{2} = 5\dfrac{1}{2}$

(c) $1\dfrac{4}{5} \div 1\dfrac{1}{2} = \dfrac{9}{5} \div \dfrac{3}{2} = \dfrac{9}{5} \times \dfrac{2}{3} = \dfrac{\cancel{9}^{3} \times 2}{5 \times \cancel{3}_{1}} = \dfrac{3 \times 2}{5} = \dfrac{6}{5} = 1\dfrac{1}{5}$

If you have a scientific calculator, it may have a fraction key on it. If it does, it is worth consulting the manual to find out how to use it for these calculations.

4 Decimals

This section will help you to add, subtract, multiply and divide decimal numbers. It will also show you how to change decimals into fractions and vice versa.

When you write down a whole number such as 492, the order in which you write down the 2, the 4 and the 9 is important: 492 means 4 hundreds, 9 tens and 2 units (or ones). The position of each digit tells you what it represents – tens, hundreds, thousands and so on. (A digit is one of the numbers 0, 1, 2, 3, 4, 5, 6, 7, 8 or 9.) You can use this system to write down both whole numbers and fractions. The 'place value' table below shows the values of the different positions.

Whole numbers				Decimal point	Fractions		
thousands	hundreds	tens	units		tenths	hundredths	thousandths
		2	1	•	5	3	6

If you look at the column headings for whole numbers, you can see that the value of each column is ten times bigger than that of the column to its right. So, the next column on the left would be 'ten thousands', then 'hundred thousands', and so on. And the value of each column is ten times smaller than that of the one to its left. So, the column to the right of the units column is the 'tenths' column, and to the right of that is the 'hundredths' column, and so on. This way of writing numbers is called the decimal system because it is based on the number 10 (*decem* is Latin for 10).

You can work out the value of a decimal number by reading off the column headings just as you would with whole numbers. In the 'place value' table, the number 21.536 (which you would say as 'twenty one point five three six') means 2 tens, 1 unit, 5 tenths, 3 hundredths and 6 thousandths. In the same way, 0.1 means '1 tenth' or $\frac{1}{10}$;

0.01 means '1 hundredth' or $\frac{1}{100}$; and so on.

It is easy not to notice the decimal point with numbers less than 1, so you always put a zero in the units column (for example, write .1 as 0.1). It is good manners as it warns the reader to look for a decimal point.

You can use a 'place value' table to compare the sizes of two decimal numbers.

For example: which is bigger, 0.008 or 0.02?

	units		tenths	hundredths	thousandths
Set up a 'place value' table and put the numbers in it:	0	•	0	0	8
	0	•	0	2	

Look along the columns, from the left, and find the first column which has a digit in it which is not zero:

It is the hundredths column

Compare the digits in this column:

2 is bigger than 0

So, 0.02 is bigger than 0.008

*M*aths Activity

1 Which is bigger:

(a) 0.07 or 0.1? (b) 10.37 or 10.364?

Answers

1 (a) Put the numbers in a 'place value' table:

units		tenths	hundredths
0	•	0	7
0	•	1	

The tenths column shows that 0.1 is bigger.

(b)

tens	units		tenths	hundredths	thousandths
1	0	•	3	7	
1	0	•	3	6	4

The hundredths column shows that 10.37 is bigger.

You can also use the 'place value' table to convert decimals into fractions.

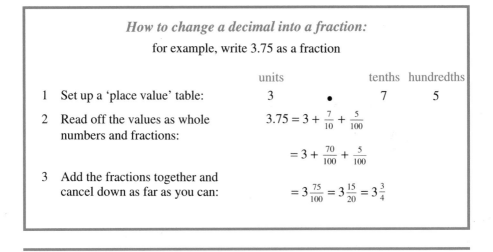

How to change a decimal into a fraction:

for example, write 3.75 as a fraction

	units		tenths	hundredths

1 Set up a 'place value' table: 3 • 7 5

2 Read off the values as whole numbers and fractions:
$$3.75 = 3 + \frac{7}{10} + \frac{5}{100}$$
$$= 3 + \frac{70}{100} + \frac{5}{100}$$

3 Add the fractions together and cancel down as far as you can:
$$= 3\frac{75}{100} = 3\frac{15}{20} = 3\frac{3}{4}$$

*M*aths Activity

2 Write the following decimals as fractions.

(a) 0.4 (b) 0.025 (c) 2.465

Answers

2 (a) $0.4 = \dfrac{4}{10} = \dfrac{2}{5}$

(b) $0.025 = \dfrac{2}{100} + \dfrac{5}{1000} = \dfrac{25}{1000} = \dfrac{1}{40}$

(c) $2.465 = 2 + \frac{4}{10} + \frac{6}{100} + \frac{5}{1000} = 2\frac{465}{1000} = 2\frac{93}{200}$

You can change fractions back into decimals too. A fraction can be interpreted as another way of writing a division. Suppose that you have two cakes to divide equally between five people. One way of doing it would be to cut each cake into five pieces and give each person one slice from each cake. Each person would end up with two slices or $\dfrac{2}{5}$ of a cake. So, $\dfrac{2}{5}$ is what you get when you divide 2 by 5: $\dfrac{2}{5}$ means $2 \div 5$ which equals 0.4

How to change a fraction into a decimal

for example, change $\dfrac{7}{8}$ into a decimal

1 Write the fraction as a division: $\dfrac{7}{8} = 7 \div 8$ or $8\overline{)7}$

2 Put a decimal point after the units digit and one directly above it in the answer. Add zeros after the point and divide out:

$$0.\,8\,7\,5$$
$$8\overline{)\,7.\,{}^{7}0\,{}^{6}0\,{}^{4}0}$$

3 So: $\dfrac{7}{8} = 0.875$

(Or you can use your calculator to work out $7 \div 8$ directly.)

Maths Activity

3 Write the following fractions as decimals.

(a) $\dfrac{4}{5}$

(b) $1\frac{3}{4}$

(c) $\dfrac{19}{20}$

Answers

3   (a) $\dfrac{4}{5} = 4 \div 5 = 0.8$

(b) $\dfrac{3}{4} = 3 \div 4 = 0.75$ So, $1\dfrac{3}{4} = 1.75$

(c) $\dfrac{19}{20} = 19 \div 20 = 0.95$

Now convert $\dfrac{4}{9}$ into a decimal using the same method. You'll learn most if you do it by hand. Stop when you get bored. Try the same with $\dfrac{3}{7}$ and $\dfrac{5}{11}$. In each of these cases you will find that the division never ends. These fractions cannot be written as exact decimals and are known as 'recurring decimals' because a group of digits keeps repeating as you divide out.

For example, $\dfrac{3}{7} = 0.428\,571\,428\,571\,428\,571\ldots$ This is written $0.\dot{4}28\,47\dot{1}$, with small dots over the first and last digits of the recurring group. In the same way, $\dfrac{4}{9} = 0.444\ldots$ is written $0.\dot{4}$ and $\dfrac{5}{11} = 0.454\,545\ldots$ is written $0.\dot{4}\dot{5}$

Putting dots over the recurring group doesn't enable you to do arithmetic with recurring decimals – there isn't an easy way of working with these numbers – but it's rarely a problem in practice. Scientists are normally working with measured quantities. These quantities are rarely, if ever, exactly known, so decimals which are rounded up or down are perfectly adequate (see Section 6). Mathematicians, however, *do* worry about numbers being exact, so they tend to work with fractions instead.

Decimal calculations

Most of the time you will use a calculator to do arithmetic. The advantage of having some experience of doing calculations involving decimals 'by hand' is that it enables you to make estimates of the answers. This is essential when you use a calculator. It is very easy to press the wrong keys, or the right keys in the wrong order, so you need some indication of the size of the answer before you start. Paper and pencil methods can be used to provide a working estimate.

You can add and subtract decimal numbers in the same way as for whole numbers.

How to add decimals
for example, work out 24.023 + 6.892 + 0.0345

1 Write the numbers underneath each other with the decimal points and columns lined up (you can put zeros in the gaps if it helps):

      24.0230
       6.8920
       0.0345 +

2 Add up the numbers in each column, starting at the right-hand side:

      30.9495

(Or use your calculator.)

How to subtract decimals
for example, work out 10.87 − 8.043

1 Write the numbers underneath each other with the decimal points and columns lined up:

     10.870
      8.043 −

2 Subtract the numbers in each column. Start at the right-hand side and use whichever of the methods below you prefer.

$$\begin{array}{c} {}^{0}\!\!\not{1}\,{}_{1}\,0.8\,{}^{6}\!\!\not{7}{}_{1}0 \\ \underline{8.043 -} \\ 2.827 \end{array} \qquad \text{or} \qquad \begin{array}{c} {}^{1}1\,0.8\,{}^{1}7\,0 \\ \underline{{}^{1}\!\not{8}\,8.0\,{}^{5}\!\!\not{4}\,3 -} \\ 2.827 \end{array}$$

(Or use your calculator.)

Now work out 0.62 + 0.28

You should get 0.90 as the answer. The last digit on the right is zero: this means that there are no hundredths. We can remove the zero and write the number as 0.9 You wouldn't write 426 as 0 000 426, because the zeros are not necessary to indicate the size of the number. In the same way, the zero after 0.9 is not necessary to show the size of the number. However, why can't you write 0.006 as 0.6?

Well, 0.006 means 'six thousandths' and 0.6 means 'six tenths', so it is important to leave the zeros in – they do indicate the size of this number.

If you are working to a level of accuracy of two decimal places in a calculation, using scientific data for instance, then you *should* include the zero after the nine and write 0.90 In a strictly mathematical context, however, the number of decimal places may not matter, so 0.9 is as good as 0.90 See Section 6 for more about rounding numbers.

---

*M*aths Activity

4 Work out:

    (a) 3.64 + 0.785   (b) 7.943 + 2.082 + 0.75   (c) 0.005 13 + 0.009 87 + 3.733

5 Work out:

(a) 2.356 − 1.134   (b) 0.0348 − 0.0297   (c) 0.0035 − 0.000 76

Answers

4 (a) 3.640   (b) 7.943   (c) 0.005 13
   0.785 +   2.082   0.009 87
   4.425   0.750 +   3.733 00 +
                        10.775   3.748 00

(In part (c) the two zeros on the right don't tell us anything about the size of the number, so the final answer is 3.748)

5 (a) 2.356   (b) 0.0348   (c) 0.003 50
   1.134 −   0.0297 −   0.000 76 −
   1.222   0.0051   0.002 74

Multiplication and division by 10, 100, 1000 and so on

When you multiply a decimal number by 10, the number gets bigger and the decimal point appears to move to the right. For example, 64.87 × 10 = 648.7 When you do the multiplication, the tenths change to units, the hundredths to tenths and so on. So, the digits have all moved one place to the left. This has the effect of moving the decimal point one place to the right. Work out what happens when you multiply by 100, by 1000 and by 10000.

100 is the same as 10 × 10. To multiply by 100, you can multiply by 10 and then by 10 again. In effect, this is the same as moving the decimal point two places to the right.

To *multiply* by 10, move the decimal point *one* place to the *right*.

0 . 2 3 × 10 = 2.3   0 . 0 0 8 7 × 10 = 0.087   25 × 10 = 2 5 . 0 × 10 = 250.

To *multiply* by 100, move the decimal point *two* places to the *right*.

0 . 8 7 6 × 100 = 87.6   0 . 0 0 0 0 4 5 × 100 = 0.0045   2 . 7 × 100 = 270.

To *multiply* by 1000, move the decimal point *three* places to the *right*.

0 . 4 × 1000 = 400.   2 . 4 4 5 6 × 1000 = 2445.6   0 . 0 0 0 6 2 × 1000 = 0.62

Note that you sometimes need to add zeros to the end of the decimal fraction to give you enough places to move the decimal point.

What happens when you divide a number by 10? What is 64.87 ÷ 10?

Did you get the answer 6.487?

When you divide by 10, tenths are changed into hundredths, hundredths into thousandths and so on. All the digits in the number have now moved one place to the right. This is the same as moving the decimal point one place to the left in the original number.

To *divide* by **10**, move the decimal point *one* place to the *left*.

$$0.8 \div 10 = 0.08 \qquad 23.87 \div 10 = 2.387 \qquad 0.000521 \div 10 = 0.0000521$$

To *divide* by **100**, move the decimal point *two* places to the *left*.

$$0.765 \div 100 = 0.00765 \qquad 34.9 \div 100 = 0.349$$

To *divide* by **1000,** move the decimal point *three* places to the *left*.

$$5.442 \div 1000 = 0.00542 \qquad 213.67 \div 1000 = 0.21367$$

You can see that the decimal point moves the same number of places as the number of zeros in the 10, 100 or 1000. This rule works for other numbers which have a 1 followed by zeros. For example, to multiply by 1 000 000 you need to move the decimal point six places to the right.

Maths Activity

6   Work out:
   (a) 2.6×10 (b) 0.032×100 (c) 41.036×1000 (d) $0.058 \times 10\,000$

7   Work out:
   (a) $3.42 \div 100$ (b) $0.73 \div 10$ (c) $0.23 \div 10\,000$ (d) $64.93 \div 1000$

Answers

6 (a) $2.6 \times 10 = 26.$

(b) $0.032 \times 100 = 3.2$

(c) $41.036 \times 1000 = 41\,036.$

(d) $0.058 \times 10\,000 = 580.$ Note that you have to add extra zeros at the end of the fraction here.

7 (a) $3.42 \div 100 = 0.0342$

(b) $0.73 \div 10 = 0.073$

(c) $0.23 \div 10\,000 = 0.000023$

(d) $64.93 \div 1000 = 0.06493$

If you want to multiply or divide two decimals using paper and pencil, the boxes below show you what to do.

How to multiply decimals

for example, work out 0.25×0.008

1 Take out the decimal points and multiply the numbers as normal:

$$
\begin{array}{r}
25 \\
8 \times \\
\hline
200
\end{array}
$$

2 Count the number of digits *after* the decimal point in each of the numbers you are multiplying and add them up:

0.25 has **2** digits after point

0.008 has **3** digits after point

Total no. of digits $= 2 + 3 = 5$

3 This is the number of digits your answer should have after the decimal point. Starting at the right of your answer, count the number of digits to the left. Add zeros if you need them. This gives the position of the decimal point ·

5	4	3	2	1
0	0	2	0	0

So, $0.25 \times 0.008 = 0.002$

Why does the 'add the decimal places' rule work?

Suppose you have to work out 13.2×0.04 The smallest part of the first number is the 2 tenths and the smallest part of the second number is the 4 hundredths. When you multiply, the smallest parts you can obtain are tenths of hundredths, that is, thousandths

($\frac{1}{10}$ of $\frac{1}{100}$ is $\frac{1}{10} \times \frac{1}{100} = \frac{1}{1000}$). So, you will need three $(1 + 2)$ decimal places. Work it out; you should get 0.528·

How to divide decimals

for example, work out $0.287 \div 0.07$

1 Write as a fraction: $0.287 \div 0.7 = \dfrac{0.287}{0.07}$

2 Make the bottom number a whole number by moving the decimal point to the right.

Then move the decimal point the same number of places to the right for the top number: $\dfrac{0.287}{0.07} = \dfrac{28.7}{7}$

(In this case, move the decimal point two places – this is the same as multiplying top and bottom by 100.)

3 Divide out as usual, keeping the decimal points in line! $7\overline{)28.7}$ with 4.1 above.

So, $0.287 \div 0.07 = 4.1$

Maths Activity

8   Work out:

   (a) 0.3×0.04 (b) 3.2×0.006 (c) 0.05×0.0021

9   Work out:

   (a) $5.6 \div 0.07$ (b) $0.00048 \div 0.2$ (c) $100 \div 0.01$

10 Work out:

   (a) 3.42×20 (b) 0.032×300 (c) $2.6 \div 200$

Answers

8   (a) $3 \times 4 = 12$ Three digits to the right of the decimal points. So, $0.3 \times 0.04 = 0.012$

   (b) $32 \times 6 = 192$ Four digits to right of the decimal points. So, $3.2 \times 0.006 = 0.0192$

   (c) $5 \times 21 = 105$ Six digits to the right of the decimal points. So, $0.05 \times 0.0021 = 0.000105$

9   (a) $5.6 \div 0.07 = \dfrac{5.6}{0.07} = \dfrac{560}{7} = 80$

   (b) $0.00048 \div 0.2 = \dfrac{0.00048}{0.2} = \dfrac{0.0048}{2} = 0.0024$

   (c) $100 \div 0.01 = \dfrac{100}{0.01} = \dfrac{10000}{1} = 10000$

10 (a) $3.42 \times 20 = 3.42 \times 2 \times 10 = 6.84 \times 10 = 68.4$

   (b) $0.032 \times 300 = 0.032 \times 3 \times 100 = 0.096 \times 100 = 9.6$

   (c) $2.6 \div 200 = 2.6 \div 2 \div 100 = 1.3 \div 100 = 0.013$

Note how you can split 20 into 2×10 and 300 into 30×100 to make the calculations easier to work out.

5 Percentages

This section will help you to understand what a percentage is and explain how percentages are used.

Like fractions and decimals, a percentage is a way of describing part of something. You can recognize percentages by the symbol %, which is pronounced 'per cent' and means 'out of a hundred'. So, if in a group of 100 people there are 25 people who do not eat meat, you could say that 25% of the group are vegetarians and 75% are meat eaters.

Another way of writing 25% or '25 out of 100' is as the fraction $\dfrac{25}{100}$, which can be cancelled down to $\dfrac{1}{4}$ Here, '25 out of 100' means '25 divided by 100'. Don't confuse this with '25 lots of 100', which means '25 multiplied by 100'. The notion of 'lots of' was introduced on page 325.

You can write 25% as a decimal too:

25% is the same as $\dfrac{25}{100}$ which means $25 \div 100$ or 0.25

So, $25\% = \dfrac{1}{4} = 0.25$

In fact, percentages, fractions and decimals are all interchangeable. You can change from one to another as follows.

> To change a percentage to a fraction or a decimal, divide the percentage by 100.

For example:

$$17.5\% = 17.5 \div 100 = 0.175$$

(Remember, to divide by 100 move the decimal point two places to the left.)

$$60\% = \frac{60}{100} = \frac{3}{5}$$

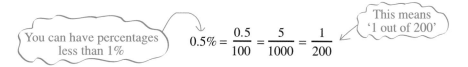

You can have percentages less than 1%

$$0.5\% = \frac{0.5}{100} = \frac{5}{1000} = \frac{1}{200}$$

This means '1 out of 200'

Don't forget to cancel down the fractions if you can.

Maths Help

> To change a fraction or a decimal to a percentage, multiply by 100%.

For example:

$$\frac{3}{4} = \frac{3}{4} \times 100\% = \frac{300}{4}\% = 75\%$$

$$\frac{1}{3} = \frac{1}{3} \times 100\% = \frac{100}{3}\% = 33\frac{1}{3}\%$$

$$0.825 = 0.825 \times 100\% = 82.5\%$$

$$1.25 = 1.25 \times 100\% = 125\%$$

> You can have percentages bigger than 100% too. Read on to find out how

Why does multiplying by 100% give the correct percentage?

You can write 100% – that is, '100 in every 100' – as $\frac{100}{100}$, which has the value 1 (that is, one whole).

If you multiply a number by 1, the number doesn't change.

So, when you multiply a fraction or a decimal by 100%, you don't change its value; you are just writing the number in a different form. That it is why it is OK to use this rule.

*M*aths Activity

1 Write the following percentages as fractions.

    (a) 50%   (b) 35%   (c) 8%   (d) 2.5%

2 Write the following percentages as decimals.

    (a) 45%   (b) 6%   (c) 0.7%   (d) 15.6%

3 Write the following fractions and decimals as percentages.

    (a) $\frac{4}{5}$ (b) 0.925   (c) $\frac{3}{20}$ (d) 0.007 2

Answers

1 (a) $50\% = \frac{50}{100} = \frac{1}{2}$ (c) $8\% = \frac{8}{100} = \frac{2}{25}$

    (b) $35\% = \frac{35}{100} = \frac{7}{20}$ (d) $2.5\% = \frac{2.5}{100} = \frac{25}{1000} = \frac{1}{40}$

2 (a) $45\% = 45 \div 100 = 0.45$ (c) $0.7\% = 0.7 \div 100 = 0.007$

   (b) $6\% = 6 \div 100 = 0.06$ (d) $15.6\% = 15.6 \div 100 = 0.156$

3 (a) $\dfrac{4}{5} = \dfrac{4}{5} \times 100\% = \dfrac{400}{5}\% = 80\%$

   (b) $0.925 = 0.925 \times 100\% = 92.5\%$

   (c) $\dfrac{3}{20} = \dfrac{3}{20} \times 100\% = \dfrac{300}{20}\% = 15\%$

   (d) $0.0072 \times 100\% = 0.72\%$

Suppose you plant two trays of flower seeds. The first tray has 50 seeds in it and 41 of them grow into plants. The second tray has 125 seeds in it and 105 of them grow into plants. How do you decide which tray gave the better results?

Saying that the second tray is better because it produced more plants won't do because more seeds were planted in that tray. You need to compare the fraction or percentage of seeds that grew into plants in each tray. In fact, comparing percentages is better (and easier) than comparing fractions, because it is like saying 'If there had been 100 seeds in each tray, how many would have grown into plants?'

For the first tray, the fraction is '41 out of 50' or $\dfrac{41}{50}$

So, the percentage is $\dfrac{41}{50} \times 100\% = \dfrac{4100}{50}\% = 82\%$

(You can also get this answer by cancelling down the fractions and multiplying out, or by using your calculator to work out $41 \div 50 \times 100$)

For the second tray, the fraction is '105 out of 125' or $\dfrac{105}{125}$

So, the percentage is $\dfrac{105}{125} \times 100\% = \dfrac{10\,500}{125}\% = 84\%$

Since the percentage for the second tray (84%) is higher than the percentage for the first tray, the second tray gave the better results. In general:

> *To express one number as a percentage of another, divide the first number by the second and multiply by 100%*
>
> for example, if you get 42 marks out of 70 for an assignment, what is your mark as a percentage?
>
> The percentage is $\dfrac{42}{70} \times 100\% = \dfrac{4200}{70}\% = 60\%$

*M*aths Activity

4 In a group of 325 people, 65 own their own computer. What percentage of the group own their own computer?

5 On a production line, 4 articles out of 320 are defective. What percentage of the articles are defective?

6 In a drug trial, 72 out of 480 people suffer side effects from Drug A and 98 people out of 560 suffer side effects from Drug B. Work out the percentage of patients suffering from side effects for each drug. Which drug causes less side effects?

Answers

4 Percentage of group with own computer $= \dfrac{65}{325} \times 100\% = 20\%$

(or $65 \div 325 \times 100\%$)

5 Percentage of defective articles $= \dfrac{4}{320} \times 100\% = 1.25\%$

(or $4 \div 320 \times 100\%$)

6 Drug A: percentage with side effects $= \dfrac{72}{480} \times 100\% = 15\%$

(or $72 \div 480 \times 100\%$)

Drug B: percentage with side effects $= \dfrac{98}{560} \times 100\% = 17.5\%$

(or $98 \div 560 \times 100\%$)

So, in this trial, Drug A causes less side effects.

Percentages are often used to measure how numbers change. You have probably seen sales discounts like '10% off all stock', or newspaper headlines like 'Reported crime rises by 5%'. If you know the original value, as well as the final value, you can express any change as a percentage of the original value using the formula:

$$\text{Percentage increase or decrease} = \frac{\text{Actual increase or decrease}}{\text{Original value}} \times 100\%$$

For example, in an experiment, a piece of metal stretches from 5 cm to 5.2 cm. What is the percentage increase in its length?

The actual increase is 5.2 cm − 5 cm = 0.2 cm, and the original length is 5 cm.

So, the percentage increase $= \dfrac{0.2}{5} \times 100\% = 4\%$

In other words, the length has increased by 4%.

In some cases, the change turns out to be larger than the original value. Suppose you stretch a piece of elastic from 5 cm to 15 cm. What is the percentage increase?

The formula above gives the percentage increase as $\dfrac{10}{5} \times 100\% = 200\%$

Percentages greater than 100%, like this one, occur quite often when you are talking about change. They just show that the change is greater than the original number. In this case, the change (10 cm) is twice the original length of 5 cm.

It is often useful to be able to work out quantities from percentages. For example, a tin of soup is advertised as '20% extra free'. If the soup usually weighs 350 g, how much extra soup do you get?

You need to be able to work out 20% of 350 g:

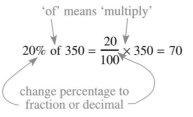

'of' means 'multiply'

$$20\% \text{ of } 350 = \frac{20}{100} \times 350 = 70$$

change percentage to fraction or decimal

So, you get 70 g extra soup and the tin will now hold 420 g of soup, since $350 + 70 = 420$.

In general:

To find a given percentage of a number, change the percentage to a fraction (or a decimal) and multiply it by the number

for example, find 35% of 64

$$35\% \text{ of } 64 = \frac{35}{100} \times 64 = 22.4$$

(Or 35% of 64 = $0.35 \times 64 = 22.4$)

M aths Activity

7   Work out:
   (a) 15% of 720   (b) 17.5% of £56

8   38% of a group of 450 plants have red flowers. How many red-flowered plants are there?

9   82% of a group of 850 students are happy with their progress. How many students are not happy?

Maths Help

Answers

7   (a) 15% of 720 = $\dfrac{15}{100} \times 720 = 108$

   (b) 17.5% of £56 = $\dfrac{17.5}{100} \times £56 = £9.80$

8   38% of 450 = $\dfrac{38}{100} \times 450 = 171$ So, 171 plants have red flowers.

9   82% of 850 = $\dfrac{82}{100} \times 850 = 697$

So, 697 people are happy with their progress, and 850 − 697 = 153 people are not happy. (You could also have worked this out by calculating 18% of 850, because 18 is 100 − 82)

In the soup-tin example, we worked out the new amount of soup by adding the increase (70 g) on to the original amount (350 g). You can deal with any change in terms of percentages in this way:

Changes in terms of percentages: percentage increases and decreases
for example, reduce 85 by 15%

1   Work out the increase (or decrease)

   Decrease is 15% of 85 or $\dfrac{15}{100} \times 85 = 12.75$

2   Add the increase (or subtract the decrease) to the original number
   New number = 85 − 12.75 = 72.25

 *aths Activity*

10 A rain forest has an area of 1600 square kilometres (or km² – see page 388). If 15% is destroyed, what area is left?

11 Equipment for a science course costs £24.50, and postage and packing is charged at 6% of the cost of the equipment. What is the total price?

Answers

10 The area destroyed is 15% of 1600 km². Now, $\dfrac{15}{100} \times 1600 = 240$ So, the area destroyed is 240 km², and area left is 1360 km², since 1600 − 240 = 1360

11 The postage and packing is 6% of £24.50 = $\dfrac{6}{100} \times £24.50 = £1.47$ So, the total cost is £24.50 + £1.47 = £25.97

In the problems above, you were told the original quantity and the percentage change and asked to work out the final quantity. Sometimes, you may be given the *final* quantity and the percentage change and be asked to work out the original quantity. This is a different type of problem, because the change refers to an original quantity which is unknown.

For example: in an experiment, a string stretches by 25% and now measures 10 cm. What was the original length of the string?

The stretched length is 100% + 25% = 125% of the original length.

So, 125% of the original length is 10 cm.

Therefore, 1% of the original length is $\dfrac{10}{125}$ cm and 100% will be $100 \times \dfrac{10}{125}$ cm = 8 cm.

Hence, the original length was 8 cm. Check this result by calculating 25% of 8 cm and adding the result to the original 8 cm. The answer, of course, is 10 cm.

Note that this answer is *not* the same as decreasing 10 cm by 25%, because

25% of 10 cm = $\dfrac{25}{100} \times 10$ cm = 2.5 cm and 10 − 2.5 cm = 7.5 cm. The two answers are different because the change has been calculated using different lengths: the original length in the first calculation; the final length in the second calculation.

Maths Activity

12 This year, there are 90 applications for a technology course. In fact, there are 20% more applications this year than last year. How many people applied for the course last year?

13 Over the past ten years, the number of species of rare plants in a nature reserve has dropped by 35%, with only 26 species now remaining. How many rare species were present a decade ago?

Answers

12 Applications for this year are 100% + 20% = 120% of the previous year.

So, 120% of the applications last year = 90

Hence, the number of applications last year = $\dfrac{90}{120} \times 100 = 75$

Therefore, 75 people applied for the course last year.

13 There are 100% − 35% = 65% of the species ten years ago. The number of species then was $\dfrac{26}{65} \times 100 = 40$ Hence, there were 40 species present a decade ago.

6 Approximations and uncertainties

This section shows you how to round numbers to a specified degree of precision. It explains how to produce numbers correct to a given number of decimal places or significant figures, as well as rounding them to the nearest ten, hundred or thousand.

Doing science involves a lot of accurate measuring – but, however accurate scientists try to be, measurement is hardly ever exact. There is almost always a margin of error (or uncertainty)* and it is important to have an idea of how big this error might be. It is also important not to write measurements in a way that makes them look more accurate than they really are. If you were measuring something with an ordinary ruler, it would be silly to write down the measurement as 6.734 centimetres, because the marks on the ruler are not fine enough, and your eye is not keen enough, to measure anything as accurately as that. Say you wanted to cut a two-metre cane into seven equal pieces. You would be able to *count* the exact number of pieces (counting *can* be exact), but you would not be able to mark off seven pieces which were *exactly* the same size. If you divide 2 metres by 7, the answer is 0.285 714 285 714 … metres. So, however hard you try, you will not be able to measure the lengths exactly. The best you can hope to do is to mark your lengths to the nearest millimetre. So you need to 'round off', or approximate, your measurements.

We want to be able to write 0.285 714 285 714 … m to the nearest mm. Changing the measurement into millimetres, by multiplying it by 1000, gives the length as 285.714 285 714 … mm – and we want to know whether this measurement is closer to 285 mm or to 286 mm. Look at the ruler below, which has been magnified to make it easier to read:

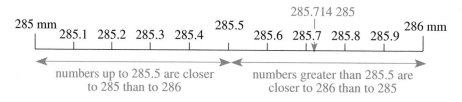

You can see that the measurement is closer to 286 mm than to 285 mm. So, the length is 286 mm, *correct to the nearest mm.*

From the ruler, we can see that any number between 285 and 285.5 rounds down to 285, and that any number between 285.5 and 286 rounds up to 286.

What about 285.5? As this number is exactly halfway between 285 and 286, you could round it up to 286 or down to 285. In practice, 285.5 is rounded up to 286.

You can work out this approximation directly from the number. First, decide which digit represents the millimetres (in this case, it is the 5). Then round up if the *next* digit is '5 or more', and round down if the *next* digit is 'less than 5'.

You can use this '5 or more' rule to round off any number to a specified degree of precision.

---

* Here, 'error' does not mean 'mistake' – it means the difference between the measurement you write down and the actual length. This is why the word 'uncertainty' is often used instead of 'error'.

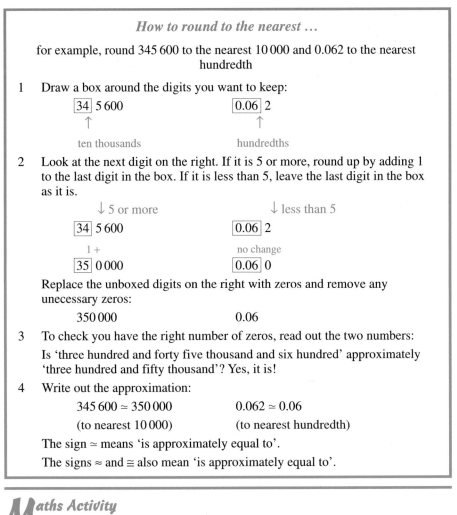

How to round to the nearest …

for example, round 345 600 to the nearest 10 000 and 0.062 to the nearest hundredth

1   Draw a box around the digits you want to keep:

     34 5 600   0.06 2

       ↑   ↑

    ten thousands   hundredths

2   Look at the next digit on the right. If it is 5 or more, round up by adding 1 to the last digit in the box. If it is less than 5, leave the last digit in the box as it is.

      ↓ 5 or more   ↓ less than 5

     34 5 600   0.06 2

      1 +   no change

     35 0 000   0.06 0

Replace the unboxed digits on the right with zeros and remove any unecessary zeros:

    350 000   0.06

3   To check you have the right number of zeros, read out the two numbers:

Is 'three hundred and forty five thousand and six hundred' approximately 'three hundred and fifty thousand'? Yes, it is!

4   Write out the approximation:

    345 600 ≈ 350 000   0.062 ≈ 0.06

    (to nearest 10 000)   (to nearest hundredth)

The sign ≈ means 'is approximately equal to'.

The signs ≈ and ≅ also mean 'is approximately equal to'.

Maths Activity

1   Round 742.819156 to the nearest:

  (a) hundred   (c) whole number
  (b) ten   (d) hundredth.

Answers

1   (a)   742.819 56 = 7 42.819 56 ≈ 700.000 00 = 700 (to the nearest 100).

   (b)   742.819 56 = 74 2.819 56 ≈ 740.000 00 = 740 (to the nearest 10).

   (c)   742.819 56 = 742 .819 56 ≈ 743.000 00 = 743 (to the nearest whole number).

   (d)   742.819 56 = 742.81 9 56 ≈ 742.820 00 = 742.82 (to the nearest hundredth).

Now, suppose you want to round 742.819 56 to the nearest thousandth?

Boxing the digits gives us: $\boxed{742.819}\,56$

Now I add 1 to the 9 to get $\boxed{742.820}$ This time you have to carry 1.

So, 742.819 56 ≈ 742.820

Note that you keep the zero that was in the box, even though it doesn't contribute anything to the number. 3.0 has exactly the same value as 3 – the zero tells you that the number has been rounded to the nearest tenth. To see why this is important, suppose you were presented with the rounded number 3.

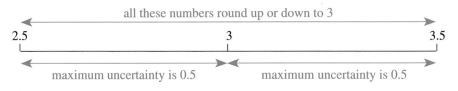

Any number from 2.5 up to (but not including) 3.5 could have been rounded to 3. Using the approximate value 3 means the maximum error you could make on the original number is 0.5

What numbers could be rounded to 3.0?

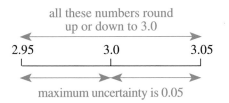

Any number from 2.95 up to (but not including) 3.05 could be rounded to 3.0

So, by using the approximate value 3.0, the maximum uncertainty on the original number is 0.05. Although 3.0 and 3 have the same value, 3.0 is written to a higher degree of precision. Note also the size of the maximum error: it is half the value of a 1 in the position of the last digit you keep. So, if you round to the nearest whole number, the maximum error or uncertainty is 0.5; if you round to the nearest 0.1, the maximum error is 0.05; and so on.

Maths Activity

2 The speed of light is defined as 299 792 458 m s^{-1}.

Write this value to the nearest:

(a) million m s^{-1} (b) ten million m s^{-1} (c) hundred million m s^{-1}

3 Write down the maximum error for each of the approximations in Question 2.

Answers

2 (a) 299 792 458 m s⁻¹ = $\boxed{299}$ 792 458 m s⁻¹ ≈ 300 000 000 m s⁻¹

    (b) 299 792 458 m s⁻¹ = $\boxed{29}$ 9 792 458 m s⁻¹ ≈ 300 000 000 m s⁻¹

    (c) 299 792 458 m s⁻¹ = $\boxed{2}$ 99 792 458 m s⁻¹ ≈ 300 000 000 m s⁻¹

3 (a) The maximum error is half of one million m s⁻¹ = 500 000 m s⁻¹

    (b) The maximum error is half of ten million m s⁻¹ = 5 000 000 m s⁻¹

    (c) The maximum error is half of a hundred million m s⁻¹ = 50 000 000 m s⁻¹

In Question 2, you got the same value for each of the three approximations. So, if you were given the value of the speed of light as 300 000 000 m s⁻¹, without any further explanation, you would not know the level of approximation that had been used. That is why it is helpful to write 'to the nearest …' when you round numbers. For example, in Question 2(b) 299 792 458 is 300 000 000 to the nearest ten million.

Decimal places and significant figures

In science, two other ways of showing the degree of precision are commonly used.

Decimals are often rounded to a given number of decimal places. The decimal places are those digits to the right of the decimal point:

$$7 \quad 4 \quad 2 \quad \bullet \quad 8 \quad 1 \quad 9 \quad 5$$

					1st	2nd	3rd	4th

Decimal places

How to round numbers to a given number of decimal places

for example, round 0.045 67 to 3 decimal places

1 Box the required number of decimal places: $\boxed{0.045}$ 6 7

                                             3rd decimal place ↑

2 Apply the '5 or more' rule to the next digit on the right: $\boxed{0.046}$ 0 0

3 Write the approximation, including the degree of precision:
    0.045 67 = 0.046 (3 d. p.)

    You can use the abbreviation d. p. for 'decimal places' (d. pl. is also used).

Maths Activity

4 Round the following numbers to the number of decimal places stated.

    (a) 23.845 to 1 d. p.   (b) 0.899 56 to 2 d. p.   (c) 2.222 25 to 4 d. p.

5 The tax on a purchase works out at £56.679 How much do you have to pay?

Maths Help

Answers

4 (a) 23.845 = $\boxed{23.8}$45 ≈ $\boxed{23.8}$00 = 23.8 So, 23.845 = 23.8 (1 d. p.)

(b) 0.8995 = $\boxed{0.89}$9 56 ≈ $\boxed{0.90}$0 00 = 0.90 So, 0.8995 = 0.90 (2 d. p.)
Did you remember to keep the last zero to show the precision?

(c) 2.222 25 = $\boxed{2.222\ 2}$5 ≈ $\boxed{2.222\ 3}$0 = 2.2223 So, 2.222 25 = 2.2223 (4 d. p.)

5 Since the smallest unit of currency is 1 p or £0.01, you have to round the number to 2 decimal places: £56.679 = £56.68 (2 d. p.). So, you pay £56.68

If you are dealing with very large or very small numbers, rounding to a number of decimal places is not convenient. Instead, you need a way of rounding numbers which just considers the most important digits in each number. These are called the most significant digits or figures, and they tell you roughly how big or how small the number is.

> The first *significant figure* (or significant digit) in a number is the first *non-zero* digit on the left.

So, the first or most significant figure in 3 246 485 is the 3. It tells you that the number is between 3 and 4 million. Similarly, the first significant figure in 0.000 245 is 2, which tells you that the number is between 2 and 3 ten thousandths. You can round a value off to any number of significant figures in a similar way to rounding to decimal places. The abbreviations 'sig. fig.', 'sig. figs' or 'S.F.' are often used instead of 'significant figures'.

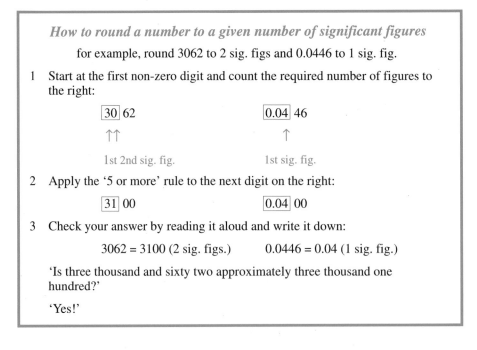

How to round a number to a given number of significant figures

for example, round 3062 to 2 sig. figs and 0.0446 to 1 sig. fig.

1 Start at the first non-zero digit and count the required number of figures to the right:

$\boxed{30}$ 62 $\qquad\qquad$ $\boxed{0.04}$ 46

↑↑ $\qquad\qquad\qquad\qquad$ ↑

1st 2nd sig. fig. $\qquad\qquad$ 1st sig. fig.

2 Apply the '5 or more' rule to the next digit on the right:

$\boxed{31}$ 00 $\qquad\qquad$ $\boxed{0.04}$ 00

3 Check your answer by reading it aloud and write it down:

3062 = 3100 (2 sig. figs.) $\qquad$ 0.0446 = 0.04 (1 sig. fig.)

'Is three thousand and sixty two approximately three thousand one hundred?'

'Yes!'

*M*aths Activity

6 Round the following numbers to the degree of precision stated.

(a) 237 986 to 2 sig. figs ,

(d) 153 432 553 to 4 sig. figs

(b) 0.056 749 to 3 sig. figs

(e) 1.0678 to 3 sig. figs

(c) 0.009 82 to 1 sig. fig.

7 Which answer is more precise: 0.008 76 rounded to 2 d. p. or to 2 sig. figs?

8 What numbers can be rounded to 1 significant figure to give the approximation:

(a) 40

(b) 100?

Hint: use a number line if it helps.

9 Round each of the numbers in the following calculation to 1 sig. fig.:

$0.008 23 \times (1854 + 6798)$

Using the rounded numbers, work out an estimate for the answer to the calculation.

Then use your calculator to work out the answer. Give your answer to 3 sig. figs. Does your estimate agree with the answer?

Answers

6 (a) $237 986 = \boxed{23}7 986 \approx \boxed{24}0 000$ So, $237 986 = 240 000$ (2 sig. figs).

(b) $0.056 749 = \boxed{0{\cdot}056\ 7} 49 \approx \boxed{0.056 7} 00$
So, $0.056 749 = 0.0567$ (3 sig. figs).

(c) $0.009 82 = \boxed{0.009} 82 \approx \boxed{0.010} 00$
So, $0.009 82 = 0.01$ (1 sig. fig.).

Here, the last zero in the box is significant as well as the 1, but you are asked for only one significant figure, so write 0.01 not 0.010

(d) $153 432 553 = \boxed{153 4} 32 553 \approx \boxed{153 4} 00 000$
So, $153 432 553 = 153 400 000$ (4 sig. figs)

(e) $1.0678 = \boxed{1.06} 78 \approx \boxed{1.07} 00$ So, $1.0678 = 1.07$ (3 sig. figs).

7 To discover which is the more accurate answer, work out 0.008 76 to 2 decimal places and to 2 significant figures. $0.008 76 = 0.01$ (2 d. p.) and $0.008 76 = 0.0088$ (2 sig. figs). Since 0.0088 is closest to 0.008 76, rounding to two significant figures gives the more precise approximation.

8 (a)

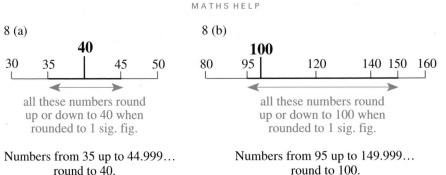

40

30 35   45 50

all these numbers round
up or down to 40 when
rounded to 1 sig. fig.

Numbers from 35 up to 44.999…
round to 40.

8 (b)

100

80 95   120   140 150 160

all these numbers round
up or down to 100 when
rounded to 1 sig. fig.

Numbers from 95 up to 149.999…
round to 100.

Note that when you are rounding to significant figures, the 'maximum error' (or 'uncertainty') on either side of the rounded number is not always the same.

9   0.008 23 = 0.008 (1 sig. fig.); 1854 = 2000 (1 sig. fig.) and 6798 = 7000 (1 sig. fig.).

So, an estimate for the calculation is $0.008 \times (2000 + 7000) = 0.008 \times 9000 = 72$

The calculator answer is $71.205\,96 = 71.2$ (3 sig. figs). This agrees with the estimate.

Significant figures are used a lot in science and technology because the uncertainties have some relationship to the size of what has been measured. Rounding to the 'nearest metre' or to '2 decimal places' does not take any account of the size of the original measurement or number.

For example, to the nearest metre, the height of Mount Everest is 8848 metres. This means that the actual height is somewhere between 8847.5 m and 8848.4999… m. That gives us a good idea of the real height, since the uncertainty in the measurement is small compared with the overall height. A person's height to the nearest metre may be 2 m. This tells you that the actual height is somewhere between 1.5 m and 2.4999… m. Here, the uncertainty in the measurement is so large compared with the actual number that the information on the person's height is not much use at all!

Now, look at the same information again, but this time with the values rounded to 3 significant figures:

height of Everest = 8850 m (3 sig. fig)

person's height = 1.88 m (3 sig. fig.).

For each height, work out the smallest and largest numbers which round to that value.

You should find that all heights from 8845 m up to 8854.999… m round to 8850 m, and that all heights from 1.875 m up to 1.884 999… m round to 1.88 m. In other words, the height of Everest has been given to the nearest ten metres, and the person's height to the nearest centimetre. Both are acceptable approximations.

7 Powers and roots

This section shows you how to work out calculations involving positive and negative powers (or indices) and square roots.

You have already met calculations which involve powers – for example, $3^2 + 5^2$ (see Section 1 of Maths Help). To work out the answer, you have to change the power notation back into ordinary arithmetic:

$$3^2 + 5^2 = 3 \times 3 + 5 \times 5 = 9 + 25 = 34$$

However, if the calculation involves multiplying or dividing numbers which have the *same base number*, there is a quicker way of working out the answer.

Consider $3^2 \times 3^4 = (3 \times 3) \times (3 \times 3 \times 3 \times 3) = 3 \times 3 \times 3 \times 3 \times 3 \times 3 = 3^6$

six 3s multiplied together

So $3^2 \times 3^4 = 3^6$

You can get the same result by adding the powers together: $3^2 \times 3^4 = 3^{2+4} = 3^6$

Try working out $2^3 \times 2^5$ the 'long way' and by adding the powers together.

Do your answers agree?

This rule applies in general:

> To multiply two numbers with the *same base number, add* the powers.

M aths Activity

1   Work out:

   (a) $2^2 \times 2^4$

   (b) $(-3)^2 \times (-3)^3$

   (c) $10^4 \times 10^3$

Answers

1   (a) $2^2 \times 2^4 = 2^{2+4} = 2^6 = 64$

   (b) $(-3)^2 \times (-3)^3 = (-3)^{2+3} = (-3)^5 = -243$

   (c) $10^4 \times 10^3 = 10^{4+3} = 10^7 = 10\,000\,000$

You can work out a similar rule for dividing two numbers with the same base number.

Maths Help

Consider $5^6 \div 5^2$. This can be written as a fraction, and then cancelled, as follows.

$$\frac{5^6}{5^2} = \frac{5 \times 5 \times 5 \times 5 \times \overset{1}{\cancel{5}} \times \overset{1}{\cancel{5}}}{\underset{1}{\cancel{5}} \times \underset{1}{\cancel{5}}} = 5 \times 5 \times 5 \times 5 = 5^4$$

So, $5^6 \div 5^2 = 5^4$

This time you can get the same result by *subtracting* the powers: $5^6 \div 5^2 = 5^{6-2} = 5^4$

Try working out $3^8 \div 3^3$ the long way and by subtracting the powers. Are you convinced that the following rule works?

> To divide two numbers with the *same base number*, *subtract* the powers.

What happens if you work out $4^3 \div 4^3$?

The 'long way' gives $4^3 \div 4^3 = \dfrac{4^3}{4^3} = \dfrac{4 \times 4 \times 4}{4 \times 4 \times 4} = \dfrac{1}{1} = 1$

The rule gives $4^3 \div 4^3 = 4^{3-3} = 4^0$

But what does 4^0 mean? '4 multiplied by itself zero times' doesn't make sense. In order for the rule to work, 4^0 is defined as having the value 1.

This works for any number:

> Any number to the power zero has a value of 1.
> For example: $2^0 = 1$ $3.25^0 = 1$ $(-6)^0 = 1$

Now try $3^2 \div 3^6$

The 'long way' gives $3^2 \div 3^6 = \dfrac{3^2}{3^6} = \dfrac{3 \times 3}{3 \times 3 \times 3 \times 3 \times 3 \times 3} = \dfrac{1}{3 \times 3 \times 3 \times 3} = \dfrac{1}{3^4}$

The rule gives $3^2 \div 3^6 = 3^{2-6} = 3^{-4}$

In order to develop a rule here, we define 3^{-4} as $\dfrac{1}{3^4}$

3^{-4} is said as 'three to the power minus four'. (Sometimes, the word 'power' is left out and we say 'three to the minus four' instead.)

It means 1 divided by 3^4 or $\dfrac{1}{3 \times 3 \times 3 \times 3} = \dfrac{1}{81}$

In the same way, 5^{-2} is said as 'five to the minus two' and means $\dfrac{1}{5^2}$ or $\dfrac{1}{5 \times 5}$ or $\dfrac{1}{25}$

*M*aths Activity

2   Write the following numbers as fractions (or whole numbers, if appropriate).

   (a) 2^{-3} (b) 3^{-2} (c) 4^{-4} (d) 5^0 (e) 10^{-5}

3   Work out:

   (a) $4^7 \div 4^5$ (b) $3^4 \div 3^7$ (c) $2^4 \div 2^{-2}$ (d) $10^{-2} \div 10^2$

4   Work out:

   (a) $10^2 \times 10^{-3}$ (b) $4^{-2} \times 4^4$ (c) $5^4 \times 5^{-2} \div 5^{-3}$

Answers

2   (a) $2^{-3} = \dfrac{1}{2^3} = \dfrac{1}{2 \times 2 \times 2} = \dfrac{1}{8}$

   (b) $3^{-2} = \dfrac{1}{3^2} = \dfrac{1}{3 \times 3} = \dfrac{1}{9}$

   (c) $4^{-4} = \dfrac{1}{4^4} = \dfrac{1}{4 \times 4 \times 4 \times 4} = \dfrac{1}{256}$

   (d) $5^0 = 1$

   (e) $10^{-5} = \dfrac{1}{10^5} = \dfrac{1}{100\,000} = 0.000\,01$

3   (a) $4^7 \div 4^5 = 4^{7-5} = 4^2 = 4 \times 4 = 16$

   (b) $3^4 \div 3^7 = 3^{4-7} = 3^{-3} = \dfrac{1}{3^3} = \dfrac{1}{3 \times 3 \times 3} = \dfrac{1}{27}$

   (c) $2^4 \div 2^{-2} = 2^{4-(-2)} = 2^{4+2} = 2^6 = 2 \times 2 \times 2 \times 2 \times 2 \times 2 = 64$

   (d) $10^{-2} \div 10^2 = 10^{-2-2} = 10^{-4} = \dfrac{1}{10^4} = \dfrac{1}{10 \times 10 \times 10 \times 10} = \dfrac{1}{10\,000} = 0.0001$

4   (a) $10^2 \times 10^{-3} = 10^{2+(-3)} = 10^{2-3} = 10^{-1} = \dfrac{1}{10} = 0.1$

   (b) $4^{-2} \times 4^4 = 4^{-2+4} = 4^2 = 4 \times 4 = 16$

   (c) $5^4 \times 5^{-2} \div 5^{-3} = 5^{4+(-2)-(-3)} = 5^{4-2+3} = 5^5 = 5 \times 5 \times 5 \times 5 \times 5 = 3125$

Note that if the base number is 10, it is often more convenient to express the answer as a decimal, as in Questions 2(e), 3(d) and 4(a).

Roots

We know that $6^2 = 36$ and $7^2 = 49$ Is there a number that, if we square it, would give 42 as an answer?

Use your calculator to try out some guesses. To start with, if 6 is too small and 7 is too big, you might try …? See if you can narrow the answer down to 1 or 2 decimal places.

You should get a value of about 6.48 This is an approximate value for a *square root* of 42.

> A square root of a number is a value which, when multiplied by itself, gives the number.

Some numbers have square roots which work out exactly.

For example, what are the square roots of 144? In other words, what number multiplied by itself gives 144?

Since $12 \times 12 = 144$, 12 is one square root.

But $(-12) \times (-12) = 144$ as well. So, -12 is also a square root of 144.

We write the positive square root of 144 as $\sqrt{144}$, and the negative square root as $-\sqrt{144}$.

If you want to talk about both square roots, you can use the notation $\pm\sqrt{144}$. This is said as 'the positive and negative square roots of 144' or 'the square roots of 144'.

The $\sqrt{}$ is called the square root sign. The line goes over the number for which you want to find the square root.

> A positive number has two square roots: a positive value and a negative value.

Note that you can't find square roots of negative numbers, because whenever you square any number (except zero), you always get a positive answer.

Most numbers have square roots which do not work out exactly, like 42, which you tried above. On your calculator, you should have a square root key. It is often marked $\sqrt{}$. I suggest that you now consult your calculator handbook to find out how to use this key.

aths Activity

5   Without using your calculator, find:

   (a) $\sqrt{16}$ (b) $-\sqrt{81}$ (c) $\sqrt{196}$ (d) $\sqrt{0.04}$

6   Giving your answers to 3 decimal places, use your calculator to find:

   (a) $\sqrt{222}$ (b) $-\sqrt{14.96}$ (c) $\sqrt{0.36}$ (d) $\sqrt{0.009}$

Answers

5   (a) Since $4 \times 4 = 16$, $\sqrt{16} = 4$

(b) Since $9 \times 9 = 81$, $-\sqrt{81} = -9$

(c) Since $14 \times 14 = 196$, $\sqrt{196} = 14$

(d) Since $0.2 \times 0.2 = 0.04$, $\sqrt{0.04} = 0.2$ (were you surprised to find that the answer is not 0.02?)

6   (a) $\sqrt{222} = 14.900$ (3 d. p.)

(b) $-\sqrt{14.96} = -3.868$ (3 d. p.)

(c) $\sqrt{0.36} = 0.6$ (since this is exact, we record it as 0.6)

(d) $\sqrt{0.009} = 0.095$ (3 d. p.)

Did you notice that the positive square root of a number which is between 0 and 1 turns out to be bigger than the original number?

For example, $\sqrt{0.01} = 0.1$ and $\sqrt{0.1} = 0.316$ (3 d. p.).

Some calculations which involve finding square roots must be split into several steps. To determine the order of calculation, treat the top line of the square root sign like a bracket; in other words, work out everything under the square root sign first, before you calculate the square root itself. You then use the BIDMAS order as usual.

For example, $\sqrt{3^2 + 4^2}$ is the same as $\sqrt{(3^2 + 4^2)}$, so you must work out the calculation under the square root sign first:

$$\sqrt{3^2 + 4^2} = \sqrt{9 + 16} = \sqrt{25} = 5$$

powers first   then +   then square root

Notice that this is *not* the same calculation as $\sqrt{3^2} + \sqrt{4^2}$:

$$\sqrt{3^2} + \sqrt{4^2} = 3 + 4 = 7$$

---

*M*aths Activity

7   Work out:

(a) $6\sqrt{5 + 4}$

(b) $\sqrt{5^2 - 2 \times 3 \times 4}$

Answers

7   (a) $6\sqrt{5+4}$ = $6\sqrt{(5+4)}$ = $6\sqrt{9}$ = $6 \times 3 = 18$

                              bracket first   square root   then ×

    (b) $\sqrt{5^2 - 2 \times 3 \times 4}$ = $\sqrt{(5^2 - 2 \times 3 \times 4)}$ = $\sqrt{25 - 24}$ = $\sqrt{1} = 1$

                              bracket first   then root

You can express square roots using the power notation as well. Consider $4^{\frac{1}{2}} \times 4^{\frac{1}{2}}$

Adding the powers gives $4^{\frac{1}{2}} \times 4^{\frac{1}{2}} = 4^1 = 4$

This shows that when you multiply $4^{\frac{1}{2}}$ by itself, you get 4. In other words $4^{\frac{1}{2}}$ is the square root of 4 = which is $\sqrt{4} = 2$

Cube and other roots

As well as finding square roots, you can find cube roots ($\sqrt[3]{}$ or $()^{\frac{1}{3}}$), fourth roots ($\sqrt[4]{}$ or $()^{\frac{1}{4}}$), fifth roots ($\sqrt[5]{}$ or $()^{\frac{1}{5}}$) and so on.

The cube root of a number is the value which, if multiplied by itself *three* times, gives the number. For example, $\sqrt[3]{27} = 3$ because $3 \times 3 \times 3 = 27$

-3 is not a cube root of 27 though, because $(-3) \times (-3) \times (-3) = -27$, not 27

You can find the cube root of a negative number too: $\sqrt[3]{-27} = -3$ and $\sqrt[3]{-8} = -2$ because $(-2) \times (-2) \times (-2) = -8$

In most cases, you will need to use your calculator to work out cube roots.

*M*aths Activity

8   Giving your answers to three decimal places, use your calculator to work out:

    (a) $\sqrt[3]{63}$

    (b) $\sqrt[3]{-142}$

Answers

8   (a) 3.979 (to 3 d. p.)

    (b) −5.217 (to 3 d. p.)

8 Scientific notation

This section explains how scientists deal with very small or very large numbers using scientific notation.

Numbers that are either very big or very small crop up in science all the time. This happens because scientists ask questions about things which range in size from the subatomic (a typical atom has a diameter of about 0.000 000 000 1 m) to the astronomic (our galaxy has a diameter of about 1 000 000 000 000 000 000 m across the main part). You can see that having to deal with these numbers raises problems. Even saying them or writing them down can be a tedious business, let alone doing anything with them! For example, here are two different numbers, deliberately written in different styles:

7803000000000000000000000000000000000

69306000000000000000000000000000000000

Can you tell which is bigger … easily?

Numbers like these are difficult to work with, so scientists use a clear, shorthand way of writing them down called *scientific notation* or *standard form*.

You have met a concise notation for writing some numbers already:

100 can be written as 10×10 or 10^2

1000 can be written as $10 \times 10 \times 10$ or 10^3

1 000 000 can be written as $10 \times 10 \times 10 \times 10 \times 10 \times 10$ or 10^6

In all these examples, the power of 10 tells you how many tens are multiplied together (and how many zeros are after the 1 in the original number). This notation is especially useful for writing down some large numbers in a concise form:

$1\,000\,000\,000\,000 = 10^{12}$

12 zeros   power is 12

In Section 7 you saw that small numbers can also be written in this form:

$$0.1 = \frac{1}{10} = 10^{-1} \qquad 0.01 = \frac{1}{100} = 10^{-2} \qquad 0.001 = \frac{1}{1000} = 10^{-3}$$

1st d.p. 1 zero power is −1   2nd d.p. 2 zeros power is −2   3rd d.p. 3 zeros power is −3

*M*aths Activity

1 Write the following as powers of ten.

(a) 10000   (b) 10 000 000   (c) 0.0001   (d) 0.000 000 01

2 Write the following numbers in decimal form.

(a) 10^8 (b) 10^{10} (c) 10^{-5} (d) 10^{-7}

Answers

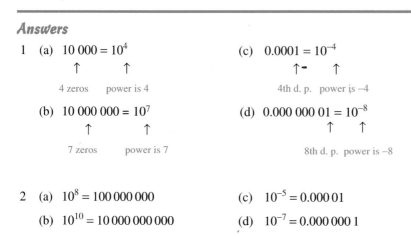

1 (a) $10\,000 = 10^4$

      ↑   ↑

    4 zeros   power is 4

(b) $10\,000\,000 = 10^7$

     ↑   ↑

   7 zeros   power is 7

(c) $0.0001 = 10^{-4}$

    ↑-   ↑

  4th d. p. power is −4

(d) $0.000\,000\,01 = 10^{-8}$

        ↑   ↑

    8th d. p. power is −8

2 (a) $10^8 = 100\,000\,000$

(b) $10^{10} = 10\,000\,000\,000$

(c) $10^{-5} = 0.000\,01$

(d) $10^{-7} = 0.000\,000\,1$

You can use this notation to write down any number in a concise form.

For example, $6\,000\,000$ can be written as $6 \times 1\,000\,000$ or 6×10^6

In the same way, $6\,500\,000$ can be written as $65 \times 100\,000$ or 65×10^5, or as $6.5 \times 1\,000\,000$ or 6.5×10^6

When a number is written in this form *and* the first number is between 1 and 10, it is said to be in scientific notation. So, the scientific notation for $6\,500\,000$ is 6.5×10^6, not 65×10^5

> A number written in *scientific notation* looks like this:
>
> (number between 1 and 10) $\times\ 10^{\text{some power}}$

You can write small numbers in scientific notation too. To write 0.0035 in this form, first find the number between 1 and 10 you need. It is 3.5 To get 0.0035 from 3.5, you have to move the decimal point 3 places to the left:

$$0\,0\,3\,.\,5$$

You could divide 3.5 by 1000 or multiply 3.5 by $\dfrac{1}{1000}$

So, $0.0035 = 3.5 \times \dfrac{1}{1000} = 3.5 \times 10^{-3}$

Hence, the scientific notation for 0.0035 is 3.5×10^{-3} This is said as 'three point five times ten to the minus three'.

How to write a number in scientific notation

for example, write 36 400 000 and 0·000 047 in scientific notation.

1 Find the number between 1 and 10 you need:

3 .64   4.7

2 Work out how many places you need to move the decimal point to get the original number:

3 . 6 4 0 0 0 0 0   0 0 0 0 4 . 7

move point 7 places   move point 5 places
to the right   to the left

3 Work out the power of ten:

this is the same as   this is the same as
multiplying by 10^7 multiplying by 10^{-5}

4 Write down the answer: ·

$36\,400\,000 = 3.64 \times 10^7$ $0.000\,047 = 4.7 \times 10^{-5}$

Check the sign of the power of 10:

If the original number was *bigger than 10*, the power should be *positive*.

If the original number was *between 0 and 1*, the power should be *negative*.

Maths Activity

3 Write the following numbers in scientific notation.

   (a) 42 500   (b) 960 000 000   (c) 0.000 625   (d) 0.000 000 2

4 Using your answers to Questions 3(c) and 3(d), what can you say about the position of the first non-zero digit in the decimal number and the power of ten when the number is written in scientific notation?

Answers

3 (a) 4.25×10^4 (b) 9.6×10^8 (c) 6.25×10^{-4} (d) 2×10^{-7}

4 $0.000\,625 = 6.25 \times 10^{-4}$ and $0.000\,000\,2 = 2 \times 10^{-7}$

    ↑   ↑   ↑   ↑

   4th d. p.   power is −4   7th d. p.   power is −7

The position of the first non-zero digit tells you the power.

You can convert a number in scientific notation back into the decimal form as follows.

Maths Help

How to convert scientific notation back into decimals

for example, write 5.83×10^5 and 3.6×10^{-4} as decimals

1   The power of ten tells you how many places to move the decimal point:

$$5.83 \times 10^5 \qquad\qquad 3.6 \times 10^{-4}$$

power is $+ 5$ power is $- 4$

If the power is *positive*, move the decimal point to the *right*.

If the power is *negative*, move the decimal point to the *left*.

move point 5 …   move point 4 …

places right   places left

5 . 8 3 0 0 0   0 0 0 3 . 6

2   Write down the answer:

$$5.83 \times 10^5 = 583\,000 \qquad 3.6 \times 10^{-4} = 0.000\,36$$

aths Activity

5   Write the following numbers as decimals.

(a) 2.845×10^6

(b) 3.2×10^{-3}

(c) 4.276×10^2

(d) 1.85×10^{-5}

Answers

5   (a) $2\,845\,000$ (move the decimal point 6 places to the right)

(b) 0.0032 (move the decimal point 3 places to the left)

(c) 427.6 (move the decimal point 2 places to the right)

(d) $0.000\,018\,5$ (move the decimal point 5 places to the left)

Using numbers in scientific notation

One of the advantages of using scientific notation is that you can see straightaway roughly how big a number is just by looking at the power of ten. Look at the two numbers at the beginning of this section (page 359). These numbers can be written as:

7.803×10^{36} and 6.9306×10^{40}

If you compare the powers of ten you can see immediately that 6.9306×10^{40} is the bigger number.

Multiplying and dividing numbers in scientific notation

A lot of the calculations with numbers written in scientific notation involve multiplying and dividing. This is much easier with scientific notation than it is with the original decimals, because you can rearrange the calculation to deal with the powers of ten and the numbers separately. For example:

$$6 \times 10^8 \times 7 \times 10^5 = 6 \times 7 \times 10^8 \times 10^5 = 42 \times 10^{13}$$

multiply numbers   ↑   ↑   ↑

same base   ... so add powers

The answer is not quite in scientific notation, however, because 42 is not between 1 and 10. Noting that $42 = 4.2 \times 10$, the answer should be $4.2 \times 10 \times 10^{13} = 4.2 \times 10^{14}$

Divisions can be treated in a similar way. Try working out $(4 \times 10^5) \div (8 \times 10^8)$

First, rearrange the calculation: $\qquad \dfrac{4 \times 10^5}{8 \times 10^8} = \dfrac{4}{8} \times \dfrac{10^5}{10^8}$

Divide the numbers and subtract the powers: $\qquad = 0.5 \times 10^{(5-8)}$

$\qquad\qquad\qquad\qquad\qquad\qquad\qquad\qquad = 0.5 \times 10^{-3}$

Rewrite 0.5 in scientific notation: $\qquad\qquad = 5 \times 10^{-1} \times 10^{-3}$

Sort out the power: $\qquad\qquad\qquad\qquad\quad = 5 \times 10^{-4}$

---

*M**aths Activity*

6   Giving your answers in scientific notation, work out:

(a) $(2 \times 10^3) \times (9 \times 10^{-2})$ (b) $(6 \times 10^{-3}) \div (3 \times 10^5)$ (c) $(2.1 \times 10^2) \div (4.2 \times 10^{-2})$

Answers

6   (a) $(2 \times 10^3) \times (9 \times 10^{-2}) = (2 \times 9) \times (10^3 \times 10^{-2}) = 18 \times 10^{3-2} = 18 \times 10^1 = 1.8 \times 10^2$

(b) $(6 \times 10^{-3}) \div (3 \times 10^5) = \dfrac{6}{3} \times \dfrac{10^{-3}}{10^5} = 2 \times 10^{-3-5} = 2 \times 10^{-8}$

(c) $(2.1 \times 10^2) \div (4.2 \times 10^{-2}) = \dfrac{2.1}{4.2} \times \dfrac{10^2}{10^{-2}} = 0.5 \times 10^{2-(-2)} = 5 \times 10^{-1} \times 10^4$

$\qquad\qquad\qquad\qquad\qquad\qquad = 5 \times 10^{-1+4} = 5 \times 10^3$

Adding and subtracting numbers in scientific notation

You have to be fairly careful when you add or subtract numbers in scientific notation, though. Before you can add or subtract the numbers directly, the *powers of ten must be the same*.

So, $2.3 \times 10^2 + 4.15 \times 10^2$ can be added to give $(2.3 + 4.15) \times 10^2$ or 6.45×10^2

But, $4.2 \times 10^{-3} - 2.1 \times 10^{-4}$ has to be rewritten as $4.2 \times 10^{-3} - 0.21 \times 10^{-3}$

    ↑   ↑   ↑   ↑

   different powers   same powers

Only then can the subtraction be carried out.

Hence, $4.2 \times 10^{-3} - 2.1 \times 10^{-4} = (4.2 - 0.21) \times 10^{-3} = 3.99 \times 10^{-3}$

Try working out these two calculations by writing all the numbers in decimal form first.

Do your answers agree with the answers given above?

Can you see why it is important for the powers to be the same?

Estimating answers

In practice, most calculations will be done on your calculator. The only calculations you need to do 'by hand' will be estimates of the answers. If you have to add or subtract two numbers in the estimate that have similar powers of ten, you can use the technique given above. If the powers are very different, then one number will be much smaller than the other. A quick check should show that the small number will probably make little difference to the estimate of the answer, and so it can be ignored.

For example, if you want to estimate the answer to:

$(6.42 \times 10^4 + 3.2 \times 10^2) \times (1.8 \times 10^2)$

6.42×10^4 is about 60 000, 3.2×10^2 is about 300 and 1.8×10^2 is about 200.

Adding 300 to 60 000 makes little difference to the sum; it will still be about 60 000.

An estimate of the answer would then be:

$6 \times 10^4 \times 2 \times 10^2 \quad = (6 \times 2) \times (10^2 \times 10^{4)}$

$$= 12 \times 10^6$$

$$= 1.2 \times 10^7$$

Using a calculator, the exact answer is:

$(6.42 \times 10^4 + 3.2 \times 10^2) \times (1.8 \times 10^2) = (6.452 \times 10^4) \times (1.8 \times 10^2)$

$$= 1.161\,36 \times 10^7$$

If you round this exact answer to 2 significant figures, you get 1.2×10^7, which agrees with the estimate.

9 Formulas and algebra

This section will help you to write down formulas using algebra and show you how to use them.

In MST subjects, patterns often emerge which apply in many different situations. You've met some of these patterns and rules already. For example, if you want to change a percentage into a decimal, you divide the percentage by 100. It doesn't matter what the percentage is, 0.3%, 46%, 99.99% or whatever, the rule is always the same. In the same way, if you want to change miles into kilometres, you always multiply the number of miles by 1.6.

Instead of describing these rules in sentences, it can be much easier and quicker to write them as word formulas.

$$\text{Decimal} = \frac{\text{Percentage}}{100}$$

Number of kilometres = 1.6 × Number of miles

 **aths Activity**

Write the following rules as word formulas.

1   To work out the average speed of a car, divide the distance travelled by the time taken.'

2   To work out the area of a rectangle, multiply the length by the width.'

Answers

1   Average speed = Distance ÷ Time   or

$$\text{Average speed} = \frac{\text{Distance}}{\text{Time}}$$

2   Area = Length × Width

You can make these formulas more concise by using letters or symbols instead of words. So, writing 'D' for 'Decimal' and 'P' for 'Percentage', the percentage formula becomes:

$$D = \frac{P}{100}$$

Similarly, if you write M for the number of miles and K for the number of kilometres, the formula 'Number of kilometres = 1.6 × Number of miles' can be written:

$$K = 1.6 \times M$$

Note that when you use letters in formulas, you must explain what the letters stand for and the units in which they are measured. For example, 'let t be the time in hours' or 'suppose the area is A in square metres'.

You can choose whichever letters you like, although if you choose them in a meaningful way it will help you to remember the formula. The first letter of the word is often a sensible choice. But be careful! Don't choose the same letter for different things. So, if you are writing down a formula that involves both your gross pay and your net pay, don't call them both 'P'. Think of another letter for one or both: 'G' and 'N' would be better labels. It's not a good idea to use 'O' either, because it can easily be mistaken for zero. Both capital and lower-case letters can be used, as well as italics, but be consistent. Apart from these restrictions, and a few special letters reserved for mathematical constants (such as 'e', 'i' and 'π'), you are free to choose whichever letters you like, including letters from the Greek, Russian and Hebrew alphabets. In science, particular letters can have a specific meaning – for example, 'c' is often used to mean 'the speed of light in a vacuum in m s^{-1}'. But in maths, 'c' is often used to mean 'any constant'. So, be careful when you meet the same letter in different circumstances.

When you come across a letter formula, you can write it as a word formula, or as a rule, once you know what the letters stand for. For example:

$$C = \frac{F - 32}{1.8}$$

C is temperature in degrees Celsius

F is temperature in degrees Fahrenheit

You could write this letter formula as a word formula:

$$\text{Temperature in degrees Celsius} = \frac{\text{Temperature in degrees Fahrenheit} - 32}{1.8}$$

or as a rule:

'To work out the temperature in degrees Celsius, subtract 32 from the temperature in degrees Fahrenheit, and divide by 1.8.'

Maths Activity

Write the following letter formulas as word formulas, and then write out the rule as a sentence.

3    $B = \dfrac{m}{h^2}$ B is body mass index

m is mass (in kilograms)

h is height (in metres)

(In Chapters 4 and 5, we used the everyday term 'weight' rather than 'mass', see page 94.)

4    $H = W \times N + T$ H is the cost of a holiday (in pounds)

W is the cost of each week (in pounds)

N is the number of weeks

T is the travel cost (in pounds)

Answers

3 Body mass index $= \dfrac{\text{Mass}}{\text{Height}^2}$

'To work out the body mass index, divide the mass in kilograms by the square of the height in metres.'

4 Cost of holiday = Cost of each week × Number of weeks + Travel costs

'To work out the cost of a holiday, multiply the cost of each week by the number of weeks, and add the travel costs.'

Algebra vocabulary

In algebra, letters are used instead of numbers. Because a letter can represent different values, these letters are called *variables*. The meaning of each letter should be stated when the formula is first used. In some formulas, there are numbers as well. These numbers stay the same in every situation, so they are called *constants*. An *expression* is a group of numbers and letters with arithmetic symbols (for example, $3a + 2b^2 - 4x$).

An *equation* is formed when two expressions have the same value. An equation has an equals sign '=' between these two expressions. The equals sign '=' in an equation means that the left-hand side (LHS) must have the same value as the right-hand side (RHS).

A *formula* is an equation that tells you how to find the value of one particular variable. This variable is called the *subject* of the formula, and it appears alone on one side of the equation (usually the left-hand side). You can find the value of the subject by putting in values for all the other variables in the formula. This process is called *substitution*.

When you write formulas in this way, you can see that they contain letters and numbers. The letters allow you to use the formula in many different situations. In each case, you just replace the letters with the appropriate numbers and work out the calculation. This process is called *substitution*.

For example, suppose you are going on a three-week holiday. The cost of each week is £200 and the travel cost is £150. Using the formula in Question 4, we replace W by 200, N by 3 and T by 150.

$$
\begin{aligned}
H &= W \times N + T \\
&= 200 \times 3 + 150 \\
&= 750
\end{aligned}
$$

So, the total cost of the holiday is £750.

---

*M*aths Activity

5 Use the formula above to work out the cost of a two-week holiday, if each week costs £150 and the travel costs £50.

6 Use the formula $C = \dfrac{F - 32}{1.8}$ to work out what 82 °F is in °C, to the nearest degree.

Answers

5 $H = W \times N + T$ $W = 150;\ N = 2;\ T = 50$

   $= 150 \times 2 + 50$

   $= 350$

So, the total cost of the holiday is £350.

6 $C = \dfrac{F - 32}{1.8}$ $F = 82$

   $= \dfrac{82 - 32}{1.8} = \dfrac{50}{1.8}$

   $= 28$ (to the nearest whole number)

So, 82 °F is 28 °C.

Expressing rules and patterns in this general way, using letters instead of numbers, is called *algebra*. It is a clear and concise method of expressing complicated ideas without using words. That's why mathematicians and scientists use it so much. You have already seen that the letters just stand in place of numbers. So, the rules of arithmetic apply to algebra as well. The following box summarizes some of the special rules and conventions used in algebra.

Rules and conventions in algebra

◆ Addition, subtraction, brackets and powers are written in the same way as in arithmetic:

   $a + b$ means 'add a to b'

   $c - 3$ means 'c subtract three'

   $f(d + e)$ means 'add d to e and then multiply your result by f'

   a^3 means 'a $\times$ a $\times$ a' and cd^2 means 'c $\times$ d $\times$ d'

   a^3 is said 'a cubed' and cd^2 is said 'c times d squared'.

◆ When you multiply two or more variables together, you can miss out the '$\times$' sign. So, $s = v \times t$ is written $s = vt$. You can also miss out the '$\times$' sign between a constant and a variable. So, $3 \times a \times b \times c$ can be written $3abc$. (But you can't miss out the '$\times$' sign between two numbers, because $2 \times 3 = 6$, not 23!)

◆ When you multiply a variable by a constant, you write the constant first: $4a$ (not $a4$). If the constant is 1, as in '$1z$', you can leave it out and just write 'z'.

◆ When several variables are multiplied together, it often helps if you write them in alphabetical order: '$5pqr$' instead of '$5rpq$' or '$5rqp$'.

◆ Divisions are usually written as fractions. So, $g \div h$ (said 'g divided by h') is written $\dfrac{g}{h}$ (said 'g over h').

These conventions, and the notation you have already met in arithmetic, enable you to use complicated formulas. For example, the distance travelled by a particle is given by the formula:

$$s = ut + \frac{1}{2}at^2$$

s is the distance in metres

u is the initial speed in m s^{-1}

t is the time the particle has been travelling, in seconds

a is the constant acceleration in m s^{-2}

How far does a particle travel if the initial speed is 5 m s^{-1}, the acceleration is 10 m s^{-2} and the particle travels for 2 seconds?

Substituting the values $u = 5$, $a = 10$ and $t = 2$ gives:

$$s = 5 \times 2 + \frac{1}{2} \times 10 \times 2^2$$

Now, work out the calculation.

Powers first: $\quad s = 5 \times 2 + \frac{1}{2} \times 10 \times 4$

Then ×: $\qquad s = 10 + 20$

Then +: $\qquad s = 30$

Finally, interpret your answer: the particle travels 30 metres.

Remember that including units in your answer is essential. From habit, I haven't include the units in the calculation itself – and this is a consistent approach throughout Maths Help. But in some courses, notably science courses, units have to be included in all the steps of a calculation. As an example, I've included the units below and added brackets to help you identify what's what:

$$s = (5 \text{ m s}^{-1}) \times (2 \text{ s}) + \frac{1}{2} \times (10 \text{ m s}^{-2}) \times (2 \text{ s})^2$$

Maths Activity

7   Foresters often have to estimate the volume of wood in logs of different sizes. The volume of a log is given by the following formula.

$$V = \frac{LD^2}{12.566}$$

V is the volume of the log in cubic metres

L is the length of the log in metres

D is the distance around the middle of the log in metres

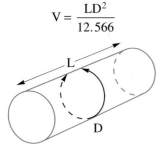

Calculate the volume of a log that is 2 m long and 0.5 m around the centre.

Answer

7   Substituting the values L = 2 and D = 0.5 gives:

$$V = \frac{2 \times 0.5^2}{12.566} = \frac{2 \times 0.25}{12.566} = \frac{0.5}{12.566} = 0.04 \text{ (to 1 sig. fig.)}$$

So, the volume of the log is approximately 0.04 cubic metres.

Rearranging equations and formulas

A formula has a single letter on the left-hand side (LHS). This is called the *subject* of the formula. For example, K is the subject of the formula K = 1.6M. If you know the values of all the other letters, you can find the value of the subject by substitution. But what if the unknown value is not the subject? Then, you need to rearrange the formula, to make the unknown into the subject, before you can substitute.

Whenever you rearrange a formula or an equation, you must keep the LHS equal to the right-hand side (RHS). So, you use the 'balancing rule'. This rule says that you can do nearly anything you like to an expression on one side of an equals sign, as long as you do *exactly* the same to the other side. 'Nearly' anything means that you must not multiply or divide by anything which could be zero. So, for example, you could add 3 to both sides, or multiply both sides by 0.5, or subtract 2.6 from each side. Or you could multiply both sides by 'y', as long as 'y' does not have the value zero. All these operations just write the equation in a different but equivalent form. It is up to you to do whatever makes the equation easier to solve. To use the 'balancing rule' to rearrange a formula or an equation, you need to remember that, in arithmetic:

◆   'add' and 'subtract' undo each other
◆   'multiply' and 'divide' undo each other
◆   'square' and 'square root' undo each other.

So, if you want to 'undo' a subtraction of 42, you add 42; to 'undo' a multiplication by 42, you divide by 42. The following example should help you to see how the balancing rule is used.

Question

Transform the formula K = 1.6M to make M the subject. M is the number of miles. K is the number of kilometres. Use the transformed formula to convert 100 kilometres into miles.

Answer

$$K = 1.6M$$

Divide both sides by 1.6 $\dfrac{K}{1.6} = M$

So: $M = \dfrac{K}{1.6}$

Substituting K = 100, gives: $M = \dfrac{100}{1.6} = 62.5$

So, 100 kilometres is 62.5 miles.

10 Interpreting and drawing graphs

This section explains how to read information from a graph and how to plot line graphs. It will help you to read scales, plot points and find the slope of a straight-line graph. Graphs are used because they can summarize numerical information, giving you a quick, overall impression of the data before you get down to the detail. Chapter 3, 'Working with diagrams', describes why you might use different kinds of graphs and charts. Here, I shall concentrate on one type – the line graph – and tell you how to use it.

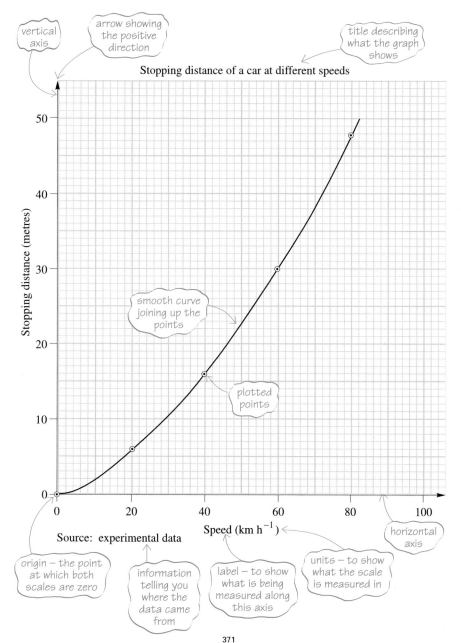

vertical axis

arrow showing the positive direction

title describing what the graph shows

Stopping distance of a car at different speeds

Stopping distance (metres)

smooth curve joining up the points

plotted points

Speed (km h^{-1})

Source: experimental data

origin – the point at which both scales are zero

information telling you where the data came from

label – to show what is being measured along this axis

units – to show what the scale is measured in

horizontal axis

371

So, what does a graph look like?

The graph on page 371 shows the stopping distance of a car at different speeds.

What information can you get from this graph? Well, you already know from the title that the graph is about the stopping distances of a car at different speeds.

Now look at the axes. The speed of the car (in kilometres per hour) is marked along the horizontal axis. (Note that the units here are expressed as km h^{-1}, rather than written out in full as kilometres per hour. This is a convention that you'll come across increasingly in future studies – it's rapidly becoming the standard way of expressing units, especially in science texts.) Each side of the large squares on the graph paper is 2 cm long, so 2 cm represents 20 km h^{-1}. This means that the scale is '1 cm represents 10 km h^{-1}'. When you're reading the scale, it often helps to know what each of the small squares represents. As there are 10 small squares along each side of a 2 cm square, the horizontal side of each small square will represent $20 \div 10 = 2$ km h^{-1}.

The stopping distance (in metres) is marked along the vertical axis. On this axis, 2 cm represents 10 metres, so the vertical side of a small square represents $10 \div 10 = 1$ metre. Note that, in this example, the scales on the two axes are different.

You can use the following method to work out the scales on any axes of this form.

How to read the scale on an axis

1 Pick two points, A and B, on the axis. Work out the difference between them:

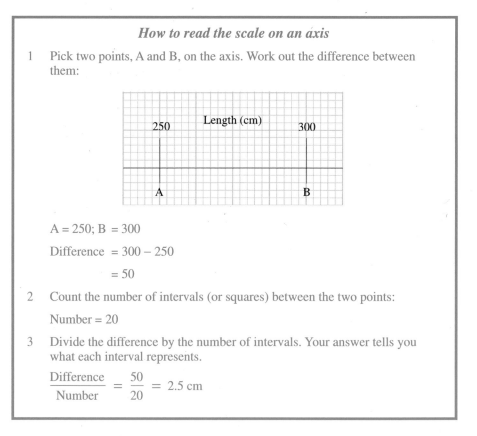

A = 250; B = 300

Difference $= 300 - 250$

$= 50$

2 Count the number of intervals (or squares) between the two points:

Number = 20

3 Divide the difference by the number of intervals. Your answer tells you what each interval represents.

$$\frac{\text{Difference}}{\text{Number}} = \frac{50}{20} = 2.5 \text{ cm}$$

Once you understand the scales, you can obtain a lot of information from a graph.

Look at the following graph and work out the scale used on each axis this time.

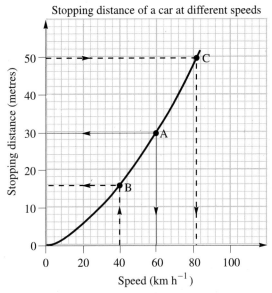

Stopping distance of a car at different speeds

You should find that the scale on the horizontal axis is '1 cm represents 20 km h^{-1}'. So, 1 small square represents $20 \div 5 = 4$ km h^{-1}. The scale on the vertical axis is '1 cm represents 10 m'. So, 1 small square represents $10 \div 5 = 2$ metres.

Now, look at point A on this graph. If you draw a line straight down from A to the horizontal axis, it crosses the axis at 60 km h^{-1}. In the same way, if you draw a straight line from A straight across to the vertical axis, it crosses the axis at 30 m. This means that the stopping distance for a car travelling at 60 km h^{-1} is 30 metres.

You can use the graph to find the stopping distances for other speeds. To find the stopping distance for a speed of 40 km h^{-1}, look along the horizontal axis until you find 40 km h^{-1}. Draw a line straight up from 40 to the curve. At the point B, where the line meets the curve, draw a line straight across to the vertical axis and read off the value. Since the vertical side of each small square represents 2 metres, and the value we want is three small squares above the 10 marked on the axis, the distance is:

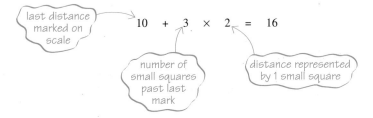

So, the stopping distance for a car travelling at 40 km h^{-1} is 16 metres.

You can also use the graph to work out the maximum speed a car can travel for a particular stopping distance. For example, what is the maximum speed a car can travel and still be able to stop in 50 metres?

Maths Help

Find 50 on the vertical axis, draw a line straight across to the curve (point C) and then straight down. Read off the value on the horizontal axis.

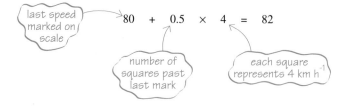

So, the maximum speed is 82 km h^{-1}.

Maths Activity

Use the graph on page 371 to answer the following questions.

1   What is the stopping distance for the following speeds?

(a) 20 km h^{-1}

(b) 70 km h^{-1}

2   What is the maximum speed a car can travel and still be able to stop in the following distances?

(a) 20 m

(b) 45 m

Answers

1   (a) $6 \times 1 = 6$ metres

(b) $30 + 8 \times 1 = 38$ metres

2   (a) $40 + 3 \times 2 = 46$ km h^{-1}

(b) $60 + 8.5 \times 2 = 77$ km h^{-1}

You can get a lot of detailed information by reading values off a graph. But it is sometimes more important to get an overall picture of the relationship between the two quantities on the axes. You can do this by looking at the scales and the shape of the graph and reading off one or two important values. Incidentally, when you read off in this way, remember to read off and write down both the number and the associated units – for example, 20 m rather than 20. Remember, too, that in many courses, particularly science courses, if you were to insert such values into an equation, for example, you would have to put in both the number and the units throughout your calculation.

The graph below shows the number of lemmings in a tundra area over a four-year period. What does it tell you about the lemming population?

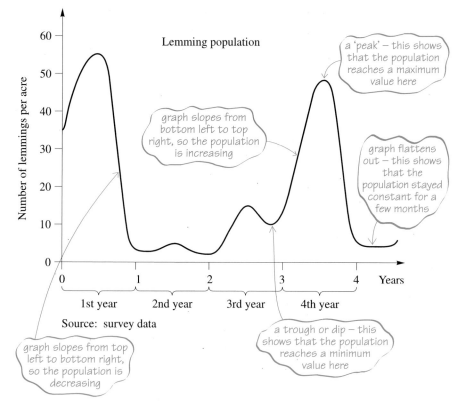

Lemming population

a 'peak' – this shows that the population reaches a maximum value here

graph slopes from bottom left to top right, so the population is increasing

graph flattens out – this shows that the population stayed constant for a few months

a trough or dip – this shows that the population reaches a minimum value here

graph slopes from top left to bottom right, so the population is decreasing

Source: survey data

As this graph has been drawn on plain paper, you will have to use a ruler to read off values on the scales. The scale on the vertical axis is 1 cm (or 10 mm) represents 10 lemmings per acre. So, 1 mm represents 1 lemming per acre.

How many lemmings per acre were there at the start of the first year? Use your ruler to measure the distance in mm from the origin to the point at which the graph crosses the vertical axis. The distance is 35 mm, so there were 35 lemmings per acre at the start of the first year.

Reading the graph from left to right, you can see that the lemming population rose to a peak of 55 lemmings per acre in the summer of the first year. This is the highest point of the whole graph, so it tells you that this was the largest population over the four-year period. The population then declined to about 2 or 3 lemmings per acre at the end of the first year. Each year, the population peaked in the summer months and then declined in the winter months. In the second year the summer population remained low, at roughly 5 lemmings per acre, but in the third summer the population increased to about 15 lemmings per acre. In the fourth summer, the population increased substantially, to almost 50 lemmings per acre. Because this represents a peak, with lower values either side, it's called a maximum value. Note that, by looking at the graph, you can tell when the population increased and decreased, but you need to look carefully at the scales to find out by how much it changed.

Drawing a graph

Graphs are often used in MST subjects – for example, to display the results of experiments. So, it is important that you feel confident about both interpreting graphs and drawing your own. If you have access to a computer, it is worth spending some time getting to grips with a graphics package, so that you can produce a variety of graphs and diagrams quickly and easily (see Chapter 7). If you are unable to use a computer, this section will help you to plot points, choose scales and draw line graphs *by hand*. It will also show you how to get information from a line graph by interpolation and extrapolation and explain how to work out the slope (or gradient) of a graph.

To draw a graph by hand, you will need some basic equipment.

◆   Squared graph paper. Common types are:

Scale: 10 intervals to 1 cm   5 intervals to 1 cm

◆   A *sharp* pencil to plot the points accurately and draw the graph. An eraser is also useful.

◆   A ruler for drawing the axes (and the graph if it is a straight line).

Plotting points

You can describe the position of a point on a graph by its distance from the two axes. On the following graph, to get to A from the origin you have to move 4 units across and 1 unit up. We say that A has the *co-ordinates* (4, 1).

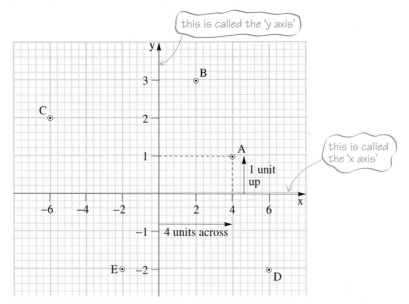

The first number in the bracket is called the *x co-ordinate* and it tells you the horizontal distance from the origin to the point. The second number is called the *y co-ordinate* and it tells you the vertical distance from the origin to the point. In the same way, B has the co-ordinates (2, 3).

Points that are to the left of the y axis have negative x co-ordinates. So, C has the co-ordinates (−6, 2). Points that are below the x axis have negative y co-ordinates. So, D is the point (6, −2) and E is the point (−2, −2). On this graph, the co-ordinates of the points could be read directly from the values marked on the axes. If co-ordinates are between the marked values, the scale is used to work out their values.

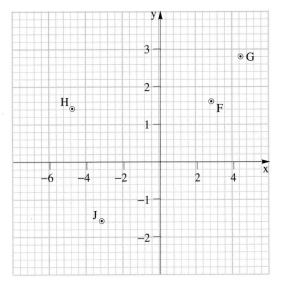

On the x axis, the scale is '1 cm represents 2 units'. There are 5 intervals between zero and the value 2. So, each interval on the x axis represents $\frac{2}{5}$ or 0.4 units.

On the y axis, the scale is '1 cm represents 1 unit'. There are 5 intervals between zero and the value 1. So, each interval on the y axis represents $\frac{1}{5}$ or 0.2 units. (You can write the intermediate values on the axis in pencil if it helps.)

Now, read off the co-ordinates of the point marked F.

F has the co-ordinates (2.8, 1.6).

Can you write down the co-ordinates of G, H and J?

You should find that G has the co-ordinates (4.4, 2.8), H has the co-ordinates (−4.8, 1.4) and J has the co-ordinates (−3.2, −1.6).

Maths Activity

3 Plot the following points on a graph:

K at (7, 1.5), L at (−3, 2.2), M at (2.5, −1.6) and N at (−12, −0.8).

Use the following scales: '1 cm represents 5 units' on the x axis, and '1 cm represents 1 unit' on the y axis.

Answer

3 Check your answer against the following graph.

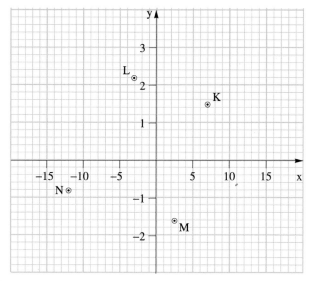

The scales show that: '1 interval on the x axis represents 1.0 units', and '1 interval on the y axis represents 0.2 units'.

Working from data

The easiest way to show you how to draw a graph is to look at an example. In an experiment, the height of a fast-growing seedling is measured at 9 a.m. on most mornings. The results are show below.

Time (days)	1	2	3	5	8
Height (mm)	22	31	50	68	106

The values for the time and height vary during the experiment, so these quantities are referred to as 'variables'. Since the time intervals were chosen, and the height then measured at these intervals, the height depends on the time. In other words, time is the *independent variable* and height is the *dependent variable*. When scientists draw graphs, they use the following convention.

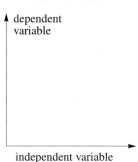

That is, you should plot the independent variable on the horizontal axis (these are the values you have chosen) and plot the dependent variable on the vertical axis (these are the values you have measured at the chosen intervals).

So, in this example, the axes should look like this:

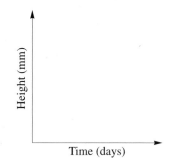

We say that 'the height has been plotted against the time'.

Note that each axis has been labelled with both the name of the variable and the units in which it is measured.

Having decided which way round the axes should go, the next step is to decide on the scales.

Choosing the scales

You should choose the scales so that you get a graph of a reasonable size, say, half a page or a full page. Most of the graphs in this section have been drawn to a smaller scale to fit the page. If you were plotting this data on full-size graph paper, you should use larger scales than the ones used here.

First, look at the range of the values that you need to plot on each axis. On the horizontal axis, we need to plot values between 1 and 8 days. On the vertical axis, we need to plot values between 22 and 106 mm.

For each axis, consider whether you need to start the scale from zero. In most cases, it makes life easier if you do. On the other hand, if one set of data contains similar values, and all of them are a long way from zero (for example, 230, 220, 260, 210 and 280), then it is better to start the scale from a value close to the lowest of these data values to make the best use of the paper. If you do decide to start the scale at some value other than zero, draw it to your reader's attention, either by labelling the axes clearly or by breaking the axis:

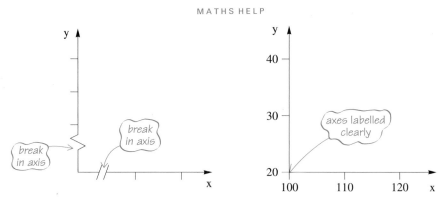

In this example, we shall include zero on both scales, since each set of data contains fairly small values.

If you look at a piece of graph paper, you can see that the small squares are grouped together to form larger, darker squares. Try to pick a scale in which both the large and small squares are easy to interpret. In practice, multiples of 2, 5 and 10 work best. Positioning the axes and working out the scales can be quite difficult, especially when you first start drawing graphs. It helps to work with a sharp pencil and an eraser, so that you can correct any errors easily without having to abandon the rest of your graph. When you have positioned the axes, mark the scales clearly, writing the values exactly opposite the marks made on the axis. Check that you have used the same scale all the way along the axis. Then label the axis to show what is being measured and what units it is measured in. (In some courses, you'll find axes labelled height/mm rather than height (mm), as in this example. The same rules apply to table headings – see Table 5.4 on page 52.) If you are dealing with very small or very large values, it may be clearer to label the axis like this:

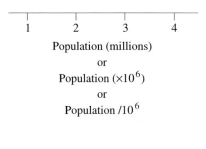

Population (millions)

or

Population ($\times 10^6$)

or

Population $/10^6$

rather than this:

1 000 000   2 000 000   - --- ---

Population

Next, plot the points carefully. Sometimes, you will find that the data are given to a greater degree of accuracy than the scales allow you to plot. If this happens, round the co-ordinates off before you plot the points. At some stage, you must add a title, so that your readers can see straightaway what your graph is about. You should also include a note of the source of your data, so that your readers can check how the data were collected if they so wish.

In this example, I have chosen the following scales: '1 cm to represent 2 days on the horizontal axis' and '1 cm to represent 20 mm on the vertical axis'.

This means that:

◆ each small interval on the time axis will represent $\dfrac{2}{5} = 0.4$ day

◆ each small interval on the height axis will represent $\dfrac{20}{5} = 4$ millimetres.

After marking the scales, labelling the axes and plotting the points, the graph should look like this:

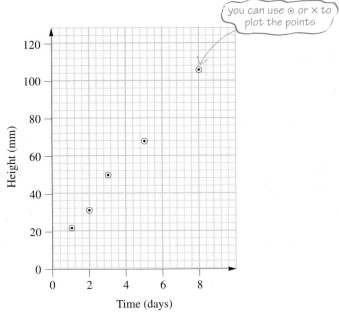

you can use ⊙ or × to plot the points

Drawing the line (straight or curved)

Here, the points appear to lie in an approximately straight line. You'll often find that the results of experiments appear to give straight-line graphs, but due to inaccuracies in measurements, the points don't fit exactly on a straight line. The problem lies in deciding which straight line best fits the data. It can be shown that the best-fitting line passes through the mean point of the data. (The mean is one of several types of average.) You can calculate the co-ordinates of the mean point by finding the mean of the x co-ordinates of the other points and the mean of the y co-ordinates.

In this example, the mean of the x co-ordinates

$$= \frac{1 + 2 + 3 + 5 + 8}{5} = \frac{19}{5} = 3.8$$

and the mean of the y co-ordinates

$$= \frac{22 + 31 + 50 + 68 + 106}{5} = \frac{277}{5} = 55.4$$

So, the mean point should be plotted at (3.8, 55.4). Plot the mean point using a different symbol from the symbol used for the other points. Note that on these scales, you can only plot points accurately to the nearest mm on the height axis, so plot the point as (3.8, 55). Now, draw a straight line going through the mean point in such a way that the other points are roughly equally balanced above and below the line. Finally, complete the graph by adding the title and the source of the data.

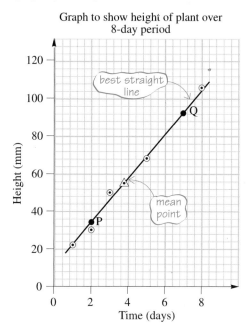

Graph to show height of plant over 8-day period

Source: experimental data

Ignore the points P and Q for the moment. Right now note that you can use this line to work out an estimate of the height of the plant at various times. For instance, to find the height on day 6, draw a line vertically up from 6 on the time axis to the best-fit line. Then draw a horizontal line across to the height axis and read off the value at the point at which the line crosses the height axis.The height was 81 mm.

Finding the values you don't know between the plotted points (the values you do know) is called *interpolation*. It can be useful in science because it enables you to get results without carrying out lots of experiments. However, interpolation only works if you are certain that you know how the graph behaves between the plotted points.

For example, the temperature at 8 a.m. on three consecutive days in summer was recorded as 20.0 °C, 20.5 °C and 21.0 °C. These data were plotted as the graph at the top of page 383. Can you estimate the temperature at midday on day 2?

The points appear to lie on a straight line. But the only information we have is the temperature at 8 a.m. By midday, the temperature will probably have risen substantially. You don't know how the graph behaves between the points, so you can't interpolate any values. So, always check that interpolation is a sensible and appropriate technique given the context of the data.

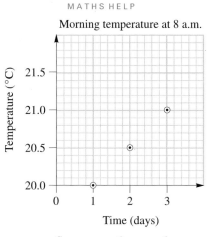

Morning temperature at 8 a.m.

Source: weather records

In some cases, you can use a graph to predict values outside the range of plotted points. For example, you might want to estimate the height of the plant would be on day 10 using the height–time graph opposite. Extending the straight line and reading off the height gives us an answer of 128 mm. Predicting values *outside* the range of plotted points like this is called *extrapolation*. But unless you are absolutely sure that the graph will continue to behave in the same way, it is a potentially dangerous technique. In the example above, you don't know exactly what will happen after 8 days. Perhaps the plant will have a spurt of growth and grow an extra 40 mm, or perhaps the cold weather will retard the growth and the plant will grow a few millimetres. So, use extrapolation with caution! It works best for straight-line graphs, such as conversion graphs, and for points that are close to the plotted values.

What happens if the points don't lie on a straight line? Sometimes they appear to lie on a curve. Drawing a good smooth curve is a skill that improves with practice. It helps if you turn your paper around, so that the curve follows the movement made naturally by your hand and wrist.

The box below summarizes the main stages in drawing a line graph.

Drawing a line graph

1 Decide which are the dependent and independent variables.

2 Work out the range of values for both variables. Decide whether you need to include zero on the scales.

3 Choose scales that are easy to interpret and make good use of the graph paper. The dependent variable goes on the vertical axis.

4 Draw and label the axes, including the units of measurement. Mark the scales at suitable and regular intervals.

5 Plot points using the scales carefully and draw in the line.

6 Check that your graph has a title and note the source of the data.

Measuring the slope of a straight-line graph

As well as reading off values from the graph on page 382, you can also use it to find the rate at which the plant was growing.

Once you have drawn the graph, choose two points which are on the line but are not from the original data (otherwise there wouldn't be much point in drawing the best-fit line). The points should be far apart. Look back at the graph on page 382 and read off the co-ordinates of the points I've chosen, labelled P and Q.

You should find that:

P has the co-ordinates $\quad\quad\quad\quad$ (2, 35)

Q has the co-ordinates $\quad\quad\quad\quad$ (7, 93)

The increase in height is $\quad\quad\quad\quad$ 93 − 35 = 58 millimetres.

The time taken to achieve this increase was 7 − 2 = 5 days.

Since the plant grew 58 millimetres in 5 days, it grew about 58 ÷ 5 = 11.6 millimetres each day, say 12 mm per day to the nearest whole number.

You can find the rate at which one quantity changes compared with another from any straight-line graph using this method. The rate of change is called the *gradient* of the graph. The gradient tells you how much the y values increase for each unit increase in the x values. This provides a way of describing the slope of the line.

*M*aths Activity

4 Work out the gradients of the following graphs.

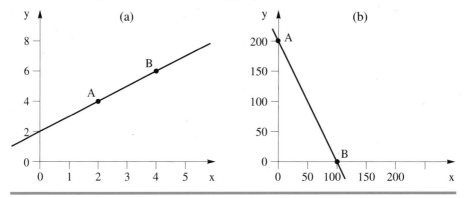

Answers

4 (a) A is (2, 4); B is (4, 6)

Run = 4 − 2 = 2

Rise = 6 − 4 = 2

So, gradient = $\dfrac{\text{Rise}}{\text{Run}} = \dfrac{2}{2} = 1$

(b) A is (0, 200); B is (100, 0)

Run = 100 − 0 = 100

Fall = 0 − 200 = −200

So, gradient = $\dfrac{\text{Rise}}{\text{Run}} = \dfrac{-200}{100} = -2$

Note that if the gradient is positive, as one quantity increases, so does the other. If the gradient is negative, as one quantity increases, the other decreases. If the gradient is zero, the quantity measured on the vertical axis remains constant.

The box below summarizes this technique.

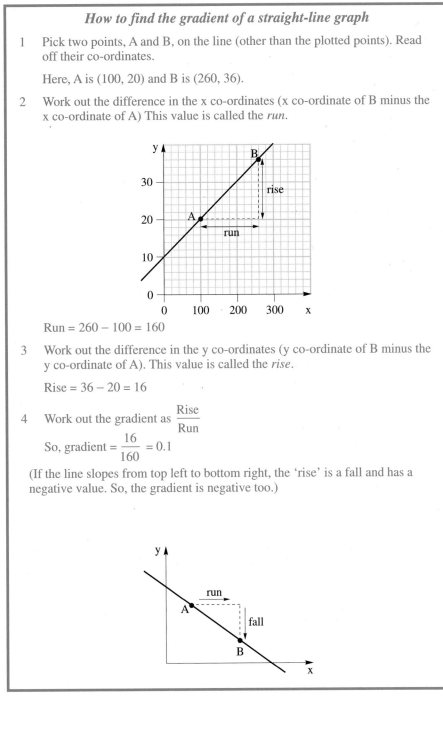

How to find the gradient of a straight-line graph

1   Pick two points, A and B, on the line (other than the plotted points). Read off their co-ordinates.

Here, A is (100, 20) and B is (260, 36).

2   Work out the difference in the x co-ordinates (x co-ordinate of B minus the x co-ordinate of A) This value is called the *run*.

Run = 260 − 100 = 160

3   Work out the difference in the y co-ordinates (y co-ordinate of B minus the y co-ordinate of A). This value is called the *rise*.

Rise = 36 − 20 = 16

4   Work out the gradient as $\dfrac{\text{Rise}}{\text{Run}}$

So, gradient = $\dfrac{16}{160}$ = 0.1

(If the line slopes from top left to bottom right, the 'rise' is a fall and has a negative value. So, the gradient is negative too.)

11 Perimeters, areas and volumes

This section will help you to understand how perimeters, areas and volumes are measured and describe how to calculate them for some common shapes and solids.

Perimeters

The perimeter of a shape is the distance around its edge. You can find the perimeter of straight-sided shapes by measuring the lengths of all the sides and adding the lengths together. (Don't forget to check that the lengths are all in the same units before you start to calculate the perimeter.)

For example:

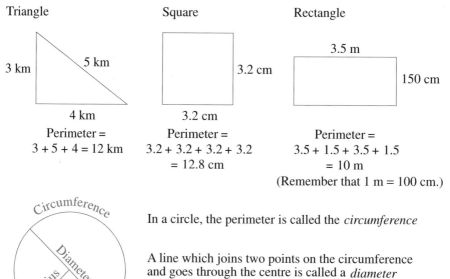

Triangle	Square	Rectangle

3 km · 5 km · 4 km

3.2 cm · 3.2 cm

3.5 m · 150 cm

Perimeter =
3 + 5 + 4 = 12 km

Perimeter =
3.2 + 3.2 + 3.2 + 3.2
= 12.8 cm

Perimeter =
3.5 + 1.5 + 3.5 + 1.5
= 10 m
(Remember that 1 m = 100 cm.)

In a circle, the perimeter is called the *circumference*

A line which joins two points on the circumference and goes through the centre is called a *diameter*

A *radius* joins the centre to the circumference

You can see that the length of the diameter is twice the length of the radius.

Try this:

Find some things like tins, mugs or buckets which have circular ends. Use a tape measure (or a piece of string) to measure the circumference and diameter in centimetres for each of the objects. Record your results in a table like the one below.

Object	Diameter	Circumference	Circumference / Diameter
Tin	7.4 cm	23.2 cm	3.14

What do you notice about the values in the last column?

You should find that the values are all just over 3. It is difficult to measure the lengths accurately, so your values will probably all be slightly different.

In fact, the value of $\dfrac{\text{Circumference}}{\text{Diameter}}$ for *any* circle will always be the same. This constant value is called 'pi' and is written using the Greek letter π. Its approximate value is known to many millions of decimal places, but for most practical situations you can use the $\boxed{\pi}$ key on your calculator or the approximation 3.142. You can use π to find the circumference (C) of a circle if you know its diameter (d) or radius (r).

> Circumference $= \pi \times$ Diameter   or $C = \pi d$
>
> Circumference $= 2 \times \pi \times$ Radius   or $C = 2\pi r$
>
> where $\pi \simeq 3.142$

For example, suppose a circle has a diameter of 4.5 cm. What is its circumference?

The circumference (C) is given by the formula $C = \pi d$, where d is the diameter.

When d is 4.5 cm , $C = \pi \times 4.5 = 14.1$ (to 3 sig. figs).

The units of C are cm, because the diameter was measured in cm.

So, the circumference is 14.1 cm to 3 significant figures.

Note that, throughout this section, all measurements are assumed to be exact. For example, when I write that 'the circle has a radius of 8 cm', I mean that it is exactly 8.00 cm. The general rule I follow is to give calculations to 3 significant figures. (See Maths Help on page 349 for more information about significant figures and decimal places.) Scientists often deal with imprecise measurements – for example, lengths given to the nearest millimetre. If these measurements are used in calculations, it is important that the final answer is given to a degree of precision that takes into account the precision of the initial measurement. You will probably be shown how to do this in your science course.

What is the circumference of a circle whose radius is 0.68 km?

Since we know the radius, we use the formula: $C = 2\pi r$

When r is 0.68 km, $C = 2 \times \pi \times 0.68 = 4.27$ (to 3 sig. figs).

The units of C are km, because r was measured in km. So, the circumference is 4.27 km (to 3 significant figures).

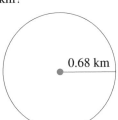

Maths Activity

1 Find the circumference of a circle of radius 8 cm.

2 Find the perimeters of the following shapes.

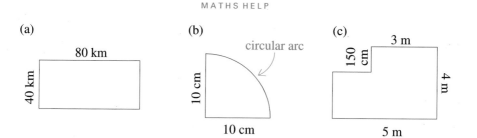

(a)

80 km

40 km

(b)

circular arc

10 cm

10 cm

(c)

150 cm

3 m

4 m

5 m

Answers

1   Circumference = $2 \times \pi \times 8 = 16\pi = 50.3$ cm (to 3 sig. figs).

2   (a)   Perimeter = $40 + 80 + 40 + 80 = 240$ km.

    (b)   The curved edge is one quarter of the circumference of a circle with a radius of exactly 10 cm. So, the curved edge has length $\frac{1}{4} \times 2 \times \pi \times 10 = 5\pi$ cm.

        The straight edges have a combined length of 20 cm.

        Hence the perimeter is $5\pi + 20 = 35.7$ cm (to 3 sig. figs)

    (c)   First, convert all measurements into the same units, say metres:

        150 cm = 1.5 m (since $150 \div 100 = 1.5$)

        The two unknown sides have lengths $5 - 3 = 2$ metres and $4 - 1.5 = 2.5$ metres

        Hence, the perimeter is $3 + 4 + 5 + 2.5 + 2 + 1.5 = 18$ m.

        Note that you could, of course, have chosen to do the calculation in cm instead.

Areas

The area of a shape is the size of its surface. You can measure an area by covering the shape in squares which are all the same size and then counting the squares. For example, suppose your bedroom measures 3 m by 4 m and you want to cover the floor with square carpet tiles. If the sides of a tile are 1 metre long, the area of each tile is said to be '1 square metre'.

You would need 3 rows of 4 tiles or 12 tiles altogether.

So, the area of the room is 12 square metres.

This can be written as 12 m².

Small areas can be measured using square centimetres (cm²) or square millimetres (mm²). Larger areas can be measured using square metres (m²) or square kilometres (km²).

1 square metre

1 m

1 m

3 m

4 m

Areas are measured in squared units. These units are written mm², cm², m², km², and so on.

A square centimetre is 10 mm long and 10 mm wide.

So, there are $10 \times 10 = 100$ square millimetres in one square centimetre.

1 square centimetre

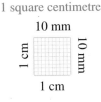

This means that you can change measurements in cm² into measurements in mm² by multiplying the measurement by 100. You can change between the other square units using the diagram below.

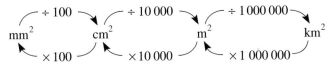

For example, change 0.056 m² into cm².

From the diagram, we can see that to change m² into cm² we must multiply by 10 000

So, $0.056 \text{ m}^2 = 0.056 \times 10\,000 \text{ cm}^2 = 560 \text{ cm}^2$

You can estimate the area of any shape by covering it with a grid of identical squares and counting how many squares it takes to cover the shape. Although this is a useful technique for estimating complicated areas, some shapes, like rectangles, triangles and circles, crop up so often that it is quicker and more accurate to use a formula to work out their areas. If you look back at the carpet tile example, you will see that the area could have been calculated by multiplying the length by the width:

Area = Length × Width = $4 \times 3 = 12 \text{ m}^2$

This formula holds for any rectangle. So, if the room measured 3.27 m by 4.15 m:

Area = Length × Width = $3.27 \times 4.15 = 13.6 \text{ m}^2$ (to 3 sig. figs).

It is worth stopping here to think about why areas are measured in squared units. For a rectangle, Area = Length × Width, so we are multiplying two lengths together measured in the same units, say, cm, that is, cm × cm = cm²

In order to find the area of a triangle, we need to be able to spot right angles and perpendicular lines.

Imagine standing at the corner of a rectangular field looking due east.

Then turn so that you are looking due north.

You will have turned through an angle which is *one quarter of a full turn.*

This angle is called a *right angle*. All the corner angles of a rectangle (or a square) are right angles.

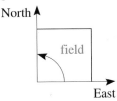

Right angles are indicated by drawing a small square in the angle as shown here.

Lines which meet at right angles are said to be *perpendicular.*

If two lines are always the same distance apart and never meet (like a railway track), the lines are said to be parallel. Parallel lines are indicated by drawing a small, matching arrow on each line as shown below.

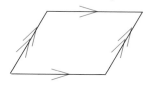

or

A parallelogram is a shape which has two sets of parallel sides.

Below are formulas for the areas of some common shapes.

Areas measured in square units

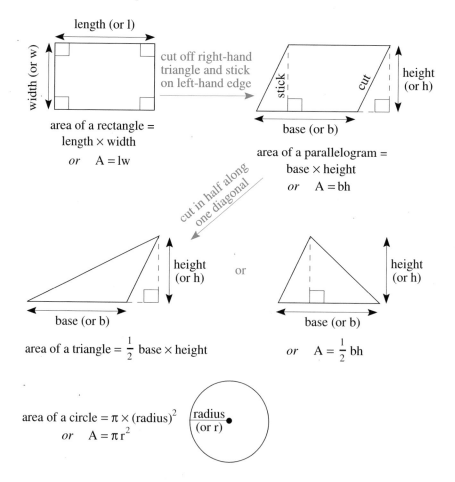

area of a rectangle =
length × width

or $A = lw$

cut off right-hand triangle and stick on left-hand edge

area of a parallelogram =
base × height

or $A = bh$

cut in half along one diagonal

area of a triangle = $\frac{1}{2}$ base × height

or $A = \frac{1}{2} bh$

area of a circle = $\pi \times (\text{radius})^2$

or $A = \pi r^2$

To find the area of a circle of radius 24.8 m, you can set the calculation out like this:

Area $= \pi \times (\text{Radius})^2 = \pi \times 24.8^2 = 1930$ (to 3 sig. figs).

So the area is 1930 m^2 (to 3 sig. figs).

Finding the area of a triangle is a bit more complicated, because you have to know the height of the triangle as well as the length of the base. The height joins the opposite angle to the base and is perpendicular to the base.

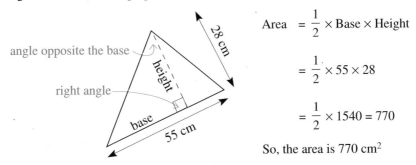

angle opposite the base

right angle

28 cm

height

base

55 cm

$$\text{Area} = \frac{1}{2} \times \text{Base} \times \text{Height}$$

$$= \frac{1}{2} \times 55 \times 28$$

$$= \frac{1}{2} \times 1540 = 770$$

So, the area is 770 cm^2

(Don't forget to include the units in your answer; some courses insist on you including them in your calculations)

Sometimes, you will have to extend the base to find the height of a triangle.

The height is 0.48 m and the base is 65 cm.

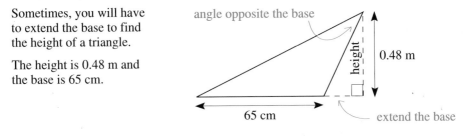

angle opposite the base

height

0.48 m

65 cm

extend the base

Remember, make sure that all the lengths you use are measured in the *same* units.

In this example, we could use either metres or centimetres. Using metres, the length of the base is $65 \div 100 = 0.65$ metres.

So, the area of the triangle $= \frac{1}{2} \times \text{Base} \times \text{Height} = \frac{1}{2} \times 0.65 \times 0.48 = 0.156$

Hence, the area of the triangle is 0.156 m^2.

Providing you can find the corresponding height, you can choose any of the three sides as the base of a triangle. So, choose the side which makes the calculation the easiest!

Maths Activity

3   Find the area of a rectangle which is 25 cm long and 32 cm wide.

4 Find the area of :

(a) a circle of radius 8.4 cm

(b) a semicircle of radius 35 m

Answers

3 Area of the rectangle = Length × Width = 25 × 32 = 800 cm²

4 (a) Area = $\pi \times (\text{Radius})^2 = \pi \times 8.4^2 = \pi \times 70.56 = 222$ cm² (to 3 sig. figs).

(b) A semicircle has half the area of the full circle.

If the radius is 35 m, the area of the circle is $\pi \times 35^2 = 1225\pi$

So, the area of the semicircle is $1225\pi \div 2 = 1920$ m² (to 3 sig. figs).

Volumes

Shapes such as rectangles, triangles and circles are flat: they have no 'thickness' to them. These shapes are said to be '*two*-dimensional', because they are described in terms of lengths and widths. Solids, like balls, boxes and tins, are described by their length, width and height. These solids are '*three*-dimensional'.

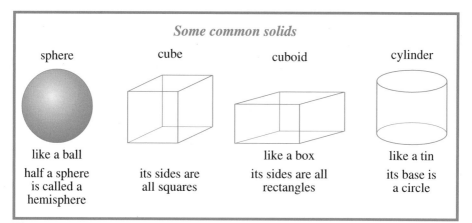

Some common solids

sphere	cube	cuboid	cylinder
like a ball		like a box	like a tin
half a sphere is called a hemisphere	its sides are all squares	its sides are all rectangles	its base is a circle

The amount of space inside a solid is called its volume, and it can be measured by counting how many small cubes of a certain size can be fitted into the shape. For example, you could measure the volume of a stock cube box by counting the number of stock cubes it takes to fill it. Cubic measures often used to measure volumes include:

◆ cubic millimetres (written as mm³)

◆ cubic centimetres (written as cm³)

◆ cubic metres (written as m³).

1 cubic centimetre

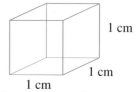

In each case, the length of an edge of the cube is one unit: 1 mm, 1 cm or 1 m.

> Solid volumes are measured in cubic units: mm^3, cm^3 or m^3.

Since there are 10 mm in 1 cm, a cubic centimetre will contain 10 layers of 10 rows of 10 cubic millimetres.

So, $1\ cm^3 = 10 \times 10 \times 10\ mm^3 = 1000\ mm^3$

In other words, to convert a measurement from cm^3 into mm^3, multiply the measurement by 1000.

Liquid volumes are usually measured in millilitres, centilitres and litres. A litre is $1000\ cm^3$. Cubic centimetres are also used for liquids – although the abbreviation 'cc' is often used instead of cm^3.

> $1\ cm^3$ or $1\ cc = 1\ ml$
>
> $1\ m^3 = 1000$ litres, which is often written as $1000\ l$

You can convert from one unit to another like this:

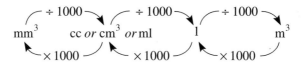

---

*M*aths Activity

5 My water bill shows that I use about $0.8\ m^3$ of water each week. How many litres is this?

6 Convert $7642\ mm^3$ into cm^3.

7 Convert $2.4\ ml$ into mm^3.

Answers

5 $0.8\ m^3 = 0.8 \times 1000$ litres $= 800$ litres

6 $7642\ mm^3 = 7642 \div 1000\ cm^3 = 7.642\ cm^3$

7 $2.4\ ml = 2.4 \times 1000\ mm^3 = 2400\ mm^3$

Suppose you have a box which measures 6 cm by 5 cm by 4 cm. What is its volume?

Since the dimensions are all given in centimetres, you can measure the volume in cubic centimetres.

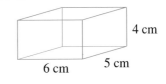

Imagine filling the box with cubes of this size.

6 rows with 5 cubes in each row would cover the bottom of the box, and the box would be filled by 4 of these layers.

So, the total number of cubes used is $6 \times 5 \times 4 = 120$

The volume of the box is therefore $120\ cm^3$.

You can work out the volumes of boxes and other solids using the formulas below.

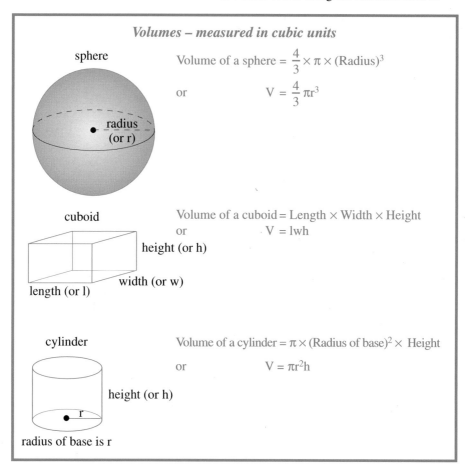

Volumes – measured in cubic units

sphere

Volume of a sphere $= \frac{4}{3} \times \pi \times (\text{Radius})^3$

or $\qquad V = \frac{4}{3}\pi r^3$

radius (or r)

cuboid

Volume of a cuboid $=$ Length $\times$ Width $\times$ Height

or $\qquad V = lwh$

height (or h)

width (or w)

length (or l)

cylinder

Volume of a cylinder $= \pi \times (\text{Radius of base})^2 \times$ Height

or $\qquad V = \pi r^2 h$

height (or h)

r

radius of base is r

Suppose a cylinder has a diameter of 3 cm and a height of 5 cm. How can you work out its volume?

From the box above, you know that the volume of a cylinder is $\pi r^2 h$, where r is the radius and h is the height.

Here, the diameter is 3 cm. So, the radius r $= 3 \div 2 = 1.5$ cm

Hence, when r is 1.5 cm and h is 5 cm:

$V = \pi \times 1.5^2 \times 5$

$= \pi \times 2.25 \times 5$

$= 35.3$ cm^3 (to 3 sig. figs).

So, the volume of the cylinder is approximately 35.3 cm^3.

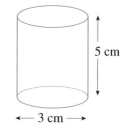

5 cm

3 cm

If a ball has a radius of 12 cm, what is its volume?

You can set out the solution like this:

Volume of a sphere, V, of radius, r is $\frac{4}{3}\pi r^3$

When r = 12 cm, $V = \frac{4}{3} \times \pi \times 12^3$

$= \frac{4}{3} \times \pi \times 1728$

$= 2304\pi \text{ cm}^3$

$= 7240 \text{ cm}^3 \text{ (to 3 sig. figs)}$

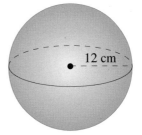

12 cm

Hence, the volume of the ball is approximately 7240 cm³.

If your answer can be expressed in terms of π, without using decimals, then it may be better to leave it in this form. The decimal answer is not precise, so mathematicians tend to leave their answers in terms of π (for example, 2304π cm³ in the answer above). Scientists, who may need answers for practical applications, tend to work with the decimal answers, rounded to an appropriate degree of precision.

*M*aths Activity

9   Find the volume of a sphere with a diameter of 40 cm.

10 What is the volume of a cube with sides 2.5 m long?

11 What is the volume of a cylinder of height 3 m and radius 2 m?

Answers

9   Since the diameter is 40 cm, the radius is 20 cm

Hence, Volume of sphere $= \frac{4}{3} \times \pi \times (\text{Radius})^3 = \frac{4}{3} \times \pi \times 20^3$

$= \frac{4}{3} \times \pi \times 8000 = \frac{32\,000}{3}\pi = 33\,500 \text{ cm}^3 \text{ (to 3 sig. figs)}$

10 Volume of a cube $= (\text{Length of side})^3 = 2.5^3 = 15.6 \text{ m}^3 \text{ (to 3 sig. figs)}$

11 Volume of a cylinder $= \pi \times (\text{Radius})^2 \times \text{Height} = \pi \times 2^2 \times 3 = \pi \times 4 \times 3 = 12\pi$

$= 37.7 \text{ m}^3 \text{ (to 3 sig. figs)}$

The Collee article

This article on food poisoning is referred to in various chapters of the book and is used to illustrate a number of important study skills. It's a shortened version of an article originally published in *New Scientist*, and I've numbered the paragraphs to make it easier to refer to specific parts of the text.

Of course, not all the texts you'll come across studying MST subjects will be like this article. Some will be harder to follow, and most will deal with topics far removed from this one. So, why choose just one article? Well, a single text can be looked at from a variety of angles and the study skills practised using the Collee article can be applied to many other types of text.

Why did I choose this particular article? First, it has lots of the features that the book highlights – diagrams, written text and a few numbers – like many of the texts you'll be working with as a beginning student. Second, it's got many features that I like and a few that I don't, so it's possible for me to take a critical approach. Third, it's written in a technical style, but is reasonably approachable. Don't be concerned if you don't understand all of the article at once. And don't be put off by some of the vocabulary it uses – for example, you'll find bacteria referred to by their Latin names, which have to be written in italics: *Clostridium botulinum*.

It'll help if you make at least one photocopy of the article. Perhaps you'll want to annotate it, writing notes or highlighting key points. Keep it to hand – you'll work with the article at several points in the book. You'll need a copy when you read Chapter 2, for example.

New Scientist, 21 October 1989

We need food to stay alive, but sometimes it makes us ill. Understanding the reasons why bacteria and other microbes may contaminate our food can help us to reduce the risk of food-borne disease

Food Poisoning

Gerald Collee

1   Most people have experienced an attack of food poisoning: an episode of diarrhoea, often associated with vomiting. Sufferers frequently assume that the cause was something that they ate or drank that was wrongly prepared, badly cooked or simply 'off'.

2   The cause of such an attack may be difficult to determine, often because none of the food eaten remains. Only when many people fall ill at the same time, having eaten the same food, does it become possible to say with any certainty that food was the source of the outbreak. This is why it is so important to report cases of food poisoning to general practitioners, who in turn inform the local environmental health department.

3   The term 'food poisoning' is a misnomer. A range of micro-organisms, including viruses, bacteria, fungi and protozoa, can cause such infections. The diseases that these organisms cause may arise as a result of two possible mechanisms. They may be true infections, in which the microbe gains access to the human body and multiplies within it; or they may occur when a microbe multiplies in the food, producing a **toxin**, which poisons the person who eats the food. So a better term is 'food-borne infections and intoxications'.

4   This article will concentrate mainly on *bacterial* infections and poisonings spread by food and water. For the sake of simplicity, I will use the term 'food poisoning' in its established sense.

5   As with almost any kind of infection, contact with disease-causing microbes does not inevitably result in a case of disease. We routinely cope with a low level of bacterial contamination in much of the food we eat, without coming to any harm. Natural defences such as acid in the stomach and other protective mechanisms in the gut are often enough to kill bacteria eaten in food. Those microbes that survive processing in the stomach have to contend with the immune system, which may be able to eliminate them, particularly if the person has encountered the microbe before and has some immunity to it.

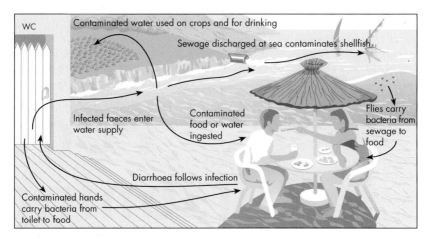

Some of the ways in which food-borne or water-borne diseases such typhoid and cholera can spread

6 Yet several factors may tip the balance in favour of the microbe being able to attack its new host. With some species of microbe, relatively few can cause disease. In other instances, diarrhoea and vomiting occurs only after someone has eaten huge numbers of them. These may have originally contaminated the food in minute quantities, which would have been harmless if the food had been eaten straight away.

7 Depending on the species of bacterium, someone who has ingested a large dose of microbes is more likely to fall ill than someone who took in relatively few microbes. If the infecting bacteria or viruses are particularly virulent, they will be more likely to cause disease. So someone may be more likely to fall ill following a smaller dose of a more virulent organism than after a bigger dose of a milder one. Usually, however, in bacterial food poisoning, the food has been mishandled in such a way as to boost the growth of bacteria in it.

8 To avoid the problem of taking in a high dose of organisms, food must be stored at temperatures too low or too high to permit bacteria to grow: either below 5 °C or above 55 °C. Storing or holding food at temperatures in between these limits allows bacteria to multiply rapidly, and often with devastating consequences.

9 Differences between individuals may also account for why some people fall ill while others do not, even though they have eaten the same food. *Listeria* bacteria, for example, do not usually attack normal healthy people, but those whose immune systems are impaired (such as may happen with pregnant women, very young babies, the elderly, and those patients taking drugs to suppress their immune systems) are much more susceptible.

10 Some bacteria produce toxins when they grow in food. The most serious example of this type of food poisoning is **botulism**, caused by the bacterium *Clostridium botulinum*. This microbe grows only in the absence of oxygen, producing a poison called **botulinal toxin**.

11 When someone eats food containing botulinal toxin, the toxin is absorbed into the blood stream and affects the nerves. Although the person remains conscious, many muscles become paralysed. Death may occur when the toxin reaches the nerves supplying the heart or respiratory muscles. Botulinal toxin is probably the most potent natural poison known. Pathologists estimate that one gram of crude botulinal toxin could kill between 100 000 and 10 million people, depending on how it is given.

12 A more common form of food poisoning due to a bacterial toxin is that caused by *Staphylococcus aureus*. This organism is frequently found in septic spots, sties, boils and infected wounds. It also occurs in the nose and elsewhere on humans who are perfectly healthy, where it may persist without harming its host.

13 When this organism gets into food under conditions in which it can grow, it may produce a toxin that can cause acute vomiting, often accompanied by dizziness and subsequent diarrhoea in the person who eats the food. The sufferer may become severely dehydrated and, as a result, mentally confused.

The longer food is left in conditions that allow bacteria to multiply, the more likely it is that someone who eats the food will fall ill. Sometimes bacteria ingested multiply inside the host, and may cause delayed disease

14 *S. aureus* can grow on salted and cooked meat. It is also associated with milk foods, custards and processed foods that have been kept in warm or inadequately refrigerated conditions.

15 Some bacteria cause disease by producing toxins not in food before it is eaten, but in the body of the host. The organism that causes cholera, for example, multiplies in non-chlorinated water. When someone drinks the water, many cholera organisms enter the gut, where they release a toxin. This has the effect of reversing the normal flow of water and salts across the membranes of the cells lining the gut. The result is a massive outpouring of fluid, causing the copious watery diarrhoea that rapidly dehydrates someone with cholera. Without adequate replacement of these lost fluids and salts, cholera can be rapidly fatal.

Warm stew
Canteen culture

16 A relative of *C. botulinum*, called *Clostridium perfringens*, causes food poisoning by producing a toxin when it multiplies inside the host.

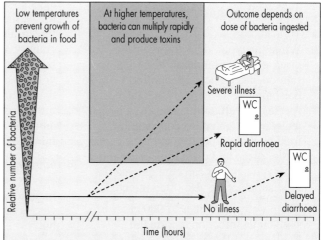

C. perfringens occurs very widely in nature. It is easy to isolate from the faeces of humans and animals and from soil and vegetation. It can also infect wounds.

17 One subgroup of this species of bacterium produces spores that are very resistant to heat. If these contaminate food, particularly meat dishes, they may survive cooking. If the dish is then kept warm, as in canteens serving large institutions, such as schools and hospitals, the spores may germinate and multiply.

18 Once eaten, these bacteria form spores in the gut. During this process, they produce a toxin which affects the intestine: cramping abdominal pains and diarrhoea occur about 9 to 12 hours after eating the meal, and last for a day or two. The illness is self-limiting and not usually severe, except in the very old or the very young, or in pregnant women.

19 Perhaps the most notorious food-poisoning agents are the **salmonella bacteria**. *Salmonella typhi* is the cause of typhoid fever, transmitted by contaminated drinking water. It is quite separate, however, from the large group of salmonellae that also belong to this genus and are linked with food-borne infections.

20 While the typhoid bacillus causes disease only in humans, the salmonellae associated with food poisoning occur in many animal species as well as humans. They infect many animals that we consume for food, including poultry and their eggs, cattle, sheep and pigs. Rats, mice and other rodents that can contaminate our food supplies are also often infected.

21 There were more than 27 000 cases of salmonella infection reported in England and Wales in 1988, and no doubt many more that were not reported. Most cases were unrelated and it was not possible to identify the source of the infection. Of 505 outbreaks of related cases, however, 60 of them were associated with eggs. Out of these 60 outbreaks, just over half were associated with a particular type of salmonella known as *Salmonella enteritidis phage type 4*.

Infected hens
Contaminated eggs

22 This strain used to be rare, but now accounts for most salmonella infections in England and Wales. Studies have shown that infected chickens are the source of this type of infection. Not only the carcases and the outer shells of the eggs (which may be contaminated with faeces) may carry the infection. The bacterium can infect the ovaries and oviducts of the hens and thus the contents of intact eggs. So, eating raw or lightly cooked contaminated eggs, in mayonnaise, home-made ice cream or as soft-boiled eggs, for example, can cause salmonella infection.

23 Although only a small proportion of eggs is infected, because people eat so many, the total numbers of salmonella infections that result throughout the country as a result of eating eggs may be considerable. Cooking eggs until the yolk sets should destroy any bacteria that are present. The government has introduced new regulations for farmers aimed at reducing the number of infected birds.

24 *Salmonella typhimurium* is another very common type that causes disease in humans. Its name means that it causes a typhoid-like disease in mice, but it can also infect a wide range of animals, including humans.

How to stop microbes making a meal of your food

512 in 3 hours

25 The organisms that can cause disease in humans are quite different from those that colonise and spoil food that has started to decay. The circumstances in which **spoilage** occurs are also distinct from those that help food-poisoning bacteria to multiply. Most significantly, food that is dangerously contaminated with bacteria capable of causing disease (**pathogens**) may appear, to the naked eye, to be entirely wholesome.

26 Bacteria can grow very rapidly. If you supply a bacterial cell with all it needs to grow and multiply, it grows a little and then promptly divides to make two cells. These cells, likewise, grow and divide. A population of bacteria can multiply in this way until it runs out of an essential nutrient, or the temperature changes, or there is an accumulation of acid that halts the process.

27 The rate of increase can be formidable. The average time needed for one of the common disease-causing bacteria to divide and create a new generation, when growing under ideal conditions in a test tube at 37 °C, may be 20 minutes or less. Within less than 12 hours, a few bacteria in a millilitre of nutrient broth can multiply to hundreds of millions. If a teaspoon holds five millilitres of fluid, imagine the dose of bacteria that someone could ingest from an average helping of stew that had been contaminated and then left for some time in a warm kitchen.

28 Bacteria such as salmonellae and staphylococci grow best at a relatively warm temperature, but bacteria can grow over a very wide range of temperatures. Some bacteria, such as listeriae and *Clostridium botulinum*, the cause of botulism, can grow at relatively low temperatures. In general, temperatures above that of **pasteurisation** (63 °C for 30 minutes) kill pathogenic bacteria, provided they are wet. Dry heat is much less effective.

29 A few of the disease-causing bacteria produce spores that resist heat. Others are protected from variations in temperature by the materials with which they are associated. Egg white and egg yolk, for example, are good at protecting bacteria within them.

30 Bacteria cannot grow without water. Many techniques of preserving food rely on this fact. Jam, for example, resists the attack of bacteria because the high concentration of sugar makes water unavailable to bacteria.

31 The bacterium's need for water explains why bacteriologists who want to reduce contamination in their laboratories like to keep all their equipment dry, and why doctors advise keeping wounds out of water.

32 Another factor that influences bacterial growth is the pH (acidity or alkalinity) of the medium in which the microbe is growing. This piece of information is not much help in reducing the risk of food poisoning, however: with the exception of foods such as pickles, the pH value of most of our food is close to neutral.

256

33 Antibiotics and other antibacterial agents can also retard bacterial growth, but the presence of antibiotics in food and water encourages the development of bacteria resistant to these drugs. In addition, if people consume antibiotics in food, they may develop serious allergic reactions.

128

Number will double every 20 minutes

64

32

16

2 4 8

Numbers of bacteria can increase dramatically in a short period, given the right conditions. Each bacterium contaminating food can give rise to 512 other bacteria within the space of just three hours

Some infections spread by food or water*

Listeria infections

34   *Listeria* organisms occur widely in soil, animals, vegetation, silage and water. They do not usually attack healthy people, but can cause serious illness in those whose immune defences are impaired. The infection usually causes an illness similar to influenza, sometimes with diarrhoea. In some cases, meningitis may result. In pregnant women, infection with *Listeria monocytogenes* can cause death of the fetus, a miscarriage, or serious infection in a newborn baby. For this reason, health officials have warned pregnant women and those with impaired immune systems not to eat food in which *Listeria* is common, such as soft cheeses and pâté, and to reheat thoroughly cooked and chilled meals and ready-to-eat poultry.

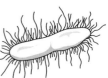

Salmonella infections

35   The typical symptoms of this type of food poisoning, which develop from 12 to 36 hours after the offending meal, are vomiting, diarrhoea and abdominal pain. The person may run a high temperature. Usually the symptoms pass off in two or three days, but the illness can sometimes be fatal especially in the very old and very young, and those who are already suffering from other diseases.

Escherichia coli

36   Most strains of this species are harmless bacteria inhabiting the human gut. Some strains, however, have a harmful effect on the gut, and are known as enteropathogenic strains. Enteropathogenic *E. coli* infections are a particular threat to young children, but they also account for some cases of travellers' diarrhoea. The symptoms may resemble those of cholera, dysentery or salmonella infection.

Most of the bacteria shown are, in life, between 1 and 5 μm (thousandths of a millimetre).

---

* The original article included descriptions of 10 infections. I have included only three examples to conserve space.

Postscript

What do I hope you've got out of studying this book? I'd like to think that it's changed you in some way. Perhaps you think and act differently. Maybe you took what you read at face value as a series of hints and tips. Perhaps you're already putting them into practice. It's possible that you've used the book as a reference source, reading just those sections relevant to your current concerns. Perhaps studying the book cover-to-cover has given you a clearer picture of what it means to be a student and made you think more deeply about what's involved in taking in and communicating information. Perhaps you've a clearer sense now of what's expected of you – of what learning tasks you'll have to undertake and how difficulties might be overcome.

However you've used the book, I hope you'll keep it close to hand as your study of MST subjects progresses. I've said before that becoming an effective learner is not a 'once and for all' skill – you have to work at it – and so the book will be of enduring value. Your academic interests and circumstances are likely to change and so different parts of the book will become more relevant over time.

I don't claim the book will have 'solved' problems for you or made study easy. Learning about MST subjects is intellectually and practically challenging – it's much more than just 'taking things in', it requires you to change and develop as an individual. You'll probably remember this being said in Chapter 1, where I introduced the idea of the *learning spiral*. Learning isn't a process whereby you passively absorb knowledge, rather it's a process of getting new information and ideas into focus, of making connections with other ideas and of putting new thoughts to use. You can then approach other information in a changed state of mind. What is so attractive about MST subjects is that they present so many opportunities for active learning – they involve investigation, both mentally and practically. When you find something out for yourself, you move a little further along the learning spiral. This process works at the communal level too. When some important finding emerges from investigations in some distant laboratory, the new information is shared with others, and soon the scientific world as a whole takes a slightly different view of particular problems – lots of learning spirals have nudged forward at the same time. So, learning is a prelude to change, for both individuals and communities.

To change and develop as a new learner, you'll need to take control of your study. In the terminology of Chapter 1, you need to get better and better at being a *self-manager*. No book can tell you what your goals are, decide which aspects of your learning have the highest priority or provide a fail-safe study plan. What I hope this book has done is to point you in the right direction. You need to step back and think about learning – in other words, to be *reflective*. Although you should take all the help you can get, you must start to work out effective approaches to study for yourself, as an independent learner. What approaches seem to work best for me? How can I change what I do to greater effect? The answers won't come straightaway. Like all learners, you'll experience highs and lows. You'll sometimes feel that you'll never get to where you want to be. But the learning journey you're now embarking on is likely to be life-long, and the process of travelling will occupy your time, not a few glorious moments of arrival. I hope this book proves a comfortable companion for the road ahead – a friendly volume that combines wayside reading, route map, phrase book, compass and good luck card.

Further reading

You'll probably find these books in larger bookshops and public libraries, so you can browse before buying. The comments here are intended to give you an idea of the level and content, but they are for general guidance – only you can decide whether a particular book is worthy of your study time.

Mathematics

Basic Mathematics by Alan Graham (Teach Yourself Books, 1995, ISBN 0-340-64418-4) is an entertaining introduction to maths for adults, especially those who haven't used mathematics for a long time. It is written for absolute beginners.

If you want more practice brushing up your mathematics, *Countdown to Mathematics* by Lynne Graham and David Sargent (Addison Wesley, 1981) has a similar style to Maths Help, but contains less explanation and takes each topic further. Volume 1 (ISBN 0-201-13730-5) includes calculations, simple equations, graphs, charts and tables. Volume 2 (ISBN 0-201-13731-3) includes angles, triangles, quadratic equations, sines, cosines, indices and logarithms.

Study skills

For a different approach to study skills, *Use Your Head* by Tony Buzan (BBC Books, 1989, ISBN 0-563-20811-2) includes note-making, mind maps and memory. It is written for beginning students.

Writing English

Plain English by Diane Collinson, Gillian Kirkup, Robin Kyd and Lynne Slocombe (Open University Press, second edition, 1992, ISBN 0-335-15675-4).

Writing by Catherine Hilton and Margaret Hyder (Letts Educational, 1992, ISBN 1-85758-092-3) covers basic grammar, punctuation and spelling, as well as different kinds of writing: for example, letters.

If you need science 'facts and figures' – information on units, for example – consult the *Science Data Book* edited by R. M. Tennent (Oliver & Boyd, 1971, ISBN 0-05-002487-6). This book is for occasional general reference, rather than detailed reading.

Index

This index covers Chapters 1 to 10, Maths Help and the Collee article. Page references to Maths Help are in italic type.